CHASING TECHNOSCIENCE

Indiana Series in the Philosophy of Technology
Don Ihde, general editor

CHASING TECHNOSCIENCE

Matrix for Materiality

Edited by
Don Ihde and Evan Selinger

INDIANA
University Press
Bloomington & Indianapolis

This book is a publication of

Indiana University Press
601 North Morton Street
Bloomington, IN 47404-3797 USA

http://iupress.indiana.edu

Telephone orders   800-842-6796
Fax orders   812-855-7931
Orders by e-mail   iuporder@indiana.edu

© 2003 by Indiana University Press

The paper used in this publication meets the minimum requirements of American National Standard
for Information Sciences—Permanence of Paper for
Printed Library Materials, ANSI Z39.48-1984.

Manufactured in the United States of America

Library of Congress
Cataloging-in-Publication Data

Chasing technoscience : matrix for materiality / edited by Don Ihde and Evan Selinger.
    p. cm. — (Indiana series in the philosophy of
technology) Includes index.
    ISBN   0-253-34253-8   (alk.   paper)   —
ISBN 0-253-21606-0 (pbk. : alk. paper)
    1. Technology—Social aspects. I. Ihde, Don,
date   II. Selinger, Evan, date   III. Series.
    T14.5 .C45 2003
    306.4'6—dc21
                                        2002152632

1   2   3   4   5   08   07   06   05   04   03

For Linda & Noreen

CONTENTS

ACKNOWLEDGMENTS

This book developed in a unique way. It is totally contemporary and all the contributing participants are active in their fields. Although the local origin was the *technoscience research seminar* at Stony Brook University, the participants met both virtually and actually across the United States and in Europe. In the process, a virtual/actual conversation community was invented. So we first want to acknowledge the wonderful cooperation of Andrew Pickering, Donna Haraway, and Bruno Latour for their openness and willingness to be a part of this project. And, since it was a collaborative project, we acknowledge the role of the interviewers in addition to the contributors: Robert Crease, Srikanth Mallavarapu, Nikos Plevris, and Jeremy Hubbell.

We also wish to acknowledge the now several years' worth of seminar participants who repeatedly sharpened the questions and issues which find expression here, our colleagues from several disciplines, both faculty members and graduate students. Beyond our local situation, we also wish to acknowledge the participation of a Danish contingent—not only were two of the authors here, Casper Bruun Jensen and Jari Friis Jørgenssen, part of the process, but Finn Olesen, Randi Markussen, and Nina Lykke, by allowing us to reprint Donna Haraway's interview, kept the project on track.

None of this would have taken place had not Lee Miller and Donn Welton, serving as chair and graduate program director, made the technoscience operation part of the philosophy program, and Ed Casey and Kelly Oliver generously kept up the support by continuing the chairing tasks of the department. The staff at Indiana University Press was also helpful and supportive of a project which did not simply fall into a standard mold, and for that we are grateful.

CHASING TECHNOSCIENCE

Introduction

PART ONE

Don Ihde

It is a commonplace to note that philosophy of technology began late, particularly in North American contexts. As late as 1979, one of the early philosophers interested in technology, Mario Bunge, claimed that "[Philosophy of technology] is an underdeveloped branch of scholarship . . . suggested by the fact that so far no major philosopher has made it his central concern or written an important monograph on it" (Bunge 1979, 68). That was the year in which my own first work in the philosophy of technology, *Technics and Praxis: A Philosophy of Technology,* appeared; it has since been often cited as the first American philosophy of technology book (Mitcham 1994, 76). It was also the year in which Bruno Latour and Steven Woolgar published *Laboratory Life,* which could be called another first in the new "sociology of science" approach to science studies. At that time, neither of us knew of the others' work. In a deep but contingent sense, however, those two beginnings now converge in *Chasing Technoscience.*

Back then, this departure from the usual traditions of an older philosophy of science, and of what might be called "theory biased" philosophical thinking, seemed a lonely enterprise. But it also carried its own rewards including a growing sensitivity to the ways in which *materiality* plays subtle and deep roles in our ways of moving about in the world. By the end of the first decade of critical reflection on many technologies, including my own special interest in instruments, I began to discover a few other thinkers who had also developed a recognizable sensitivity to instrumental materiality. My book *Instrumental Realism: The Interface between Philosophy of Science and Philosophy of Technology* explored these sympathies. Philosophers of science, particularly Ian Hacking, Robert Ackermann, Patrick Heelan, and Hubert Dreyfus, each recognized the deeper role instruments and technologies played in science. This was also the time during which the even more original insights of two individuals who have since become major figures in the fields they represent came into play—those of Peter Galison, the pre-eminent philosopher-historian of modern microphysics, and Bruno Latour, an often controversial pre-eminence in "science studies." The separate and unconnected paths of *Technics and Praxis* and *Laboratory Life* now began to converge.

One of the features of philosophy of technology that differentiates it from other styles of philosophy is its necessary sensitivity to the *concrete,* to *materiality.* The traditions of philosophy that are predisposed to precisely this concreteness are the *praxis* philosophies that include pragmatism, some strands of Marxism and neo-Marxism, and the phenomenology and hermeneutic traditions. It is not accidental that there is very little "analytic" philosophy of technology, and neither is it accidental that philosophy of technology associates with the praxis directions. Yet neither Peter Galison nor Bruno Latour seem to quite fit neatly into the mentioned traditions for philosophy of technology. But both do display sensitivity toward the materiality that marks praxis philosophies.

So, we come to this particular *chase.* This book originated from a set of studies undertaken by the technoscience research seminar at Stony Brook University. This seminar, now ongoing since 1997, brings together visiting scholars from abroad, advanced doctoral students, and occasional longer-term participating faculty members. Participants study living authors concerned with the philosophies of science, technology, and science studies. In *Chasing Technoscience,* we present and discuss contributions by four principal participants in this seminar whose work is at the forefront of technoscience: Donna Haraway, Don Ihde, Bruno Latour, and Andrew Pickering.

Why these four? Were a full panorama of social science and humanities perspectives upon technoscience to be presented, many, many others clearly would have been included. Of these, there are prominent historians, sociologists, anthropologists, and political theorists—but since the beginnings of what most popularly are called "science studies," fewer and fewer philosophers. This is partly because the new social science perspectives upon science as a social and cultural practice often challenged and disputed traditional philosophies of science. I shall not enter that terrain here in any full respect other than to note in passing that the dominant traditions in philosophy of science, even by the mid–twentieth century, remained "analytic" and tended to view science as largely a theory-producing activity. And while the earlier Logical Positivist and Empiricist strands had been challenged by philosophers in what Peter Galison calls the "positivist–anti-positivist controversy," the emphasis upon theory remained central (Galison 1997, 786–797). This chase aims to reopen the way for philosophers to engage in new analyses of technoscience.

In contrast to the philosophies of science, the new sociologies (and other social sciences) that emerged in the mid–twentieth century saw science as a wider social practice. Latour and Woolgar's *Laboratory Life* actually was an early collaboration between an English and a French approach which was to become divergent very soon thereafter. On the English side of what cannot help but recall the "Continental-analytic" battles in American philosophy, the emergence of what became known as the "Strong Program" in the sociology of scientific knowledge soon became contrasted with the French school of "Actor-Network Theory." Thus in the new sociologies, another of the "Channel Divides" opened.

Andrew Pickering records this division in a famous series of debates that began with "Epistemological Chicken" by Harry Collins and Steven Yearly in *Science as Practice and Culture*. What must be called a "social constructionist" attack upon a semiotic-based "Actor-Network Theory" position brought immediate response from both Steven Woolgar and Bruno Latour. This battle, often highly contentious, still continues!

And for those amused or titillated by the "science wars," there will be some recognition of even wider battles which rage—between the philosophers and the new sociologists, usually about some form of "realism" or "anti-realism" with any new sociologist tarred with "anti-realist" epithets. Science studies is a new, interdisciplinary field, with battlefields already littered with the corpses of arguments and publications.

There are major figures and attainments on all sides. Were I to choose a single work, monumental if for no other reason than because of its recognition and citation by virtually all sides, it would have to be *Leviathan and the Air-Pump: Hobbes, Boyle and the Experimental Life*. If Steve Shapin and Simon Schaffer are "social constructionists," then this is one of social constructionism's major works. They show how the social formation of science includes a "technology" of machines (the air pump), a "technology" of language (third person style), and a social "technology" of modest (male) witnesses. All four of our principal authors refer to this monumental work, often in extended ways.

Nor does *Air-Pump* stand alone. The field today is full of other visible authors spanning the vast spectrum of science studies. Laboratories have played a central role. Andrew Pickering's admired and also controversial *Constructing Quarks: A Sociological History of Particle Physics* is another such work, as was the even earlier *The Manufacture of Knowledge: An Essay on the Constructionist and Contextual Nature of Science* by Karin Knorr-Cetina. Similarly, technologies also underwent the social constructionist treatment in *The Social Construction of Technological Systems: New Directions in the Sociology and History of Technology* by W. Bijker, Thomas Hughes, and T. J. Pinch. This necessarily partial list indicates that by the 1980s and 1990s, the new sociologies and social science perspectives upon technoscience had burgeoned and come to prominence.

I return to the question of why we chose these four thinkers for the chase in this meditation on philosophy and materiality. Three interrelated answers suggest themselves. First, the studies we are exploring, and which include philosophy of technology itself, but now stretching to science or technoscience studies, are all deeply *interdisciplinary*. There are no neat boundaries to be found here. This interdisciplinarity is recognized by philosophers of technology as well as by the social science approaches to technologies. Interdisciplinarity is a shared perspective.

Second, each of our principal authors forefronts materiality in unique but comparable ways. Two, Donna Haraway and Andrew Pickering, were practicing scientists in the earlier days of their careers, although in quite different fields. Pickering began as a theoretical physicist, Haraway as a biologist. But both began to critically reflect upon the practices of their respective fields. Pickering's first transformation was as a sociologist and his first major work was the above-mentioned *Constructing Quarks,* one of the early "constructionist" accounts of laboratory practice in particle physics. Haraway soon found herself interested in the history of her subject, but even more in the way its social settings constructed outcomes. Her first large and successful work was *Primate Visions: Gender, Race, and Nature in the World of Modern Science,* a work in which she simultaneously showed how contemporary primatology had been revolutionized by feminist scientists and how its constructions often reflected gender biases at their very base.

Both Pickering and Haraway continued and radicalized their earlier work as well. Pickering's *The Mangle of Practice: Time, Agency and Science* plunges us into the role of materiality in science practice. A central focus of *Mangle* is the process through and by which scientists learn to use and produce knowledge through their technologies. Pickering produces a rich vocabulary of this process: "machinic agency," "resistance and accommodation," "the dance of agency," "tuning," as well as the dominant metaphor, "mangling." He shows the deeply material engagements which characterize the natural sciences. But he also frames his approach as anti-representational and performative, again an approximation of the praxis traditions.

Donna Haraway's best-known metaphor or "figure" for the role of materiality in human life is that of the "cyborg." The *cyborg* combines much more than humans and machines—it draws its strength in some ways from science fiction fantasies, but, in such creatures as "OncoMouse," it brings together a string of events and dimensions which include technologies, social enactments, modified biological processes—everything from genes to the socialized military-industrial powers. Drawing from considerable literary-critical talent, Haraway manages to depict and elicit the complexity and subtlety of so much of what is contemporary. She is particularly adept at demonstrating the *non-innocence* embedded in technoscience. In her now famous "Cyborg Manifesto," she detects in today's visual technologies a predatory nature embedded in photographic consciousness, and in the developments of genetic biologies she senses a translation of the world into being taken as a coding problem, insights which are simultaneously scary and yet, particularly today, insightful.

Among our quartet of thinkers, Bruno Latour is both the best-known and most heterodox of the group. And although this might come as a shock to those who read "Continental" thinkers in this era, Latour is cited in the standard social science indices more than is Jacques Derrida! I was probably first attracted to what could be characterized as the "hermeneutic Latour." In *Science and Action*, Latour characterizes instruments in science laboratories as complicated *inscription devices*, designed to make a visual presentation (which has to be "read"). The parallel to my own hermeneutic human-technology relations was obvious. But today Latour's approach is a modified and radicalized *semiotics*. He utilizes a radical symmetry by which humans and non-humans are both seen as *actants*. Both modify the other symmetrically. This radical analysis applies to simple materializations such as speed bumps (literally in French, "sleeping policemen"), doorstops, and handguns, as well as to complex phenomena such as Pasteur's discovery of and by microbes! Such provocation one should not ignore.

My own role within the quartet should be obvious. Philosophy of technology, which in my approach includes a phenomenology of human-technology relations as well as a hermeneutics of technology and culture, makes materiality a central feature within human and social activity. My secondary role here is to try to entice my fellow philosophers to read seriously some of their new philosophical neighbors.

The third reason for this particular set of choices is their mutual focus on problems looked at from *philosophical perspectives*. I have long argued that technologies and material complexes are *non-neutral*, and I am quite sure that each of our four holds the same conviction. But the details are where the shapes and forms of non-neutrality are revealed. This volume addresses the different ways of undertaking such analyses and investigations, but there is also a sense in which each of the four authors embraces the philosophical. In Latour's and my cases, the connection to philosophy is most explicit since it forms much of our educational background. Much of Latour's early training was philosophical and theological—as was mine. In the cases of Haraway and Pickering, the "philosophical" is a bit more indirect. Haraway claims that she "breathes Darwin and Foucault" in her thinking, but she also invokes Alfred North Whitehead as a forefather. Once again, the praxis or process philosophies play a role here. Pickering, often negative toward philosophers, nevertheless begins to see his mangle as a "theory of everything," or a nascent metaphysics, and again not foreign to Whitehead's notion of process philosophy. Note, too, that Latour also claims the metaphysical—and Whitehead—in his interview.

Here we reach the apogee of the chase that has shaped the organization of this book. Chronologically, Part Two, the analytic and comparative exercise which arose out of the technoscience seminar, occurred first. But the involvement of the principals became immediate and continuous. Electronic communication between the seminar participants and the principals occurred during the first stage of the project. In more embodied form, the paths of the principals also actually crossed. Haraway, Pickering, and I were keynote speakers at a Danish conference in Aarhus in the fall of 1999. In conversations, Donna Haraway suggested the use of interviews, a suggestion we followed, not without complication. In Haraway's case, the interview was conducted around the cyborg conference in Aarhus, Denmark, by Randi Markussen, Finn Olesen, and Nina Lykke, and was published in Danish in the journal *Kvinder, Kon og Forskning,* edited by Nina Lykke and reprinted here in the original English with permission. All the other interviews were conducted by members of the technoscience research seminar and are original to this volume. Haraway, Pickering, and I met again at the University of Oregon in 2001. Bruno Latour's original interview was "captured" at the international joint meeting of the Society for the Social Study of Science and the European Society for the Study of Science and Technology in Vienna in fall 2000. Latour and I met again at a workshop on technological accidents organized by Peter Galison at Harvard-MIT in spring 2001. It was this criss-crossing and the alternations between electronic and actual meeting which suggested our title, *Chasing Technoscience.*

Part One, then, presents an original article by each of the four, accompanied by an interview that, with the exception of Donna Haraway's, was conducted by seminar participants. This process, conducted within "real time," yielded some pleasant surprises with which I shall conclude this introduction.

Andrew Pickering's chapter, "On Becoming: Imagination, Metaphysics and the Mangle," is a reflection upon *The Mangle of Practice.* It responds to various reviews and critiques of *Mangle,* and in effect generalizes his notions of machinic agency and the interactions of human and material in science. It is a summation of this development which inclines toward philosophy.

Donna Haraway provides the biggest surprise; in her "Cyborgs to Companion Species: Reconfiguring Kinship in Technoscience," we move from her best-known figuration of the cyborg to companion species, notably *dogs.* This is a portentous change of perspective, caught in the act here, as it were. In her narrative, she tells us that dogs and humans invent each other. The domesticated dog cannot be what it is without humans—but there is a sense in which humans would not be what they are either were it not for the dogs which have invented us and which continue to invent us. If she is right, there may be much deeper significations which lie here in the interrelationships of canine-human exchanges that point to new directions concerning technoscience.

Bruno Latour offers us another transition piece, "The Promises of Constructivism." Latour, sometimes chastised these days, is returning to a more philosophical and even ethical-political dimension within his thinking. Latour chafes at any designation as a "social constructivist," although he included that designation in *Laboratory Life*. In this entry, brand-new and specifically for this collection, he re-evaluates construction. What emerges is what he calls the impossible sentence, "the more constructed, the more real." While much of this article is responding to Ian Hacking, Latour clearly deals with the role of "realism" in the continuing debate and particularly tries to decouple "constructivism" from "deconstruction."

My own essay, partly because it comes at the end of this chase, is more responsive to the other three thinkers than theirs are to any of the rest. It is by reading these philosophical neighbors that I can reflect back and reconceive my own project better. Some of the frustrations which have long surrounded "phenomenology" become clear only by reading across others.

In sum, I urge readers to look seriously at the various perspectives on materiality brought into focus here and especially recommend to our more philosophically inclined readers that they venture into these interdisciplinary contexts to broaden and deepen their own concerns.

PART TWO

Evan Selinger

The chapters making up the second half of this volume emerged from research conducted at the Technoscience Research Group (TRG) at Stony Brook University. This multidisciplinary group within Stony Brook's Department of Philosophy brings together visiting scholars and fellows with various philosophical, scientific, and technological backgrounds. The scholars have come from countries as diverse as Australia, Denmark, Holland, Hungary, Greece, Norway, Korea, and Sweden. The advanced graduate students come from Stony Brook's philosophy, English, history, and sociology departments. All active members of the TRG participate in an ongoing, weekly seminar devoted to discussing and reading *living authors* writing about science and technology. Additionally, participants often present excerpts from their own research projects to receive evaluative, pre-conference, pre-publication feedback.

In keeping with Ihde's *experimental method* of philosophizing, selected authors—such as Albert Borgmann, Andrew Feenberg, Peter Galison, Andrew Pickering, and Joseph Rouse—are brought to the seminar for a critical discussion of their works. This process has become affectionately known as a *"roast."* Despite Donna Haraway's initial concern for the seemingly patriarchal sedimentation of the term, the metaphor comes from eighteenth-century chemistry, wherein metals were "roasted" to see if they gained or lost weight. As preparation for a "roast," the seminar spends several weeks reading and critiquing the most current works an author is willing to make available. Often, this means participants in the TRG have access to unpublished manuscripts or articles. Rather than presenting a formal paper, the invited "roastees" are asked to give a five-to-ten-minute talk in which they relate their current research to the topics covered, and methods used, in previous writings.

After this succinct précis, TRG seminarians fire away questions, some of which have provoked lively debates. For example, Borgmann was asked to defend his normative position on better and worse practices, as well as clarify his understanding of the good life. Although many participants objected to the seemingly nostalgic, rural fantasies that run through his oeuvre, they also appreciated his attempt to address the morality of practices occurring in material culture. The difficult question left unanswered by Borgmann's visit centered on pluralism: How can one criticize patterns of use and consumption without simultaneously presupposing a single vision of worthwhile endeavors? The problem of the limits of modernity dominated the Feenberg discussion. While it was agreed that his criticisms of Jürgen Habermas's views on technology are insightful, he was repeatedly asked to support his political use of transcending ideals, such as nature and culture, as well as his reliance on Marcusian concepts that appear dated. Still, many participants found Feenberg's political goal of providing socialist arguments for technological use urgent and necessary. The political aporia left by Feenberg's visit was this: How can one defend political intuitions without presenting overgeneralized and empirically unsubstantiated conceptions of history, technology, and collective identity?

Pickering, Rouse, and Galison found themselves obligated to answer interdisciplinary questions. On the one hand, Pickering's provocative discussion was inspirational because he continually emphasized processes of becoming over static conceptions of being. His insight that retrospective accounts of practice are more common in philosophy, history, and sociology than they appear forced many participants to rethink their notions of intentionality and action. On the other hand, Pickering was taken to task for not seriously reckoning with philosophy. While his project resonates on the surface with philosophers like Michel Foucault and Gilles Deleuze, Pickering's discussions of them, as well as his treatment of general philosophical concepts like practice, temporality, and intentionality proved frustrating for the philosophers in the audience. The main question left unanswered by Pickering's talk: How can one be sensitive to the empirical nuances of practice, in such a way that human and non-human actors are taken into "real time" consideration, without sacrificing the rigor of philosophical concepts? Rouse was pressed on his understanding of science studies. Specifically, discussions with Rouse centered on how to best understand the relation between science studies and philosophy institutionally, as disciplines, and methodologically, as styles of research. The most important issue prompted by Rouse was how philosophy and science studies can best be interfaced. Galison emphasized the importance of meticulous research during his talk. Some of his keen remarks on Einstein's use of clocks prompted debates about immanence and transcendence, specifically as they relate to genius. The primary interdisciplinary question he faced was this: Why does he present the history of philosophy of science in terms of positivist–anti-positivist debates while obscuring contributions from Continental philosophy.

During the 1998–1999 meetings of the TRG, the seminar undertook a major comparative work on the theme of "materiality" in the works of Don Ihde, Donna Haraway, Bruno Latour, and Andrew Pickering. This research endeavor became known as the "Matrix Project" (MP). The title for this project was chosen long before the technoscientific fantasies of the movie *The Matrix* came to reorient how undergraduates are taught Plato's allegory of the cave as a cinematic brain in a vat. Generally defined, a matrix is something within or from which something else originates, develops, or takes form. In this sense, the MP focused on the comparable and differing ways "non-humans" take form and develop in the works of these authors. A more concrete definition of matrix states that a matrix can be the natural material (as soil or rock) in which something (as a fossil or crystal) is embedded. In this sense, the explicit aim of the MP was to render thematically explicit how the "non-humans," who cannot speak for themselves, are embedded, which is to say, culturally structured, in the works of these authors. Finally, a matrix can be the intercellular substance in which tissue cells (as of connective tissue) are embedded. For example, the thickened epithelium at the base of a fingernail or toenail is a matrix from which new nail substance develops. The sense of novel development depicted in this last definition points back to the etymology of matrix, which in Latin refers to a womb. Here too is a connection with the MP, as one of the goals of the seminar was to move beyond the repetition of established theories of "non-humans" by providing the basis from which new work on materiality could develop. For the delimited purpose of the MP, however, the "generative matrix" encompasses the representations and interpretations of science and technology as presented by four authors in the burgeoning field of technoscience studies.

Ihde's suggestion that the TRG research group engage in this comparative study further belies his early phenomenological training. Many critics, such as Pickering and Latour, have criticized phenomenology for being a subjectivist philosophy. Arguably, these critics are correct about certain, if not most, uses of phenomenology. They characterize phenomenology as subjective because they take phenomenological descriptions to be first person, experiential reports of data directly present to the observer's mind. They are dissatisfied with phenomenology because of the dualism that introspective accounts inevitably bring: subjective phenomena are found to be situated within a subject in contrast to the objective phenomena located outside of the subject. Unlike these styles of phenomenology, Ihde has long argued that the phenomenological core is not subjective narration, but a relational analysis capable of producing invariant structures detailing the requirements for certain perceived and occluded features of the world. According to Ihde, the primary focus of phenomenology is the structure of intentionality in which the givens of experience are not the starting and ending points of investigation, but are taken as indexical clues to be investigated as determinants of the reflexive conditions of appearance.

Ihde's defenses of phenomenology have rested upon his uses of the primacy of the variational method. The MP can be taken as an instance or application of this method. Consequently, while only a few MP participants would call themselves phenomenologists, they all agreed, as part of their participation in the MP, to engage in a distinctly phenomenological exercise. When the MP first began, Pickering skeptically inquired into the value of this comparative study. His sense was that the "he-said/she-said," textually oriented style of such studies rarely enriches fields of investigation. Implicit in his criticism is the view that comparisons begin and end with the givens of published theory and are incapable of transcending these givens to present novel insight. Pickering is clearly right as far as some comparative studies are concerned. Our objection to Pickering's understanding was that the comparative method of the MP is a means of variationally sorting out claims about "materiality" made in relevant styles of investigation.

"Materiality" is not a thing in itself, but a multi-perspectival field of inquiry, restricted in part by the internal horizons of each investigator who delimits how its complexity can be portrayed as determinate. Each view—whether it is phenomenological, material-semiotic, Actor-Network, or performative—is partial in its assessment of what "materiality" is and how it is capable of interacting. Comparing and contrasting these assessments with one another allows different levels of relational stability and instability to be shown. What the MP set out to accomplish was to shift a potential investigator's dominant concerns from foci suggested by the beliefs and habits of one of the four styles of inquiry to the development of unfamiliar modes of presentation. Variation in this sense is not repetition without difference, but the production of reshaped dominant and regressive foregrounds and backgrounds. In short, once one encounters a phenomenon as multi-stable through variational analysis, one can never return to it as "given." This is not to say that materiality is simply whatever one conceptually declares to it to be. Nothing could be further from the aim of the project, which attempts to register "material activity" without many of the dominant modern biases. Nevertheless, it remains true that how people look at "materiality" depends in part on what people are willing and unwilling to see.

Briefly stated, the following chapters attempt to interpret Haraway, Ihde, Latour, and Pickering across one another. In doing so, the idiosyncratic, technical vocabularies of each of these thinkers are clarified. Words the reader may initially be puzzled by—"lifeworld," "alterity relations," "embodiment," "dance of agency," "material agency," "mangle," "actant," "network," "cyborg," "material-semiotic," "post-human," and "post-subjectivist"—will, by the close of this second section, be more easily understood. These novel concepts are used to address philosophical issues: the problem of being and becoming; the differences between representational and non-representational epistemologies; the distinction between reason giving and causal determinism; the level of compatibility between situated and symmetrical knowledge; the limits of translation and interpretation; the discrepancy between centralized and diffuse expertise; the disparity between analytical and rhetorical demarcation; and the relation between traditional and novel horizons of understanding. In order to prepare the reader for what follows, I would like to do more than flag technical vocabulary and general investigative issues. To this end, I have selected three groups of questions as guides.

1) How is knowledge constituted? Who narrates how knowledge is constituted? How are these narratives produced? How are knowers constituted? Who narrates how knowers are constituted? How are these narratives produced?

2) How plastic is the world in its restriction and receptivity of theoretical pronouncements? What does the selective specificity of a theorist's examples indicate about the ease and range of applicability of that theorist's concepts? In short, how is the infrastructure of putatively edifying examples prejudicially suggestive of distinct interpretative horizons? Which theories can and cannot map onto extant nodes of existence and what is black-boxed in the process?

3) Whom do theorists argue against in their attempts to accrue the symbolic capital required for institutional acceptance? Do theorists present caricatured, easily defeated red herrings? Are theorists as reflexive about their own positions as they are critical of their interlocutors? Are all of the participants in the MP equally prone to misinterpreting other theorists' works?

I believe that all three of these questions are addressed in each of the following chapters. Sometimes they are posed directly. Other times, these questions operate implicitly. Although none of these questions are exhaustively answered, the reader who perseveres through all of the chapters will be exposed to enough variation to develop his or her own tentative conclusions. In a sense, when the reader draws these conclusions, he or she will also be participating in the variational method. Should the reader develop a novel perspective unaccounted for by the authors of this volume, then that reader will engage in a traditional phenomenological enterprise. Phenomenologists—even of the subjective variety—have always tried to circumvent doxic presuppositions that constrain how open one can be toward pragmatically encountered phenomena.

BIBLIOGRAPHY

Bijker, Wiebe, Thomas Hughes, and Trevor Pinch, eds. 1987. *The Social Construction of Technological Systems: New Directions in the Sociology and History of Technology*. Cambridge, Mass.: MIT Press.

Bunge, Mario. 1979. "Five Buds of Techno-Philosophy." *Technology in Society* 1: 67–74.

Galison, Peter. 1997. *Image and Logic*. Chicago: University of Chicago Press.

Haraway, Donna. 1989. *Primate Visions: Gender, Race, and Nature in the World of Modern Science*. New York: Routledge.

Ihde, Don. 1979. *Technics and Praxis*. Dordrecht: Reidel.

———. 1990. *Technology and the Lifeworld: From Garden to Earth*. Bloomington: Indiana University Press.

———. 1991. *Instrumental Realism: The Interface between Philosophy of Science and Philosophy of Technology*. Bloomington: Indiana University Press.

Knorr-Cetina, Karin. 1981. *The Manufacture of Knowledge: An Essay on the Constructionist and Contextual Nature of Science*. Oxford: Pergamon.

Latour, Bruno. 1987. *Science in Action: How to Follow Scientists and Engineers through Society*. Cambridge, Mass.: Harvard University Press.

Latour, Bruno, and Steve Woolgar. 1986. *Laboratory Life: The Construction of Scientific Facts*. Princeton, N.J.: Princeton University Press.

Mitcham, Carl. 1994. *Thinking Through Technology: The Path between Engineering and Philosophy*. Chicago: University of Chicago Press.

Pickering, Andrew. 1984. *Constructing Quarks: A Sociological History of Particle Physics*. Chicago: University of Chicago Press.

———, ed. 1992. *Science as Practice and Culture*. Chicago: University of Chicago Press.

———. 1995. *The Mangle of Practice: Time, Agency and Science*. Chicago: University of Chicago Press.

Shapin, Steven, and Simon Schafer. 1985. *Leviathan and the Air-Pump: Hobbes, Boyle, and the Experimental Life*. Princeton, N.J.: Princeton University Press.

PART ONE

I. Interview with Bruno Latour

Participants: Robert Crease, Don Ihde,
Casper Bruun Jensen, and Evan Selinger

DI: Those of us who have read your books, from *Laboratory Life* through *Artemis, Pasteur,* and up recently through *Pandora's Hope,* have noted first of all that you move somewhat from an earlier, much more descriptivist position to now considering normative factors—morality and ethics. At the same time there is a kind of parallelism between your self-identity, first as a more sociological anthropologist, following around the scientists, to *Pandora's Hope,* where you re-identity yourself as a philosopher. The opening question then is: What is motivating this transition?

BL: Well, I am not sure if it is a transition from sociology to philosophy because my disciplinary affiliations have always been rather uncertain: although I teach sociology I have always considered myself as a philosopher at heart, but of course, let me add that no one in France ever took me as really a sociologist nor as a professional philosopher, nor for that matter an anthropologist. Like the Dutch scholar Ann-Marie Mol, I would define myself as an "empirical philosopher," not as an empiricist philosopher, but as someone who tries to get at classical philosophical questions through the methods of fieldwork and case studies. I believe that the corpus provided by field work and case studies should be added to the usual corpus of canonical texts. The two have to be carefully studied together. The latest book I have just completed in French, about legal practice, *Dire le droit, une ethnographie du Conseil d'Etat* is thoroughly empirical. So I don't see a trend as if I was moving away from concrete questions to abstract ones. I try to do the two together always. It is just that sometimes I identify myself more with philosophy and sometimes more with anthropology. In fact, deep down, my real interest is in metaphysics. My longer-term project has always been to visit successively and to document the different truth production sites that make up our civilization: science of course, but also techniques, religion, law, etc. But it is really sweet of you to consider that I am a philosopher. I like the label and it is not so frequent. . . .

DI: It is an interesting question because what you are characterizing yourself as, being more empirically oriented, actually fits in more with part of the American model of philosophy, particularly in pragmatism, than it does in classical European philosophy, or certain aspects of analytic philosophy. In some sense, we have no problem with an empirically oriented philosopher.

BL: In a sense, we also have this tradition in France, if you think of the style of writing of people like Sartre (think of his *Flaubert*), or Bachelard, or Serres, or our various trends of phenomenology, think of Merleau-Ponty. There is much more data, if one can say this, in all these authors than in what other traditions would take as straight philosophy. Think of Deleuze and Guattari's *Mille Plateaux*! It is packed with other sources than canonical texts. The practical question concerns who does text studies and who does data studies.

DI: Since you raised the term phenomenology—a topic we have already had a few exchanges on—I should mention that I agree with your point that European phenomenology made more of an empirical turn than some of the classical philosophies. But in *Pandora's Hope* you claim that phenomenology has only gone part of the way in terms of recognizing the embodied subject. It seems to me that the kind of phenomenology that emerged at the end of the twentieth century is more materialist and embodiment-oriented than the phenomenology done during the beginning of the century. My guess is it that part of your reservation has to do with phenomenology not taking into account the non-humans.

BL: This may have to do with my ignorance and biases. Let's take the phenomenological tradition I know the best—the one of Merleau-Ponty. It is a very interesting tradition for embodiment. But it is an entirely human-centered account of embodiment. It is very difficult to de-center the human in this tradition and connect Merleau-Ponty with classical metaphysical questions, like the ones I am interested in that were posed by Whitehead. I know it is unfair. But in the fight to rehabilitate metaphysical questions in the Whiteheadian sense, I don't see what kind of help phenomenology can be. Certainly it is more helpful than overly rationalistic positions, because of the attention on the lived world, *le vécu* and its beautiful appraisal of the cosmic horizon, as Merleau-Ponty calls it. But the question is: Can we again gain access to agencies that are not human-centered? I don't see the use of phenomenology here. If you take the *Phenomenology of Perception,* for instance, the opposition between lived perception and the scientific objectivist definition of the same phenomena is rendered even starker than before, in the positivist days. So, for me, but you have to understand that this judgment is linked to my position, to what I want to do, I always find the tools of phenomenology widening exactly the type of gap that I am trying to close. The choice is between Merleau-Ponty and Whitehead for me.

DI: It is interesting that you should mention Whitehead because Donna Haraway does the same thing. She also fixes on his notions of concreteness.

ES: You mentioned metaphysics twice. I am hoping that you can say more about this. You claim that you have always been interested in metaphysics. This is interesting because the term is so broad one might even say that it is overdetermined. Social constructivism, which you have always distanced yourself from, has never been able to bridge the gap between local analyses and that which lies beyond the local. I take it that what you mean by "metaphysics" is that you are always working on particular case studies in order to come up with slightly more general, perhaps what Deleuze calls virtual, concepts, such as "mediation," "networks," and "translation." These concepts have a general scope and belong to the project of category building. For example, in *Pandora's Hope* you work through different levels of style and mediation in order to produce a general model of practice. Can you clarify what you mean by metaphysics by addressing the relation between the particular or singular and the universal, which, after all, is the traditional philosophical desideratum.

BL: I don't relate metaphysics to the question of the connection between the local and the global. This is a question in itself, one of social theory on which I have worked a lot, for instance in the book I did on *Paris ville invisible.* No, I relate metaphysics to the very Leibnizian and Whiteheadian traditions. According to this tradition, the ingredients of the world are accessible to inquiry. I add—because in this regard, Whitehead is not exactly a field worker!—they are accessible to some sort of empirical inquiry and it is the role of the social sciences (but the word social here becomes an inconvenience) to pursue those inquiries about the basic categories by which actors build time, space, and agency. These categories should not be fixed in advance by what I call the "metaphysics of nature," a paradoxical expression to point out that with the notion of nature one is already doing metaphysics. So metaphysics is not concerned with "meta" questions that begin "after" nature has been known, but begin at once, even in the very definition of the ingredients that are making up nature. So, for me, metaphysics starts in earnest when you grant those you study the same ability to build the basic categories as when you read a treatise by Leibniz or if you read *Process and Reality*. When I interview scientists, I consider that they are doing as much metaphysics as if I was reading the *Monadology*. In both cases they are concerned with how the world is built. This might seem strange to you but for me metaphysics is a very concrete practice. Even stranger, I take it to be a mixture of ethnomethodology and ontology.

ES: Perhaps the reason I was associating metaphysics with the relation between the particular and the universal is because in your work—at one point you call it the "Modern Settlement," at another point, you delineate it in terms of the agreement made between Socrates and Callicles—you point to meta-level trends that are located at a particular historical juncture that carry with them a metaphysical resonance from that point on, within a pervasive milieu. This is metaphysics in the sense of going beyond. I interpret this to be a move in the direction of the general because it appears that your critical aim is to classify styles of evoking "nature" and "culture" that happen with a certain amount of repetition in order to locate core elements.

BL: I disagree with the word "meta." For me it is what I call infra-theory. The vocabulary I have used is very bad and it is meant to be bad: actant, mediation, obligatory passage point, translation, delegation, they have no meaning in themselves and they do no metaphysical work whatsoever. I never put any sort of explanatory weight on them. I don't believe the world is made of mediations, entities, or agencies. Those words are simply tools deployed to travel from one site to the next. The whole vocabulary of Actor-Network Theory is a way of moving from one agency to the next. This is why, in the book I did on the politics of nature, I call what I do "experimental metaphysics." Like Whitehead—whom Isabelle Stengers defines as the greatest philosopher of the past century—I believe that to do metaphysics experimentally, one should not define the actors of the world in advance. It is the job of metaphysicians to monitor the experiment in which the world makes itself. We need a very poor vocabulary, composed of stupid terms, to function infra-conceptually. Words like modernity are even more useless since they have no empirical content, they simply dramatize some ideological questions. See, I find all those terms disgusting as well, but I don't worry if they are dirty since I put no explanatory weight in them. They simply allow me to move, in a relativist way, from one position to the next, and to see how all the ingredients of the world—space, time, agency—of what will compose a normal metaphysics are actually redone locally.

CBJ: If I can change the field a little bit; because I am not a philosopher, and would rather identify myself with STS studies, I would like to raise a different question of your development in time and spirit. Going back to the notion of infra, such as infra-reflexivity, the methodological slogan of *Science and Action* was "just follow the actors around because they will define themselves."

BL: The philosophy of *Science and Action* is not very deep. It is more like sociology of science.

CBJ: In any case, in order to let the actors define themselves with interference from meta-theories, there seems to be an appeal to pure description. This has come under attack, on normative grounds, by theorists like Langdon Winner. Now you are turning to normativity. I take this to be similar to what Isabelle Stengers does, her sort of normativity. My question is: Is there a change in methodology from *Science and Action*, in which your goal is to follow the actors around, to your recent work, in which you make claim that we can define, by following the actors around, whether they are good or bad actors, i.e., it is better to engage than negate an enemy. It seems that you go from a descriptive to an evaluative practice without changing presuppositions. I am wondering how you conceptualize that role. At what point is one able to make an evaluation instead of merely describing? Can we still have infra-reflexivity if you are evaluating the infra-reflexive practices?

BL: I have to warn you, my degree of reflexivity on myself is nil. I produce books, not a philosophy. Every book I am involved with is a work of writing that has its own categories and its own makeup. I cannot transform all of these books into a unified field of thought that would remain stable over time and of which one book would simply be coherent manifestations. On the other hand, I don't believe in being irresponsible for what I have written. I agree that I have a responsibility for being compatible, like a software designer has to maintain compatibility. I want someone who can "run" my religious and ethical software to also be able to "run" old software, such as *Laboratory Life*. Maybe this is harder to understand in your American tradition than in the text-based Continental one, but for me there is a big difference between producing books and having a philosophy simply expressed in books. Each book requires a writing strategy that is uniquely adjusted to the problem at hand, for instance *Aramis or the Love* *of Technology;* but it does not mean that you can transport this writing strategy to another book, for instance *Irreductions.* Do you see what I mean?

CBJ: Yes, but you are evading my question on normativity.

BL: On the accusation of not being normative, I have never understood what this means. It is just that it takes time to find the sites where morality can be investigated. I don't believe that morality is something that floats on top of purely descriptive or merely empiric stuff. Morality is inside the things, and thus it can also become an object for empirical enquiries. When I started writing twenty-five years ago there was a great need for descriptions of scientific activity since there was none independent of the scientists' own descriptions. Times change and now we have a lot of this type of work. I am greatly influenced, as you know, by the work of the Belgian philosopher Isabelle Stengers, especially her work on what she calls "cosmopolitics," the politics of cosmos. Now, this is neither descriptive nor normative—by the way, where does the difference come from if not from the modernist settlement that we have been throwing into doubt? In *Politiques de la Nature,* I have tried to overcome this very distinction between facts and values, descriptive and normative, and to explore its political root. So I don't accept the characterization of my earlier work as being uninterested in ethical and political questions; in this work the ethical task was to describe, describe again and again, how science and technology are done. But now I want to do other things and the scientific controversies that are pressing us from every corner require, I agree, other types of concepts and other focuses of interest. I can see why this is so completely chaotic for a professional philosopher because it is far from being tidy. Sometimes I am highly conceptual, then I do field work, then it is a variety of infra-arguments to move from one field work to the next. If that can reassure you, I too find this a disgusting *bricolage.* But I don't know how to think otherwise.

ES: Concerning your compatibility as you call it, I noticed that there is one thing, a unified metaphorical structure, that runs throughout your work. Like Nietzsche and Deleuze, you use metaphors of war as a means of generating explanatory power. Even in your last talk—and I know you were not saying it was your own term—you spoke about enemies. You have gone from talking about networks and trials of strength to enemies. All of these discussions are compatible in the sense that their force and affectivity relies on an agonistic vocabulary.

BL: I'm sure Donna Haraway would castigate me. Yesterday's talk was a bit different, though, since it was about what I call the "progressive composition of the common world." The term "enemy," which was used in Karl Schmidt's sense of what to do when there is no common referee, is not metaphorical. War is now less metaphorical than in my earlier work. It is part of a conceptual argument of what to do when there is no common referee, no accepted umpire, and especially not nature. But I agree that I use a lot of war metaphors, which I still think was really important to do to fathom the supposedly peaceful domain of science. (Have you noticed by the way that I am simultaneously accused of having been apolitical in my descriptive work and to have politicized the pure world of science and technology?) I have to confess that my first philosopher was Nietzsche. I went to a Jesuit school and, strangely enough, we read Nietzsche for a whole year preparing for the baccalauréat. So I don't deny his influence on me. I was saved from philosophy of consciousness by early high doses of Nietzsche; this is my Deleuzian influence, and this probably explains why I can't swallow much phenomenology. Philosophy is an ecosystem; there are all sort of different species, economies, diets there. So, thanks to the little niche where I have been educated, I never understood why consciousness was an important question anyway. But again, I am sorry to say that I am not a philosopher in any professional sense.

RC: You mentioned fieldwork, a term which is philosophically loaded. In Clifford Geertz's last book he opposes the critical studies mode of fieldwork to a more hermeneutically sensitive mode of fieldwork, which he sees himself as doing. In a hermeneutic mode, you have to ask who the actors think they are, what they think they are doing, what end they think they are moving toward, and the framework of meaning they move within. This doesn't mean you have to go native but you at least have to try to understand their mindset.

BL: Yes, that is a minimum definition of fieldwork! Does he mean that the cultural studies people don't do that?

RC: Yes, that's what he says.

BL: This is very mean.

RC: He opposes this to a hermeneutically sensitive sense of trying to get at the self-interpretation of the actors. So I was wondering if you could elaborate on what your own conception of fieldwork is.

BL: The hermeneutic definition given by Geertz seems to me a very minimalist one, considering the challenge of how much you need to do to get at understanding the experimental metaphysics of those we study. There is much more to understanding than meaning. Any fieldwork we do should force us to re-interpret the frame of reference of what is the world, including in its most basic elements, time, space, agency, and so on. The best anthropologists do this. It takes fieldwork to engage us into a mixture of ethnomethodology, semiotics, and metaphysics. These are three necessary tools for seeing how some events or actors can remake the world locally. This is why I take a hermeneutic sense of fieldwork to grossly oversimplify things. For instance, hermeneutics would be content in interpreting the meanings of culture, but while some of us live in cul-ture, most people don't, so if you are not ready to throw the notion of culture as well, you might end up doing fieldwork in a sophisticated hermeneutic sense, but not in my sense. I guess what I am interested in is always in remaining com-patible with philosophy. When Eduardo Viveiros de Castro does fieldwork in the Amazon, his work is for me as essential a reading as Whitehead, and then I have two sources instead of one to understand why culture and nature makes no sense either in our Western world or in theirs. Fieldwork for me is a way of mul-tiplying the sources and sides to do good comparative philosophy. But if you be-gin your fieldwork by presupposing a common world in the sense of positing that there exists a culture, that humans are defined by being in culture, having a body, genes, and neurons, then you are finished. You are not an anthropologist because you have already decided for the actors what is the world they have in common even if they refuse to have a body and a culture . . . or for that matter to be actors at all.

DI: You just mentioned the use of semiotics. Can you be more specific about what type of semiotics you're talking about. Last year I had an exchange with Donna Haraway and she claimed that my critique of symmetry vs. situatedness did not recognize her specific use of semiotics, which turned out to be Piercean. Which semiotics are you using?

BL: I think I am with Donna on this, although not with Pierce, as my training was in Greimas. And I know I am completely outdated now, but that does not bother me. I see semiotics as a toolbox. As a philosophical tool it is useful in the freedom it promotes for letting the actors build their own world as actants. Even Whitehead is not as free to let the actors build their own worlds as sometimes the average semiotician is. Yet semioticians, who normally only operate on texts, are greatly limited as well. I have tried to extend the semiotic connection by linking it with ethnomethodology. I still teach semiotics to students because it is effective for bracketing out the subject. At small doses this is useful, although at high doses it can be damaging if it convinces you that you are not dealing with something real. Basically, Deleuze and Nietzsche recognized this as well.

CBJ: So semiotics can be used to allow actors to build their own worlds.

BL: Everything that does this is good: metaphysics, ethnomethodology, and semiotics.

CBJ: I would like to ask a question that is a criticism. This criticism is not my own, but is one frequently leveled against you. Your theory defines the types of actants who define their own worlds in specific ways. You focus on antagonisms and goal-oriented rationality metaphorics. Gary Downing and J. Macgregor Wise in their recent books take issue with this.

BL: I am really sorry, but I have not read either of their books.

CBJ: Okay. But the question is how do you view trials of strength and weaknesses? Doesn't this suggest that the only worlds anthropologists can build are antagonistic, incapable of operating like Haraway's game of cat's cradle?

BL: I accept the criticism. But it has to do with priority. The priority twenty-five years ago was to open up the immunized world of science to social theory. My priority was to bring out as much force and dispute in the sciences as possible. Now, this being said, the people who say it is all about antagonism have read very little of my work. In the case of the Pasteur book, I did not focus on goal-oriented rationality or interests. Or, to put it more charitably, my critics often don't understand what I am doing, which is refusing to distinguish between force and reason, because I am interested in the force of reason. This is the heart of the matter in *Irreductions*. People claim that I attribute force to every entity in the world. Perhaps this is my Nietzschean undercurrent. Nietzsche did not do a very good job in this respect. Deleuze did a much better job. But then again Deleuze is accused of being an organicist. Bergson did a very good job. But then again he's accused of being an evolutionist. It is absolutely impossible to win. For those who are monists and do not make a distinction between force and reason, a no-win situation arises. So I think I've lost interest and don't use force often these days. I'm done with it. But if I had to defend myself, I would say that even in *Laboratory Life* I used force to describe, for instance, the scratching of a stylus onto the millimetered paper of a physiograph. Does that really resemble the force of a chest-beating gorilla, the brute force of the blonder beast of prey? I guess I recognize the criticism but don't care. I agree, though, that in the early work we overdid the power grabbing male innovator. Then again, I am not very reflexive about my own work.

ES: One of the things that Casper and I have frequently discussed is a line of thought that has gone from thinkers like Deleuze to Manuel De Landa. These thinkers seem to be trying to look at emergence while holding on to notions of complexity theory. So on the one hand, they try to locate novel forms of emergence as they appear in the world, unmediated by theoretical constraints. On the other hand, they find certain mathematical models as helpful for seeing the emergence of the world in a particular way. What does it mean to the have and hold on to these models of complexity? Does holding on to them in advance restrain the types of possible emergence?

BL: You need to ask Isabelle Stengers this question. She knows more than I do about the scientific side of Deleuze. While I have read everything of Deleuze, I am not always convinced he is so useful in my empirical enquiries. I am impatient in this otherwise beautiful book, *What Is Philosophy?*, with the way philosophy's role is exaggerated beyond any recognition, and also by the fact that on religion he has nothing much to say. Deleuze is not my all-purpose philosopher. Also, and that's a disagreement I have with Isabelle, I don't see him as a good writer, and for me the writing is very important, the crafting of books with very specific literary strategies that embody very specific theories.

DI: You mentioned religion in this context. This is another thing that seems interesting in much of your recent work. What do you have to say about religion at this point?

BL: I started with religion and was a theologian first, exegesis more exactly, again text-based practice. This has always been my interest. If it is difficult to speak of science, it is even more difficult to speak of religion. I am just writing a book, which I have been thinking about for many years, on the conditions of the enunciation of religion. The enunciation of religious speech-acts has become even less possible now than scientific discourse. But I consider that philosophies that don't deal with the truth production of religion are as incapable of dealing with real thought as those who can't deal with the truth production of science or the truth production of techniques. This is why the whole current of anti-religious thinking, which is very strong in much French critical thought, I find unhelpful. We must be prepared to handle all of the domains of truth production, including, of course, politics. That was the aim of my talk yesterday: the truth production of politics is absolutely essential.

DI: You are approaching being a genuine metaphysician.

BL: That's kind of you but alas I am genuine in nothing. But if I were genuine in something it might be in metaphysics, experimental metaphysics. It is important not to do metaphysics in the place of the actors. This is what I am interested in. I am surprised that the speech condition of religion has disappeared. This is because, I think, it has been loaded with rationalism that makes it completely unable to get at the right tone with which it should be articulated. I am trying to find a way to speak about religion without using the idiom of rationality. I have a "sermon" to appear in *Res* in case you are interested! But I know this is even more tricky and dangerous than speaking about science.

ES: I have a question about the possibilities of speech. One strategy I've often seen you use—and I've learned quite a bit from—is that you turn to situations which appear to be exclusively conflictual and find underlying points of agreement, what Goffman calls tact. These are moments of complicity that under the surface provide the conditions of the possibility for utterances of disagreement to transpire. For example, while Hobbes and Boyle appear to disagree on everything that is important, they need to agree on what nature and culture are in order to disagree in the first place. Socrates and Callicles appear to disagree on everything, until you interpret their shared sentiment about the masses as the condition of the possibility for appearing to disagree in the first place. Why do you utilize this strategy so often? I take this way of proceeding to be different than social constructivism that always centers on the *agon,* conflict, the opposition, and misses multiple levels of complicity.

BL: Your observations are right and perhaps I have overdone it. It is a strategy similar to Leibnizian diplomacy. Stengers has rehabilitated the notion of diplomacy and the figure of the philosopher as the diplomat. So, after all my talk about war, I guess I am interested in diplomacy. If there is no common world, if there is no referee, if there is no common world already made, and if you still want to produce a common world, locally at least, then the diplomat becomes a key figure. The diplomat does precisely what you say. The diplomat is the one who is hated and doesn't know what the people he represents want. I think that it is very difficult to locate disagreements, so the strategy is to look for other sources.

ES: Can you link this up with the topic of trust in any way? If you see the world as an *agon,* then it is filled with distrust. This suggests the problem to be solved is one of mediation, attempting to create bonds of trust. But if you begin your analysis differently, by using the figure of the diplomat, you appear to demonstrate that trust was there from the start.

BL: Again, in spite of the criticism leveled at me, I don't paint an agonistic portrait of the world. After all, the key words are translation and irreduction, hardly agonistic terms. . . . The fault with social constructivism is not in the agon, but in the fact that they have taken the liberty of making the metaphysics in the place of everyone else. The mistake of social constructivism comes from the social—and also from the notion of construction that might have outlived its usefulness somewhat.

ES: I am thinking of something like the expert-lay divide. Here the metaphysical presuppositions are that experts and laity need to communicate better with one another. Some people argue that experts are patronizing and need to be better sensitized to lay knowledge. Others argue that lay concerns are often too value-laden and based on irrational concerns. In both instances, commentators focus on distrust and differences, not complicity and trust. But this picture of the world, as conflict-ridden and divided, is only a social constructivist world.

BL: My worry with social constructivism is that they confuse what the world is made of with how it is made. They confuse the ingredients with the construction. They believe that the world is really made of social stuff. Like Stengers, I am a constructivist but not a social constructivist. On the other hand, there is a deep hypocrisy in rejecting the antagonistic too fast. This is why I am very interested in Schmidt. People always talk about dialogue. But to imply a dialogic condition means that we have already organized the world for the others.

DI: As an interesting coda to this, your claim about not writing a philosophy but writing books is precisely what Paul Ricoeur told me many years ago.

BL: (Laughs) I'm surprised Ricoeur said that. I don't see much craft in his books.

DI: Well, he told me two things. He told me first of all that "once I write a book, it is no longer mine. It belongs to the world." The second thing he told me is that each book written is separate and autonomous. He then asked me how I could see his different works as all relating together. Part of this of course is what we were trying to do with you.

BL: This is kind of you. I am sorry to be so unreflexive on my own work.

NOTE

This interview took place at the 2000 4S/EASST conference in Vienna.

2. The Promises of Constructivism

Bruno Latour

For Albena Yaneva, architect-watcher

What has gone so wrong? It first looked like a good idea: it was fun, it was original, it was enlightening to use the word "constructivism" to designate the work I was doing on science and technology. Laboratories indeed looked infinitely more interesting when described as so many construction sites than when portrayed as dark mastabas protecting mummified laws of nature. And the adjective "social" seemed at first rather well chosen, since I and my colleagues were bathing the venerable work of science into a hot tub of culture and society that aimed at making them young and lively again. And yet everything has gone awry. I had to withdraw the word "social" with shame—scrapping it in haste from the title of *Laboratory Life* like faces of Trotsky deleted from pictures of Red Square parades; as for the word "constructivism," it does not seem possible to salvage it from the furies triggered by the "science wars" nor from the detritus left by the passage of "deconstruction," this new Attila whose horse's hoofs leaves no grass behind. Everything I wanted to achieve, namely, to associate reality and construction into one single dynamic with one single term, has been wrecked like a badly designed aircraft. Times have changed: In order to show that one is not a dangerous outcast, it seems compulsory to swear a pledge of allegiance to "realism"—now meaning the *opposite* of constructivism. "You have to choose," roar the guardians of the temple. "Either you believe in reality or you cling to constructivism."

And yet saving constructivism is precisely what I wish to accomplish in this

discovered by sociologists and economists so much stronger than the ones constructed by chemists, physicists, and geologists? How unlikely. The *explanandum* certainly does not match the *explananda*. More importantly, how could the homogeneous stuff of almighty "society" account for the bewildering *variety* of science and technology? Constructivism, at least in our little field of science and technology, led to a completely different program than the one repeated *ad nauseam* by critical sociology. Far from trying to explain the hard facts of science with the soft facts of social science, the goal became to understand how science and technology were providing some of the ingredients necessary to account for the very making and the very stability of society. This was the only way to give the word "construction" some of its original meaning, to highlight the collective process that ends up as solid constructs through the mobilization of heterogeneous crafts, ingredients, and coordination (Haraway 1999; Pickering 1995; Rheinberger 1997; Knorr-Cetina 1999; Latour 1999a).

The two things science studies did *not* need were to replace the fascinating site it was uncovering by an unconstructed, homogeneous, overarching, indisputable "society" and of course an unconstructed, already there, indisputable "nature." This is why science studies found itself fighting on two fronts: the first against critical sociology it wrongly appeared to descend from (as if it were merely extending social explanation coming from law and religion to science and technology); and the second against nature fundamentalists who wanted facts to pop up mysteriously from nowhere.[2] If "social" means either the stuff out of which things of science are made—a position which, to the best of my knowledge, has never been defended by anyone—or the harder structure that explains the long-term solidity of scientific facades—as most people, including Hacking regarding what he calls "social kinds," still believe—it is better to abandon it altogether. This is also why, if I quickly deleted the adjective "social" from the title of my first book, I carefully kept the word "construction" since, thanks to science studies, most of the interesting connotations of the building metaphors were at last beginning to appear: history, solidity, multiplicity, uncertainty, heterogeneity, risk taking, fragility, etc. Obviously "social" did not refer to the stuff out of which other things were made—to be critically denounced—but to the *associations* of many different sources of relatively solid ingredients. The social sciences were becoming not the sciences of the social, but those of heterogeneous associations (Tarde 1999; Latour 2002a). Constructivism is like the word "Republic": the more adjectives you add—socialist, Islamic—the worse it becomes.

Miscasting Creators As Well As Creatures

Once "social" has been crossed out, the problem of construction, however, remains just as irritating as before. This time the reason has not to do with the demise of critical sociology, the weakness of our own case studies, or the persistence of the "science wars," but rather with the inner mechanism of construction itself. The problem with constructivism is that no one could account for the building of anything, even the simplest shack, by using this metaphor as it has been popularized in social sciences. Nothing in it works: neither the role given to the builder or the maker, nor the role of the material being used; neither the solidity and durability of the result, nor its contingencies or necessity; neither its history nor its lack thereof. If any mason, any architect, any Little Pig were trying to build anything with the *theory of action* implied by constructivism, they would fail hopelessly to assemble any durable whole.

Let us measure the utter inadequacy of this notion—even if this seems to render its salvation even more hopeless. First to fail is the role attributed to the *maker*. Implied in constructivism is an agent which masters its own acts of making—I use a neutral term here because society, nature, fields of force, structure, as well as humans, can be asked to fulfill the role of master-builder in some account. When someone says, "This is a construction," it is implied: "It was built *by* some agency." But then by what sort of agency? If it is an all-powerful creator who has full command of what is produced out of nothing, this is certainly not a realistic account of the building of any real structure. Even if some architects see themselves as God, none would be foolish enough to believe they create *ex nihilo* (Yaneva 2002). On the contrary, architects' stories of their own achievements are full of little words to explain how they are "led to" a solution, "constrained" by other buildings, "limited" by other interests, "guided by the inner logic of the material," "forced to obey" the necessity of the place, "influenced" by the choices of their colleagues, "held up" by the state of the art, and so on (Koolhas and Mau 1995). No God is less a Creator than an architect, even the most innovative and daring one. To "become sensitive to the many constraints that lead to a rather autonomous scheme that begins to take over a sort of life of its own" is precisely what they will try to emphasize. But then, if we become attentive to humbler ways of speaking, this agency shifts from the all-powerful master to the many "things," "agents," "actants" *with which* they have to share the action.

And of course, the vocabulary of "making" will divert attention from the maker to the materials even more quickly if one considers engineers instead of architects—numbed by the aura of the "free" modernist artist. Learning how to become responsive to the unexpected qualities and virtualities of materials is how engineers will account for the chance encounter with practical solutions: they will never think of describing themselves as little kids molding reality at will.[3] If there is one thing toward which "making" does not lead, it is to the concept of a *human* actor *fully* in *command*. This is the great paradox of the use of the word construction: it is used by critical sociology to show that things are not simply and naturally *there,* that they are the product of some human or social ingenuity, but as soon as this metaphor of "making," "creating," or "constructing" barely begins to shine, then the maker, the creator, the constructor has to *share* its agency with a sea of actants over which they have neither control nor mastery. What is interesting in constructivism is exactly the opposite of what it first seems to imply: there is no maker, no master, no creator that could be said to dominate materials, or, at the very least, a new *uncertainty* is introduced as to what is to be built as well as to who is responsible for the emergence of the virtualities of the materials at hand. To use the word "constructivism" and to forget this uncertainty so constitutive of the very act of building is nonsense.

Second to fail is the conception of the material involved in the process of construction. If you think that builders were treated unrealistically, wait for the poor portrait usually given of matter—the two being obviously linked, as we will see. To exert a determinate and obstinate blind force, to be there as the mere support for human fanciful ingenuity, or simply to offer some "resistance" to human action, these are the only three roles given to things in the constructivists' scenarios. The first one gives material agencies the exact same implausible function given to the creator in the *ex nihilo* story, but in reverse: things command assent by their sheer force that simply has to be obeyed. The second saps any possibility of agency from things: they are left merely plastic, only able to retain an abundance of shapes offered by the rich, creative, and totally free human mind. The third conception of things differs from the former by simply adding some resistance for no other reason but to provide the creator with some surprise while he retains full power over matter—and it has to be a "he." To complete this sad inventory, one should add the comical role of being-there-just-to-prove-that-one-is-not-an-idealist role invented by Kant and replayed over and over again by philosophers all the way to David Bloor: things are there but play no role except that of mute guardians holding the sign, "We deny that we deny the existence of an outside reality" (Bloor 1999). Quite a function well worth hapless "things in themselves."

Any constructivists worth their salt should be ashamed to see that everywhere things have not been given their due: the first treats matter as master, the second as no more than wet sand in a sandbox, and the third as an occasion to feel one's own force being resisted. But with such theories of forces no one could succeed in accounting for even the simplest task: baking a cake, weaving a basket, sewing a button—not to mention erecting skyscrapers, discovering black holes, or passing new bills. And yet most debates on "realism" and "constructivism" never go further than the next child's toy box—to which, for good measure, one should add a few "mugs," "mats," "cats," and "black swans." Let us be serious: If the word constructivist has any sort of meaning, it is because it leads us to agencies never falling into these silly and childish roles. Yes, they act, yes they order, yes they resist, yes, they are plastic, but what proved interesting are all the *intermediary* positions they are able to *simultaneously* occupy (Latour and Lemonnier 1994). The paradox is that critiques retain three or four points in trajectories for which artists, artisans, engineers, architects, house-persons, and even children in kindergarten have a rich and talented vocabulary. Certainly Gianbattista Vico never did build much with his hands, to believe that what he had made was for this reason fully and completely known. I have never met scientists at the bench who were content to choose between "realism" and "constructivism," except of course when giving science war pep talks. Show me one single artist who would denigrate the complex material he is shaping into form to the low point of "infinitely plastic" clay—certainly not potters (Geslin 1994). Show me one single programmer who would think in full command of the software she is writing. Have you ever seen a cook who could account for a cheese soufflé by defining its delicate and crusty substance with the simple notions of "plasticity," "resistance" and "pure obedience to the forces of nature?"[4]

Everywhere, building, creating, constructing, laboring means *to learn how to become sensitive* to the contrary requirements, to the exigencies, to the pressures of conflicting agencies where none of them is really in command.[5] Especially not the "maker" who spends nights and days trying to live up to his or her responsibility to what Etienne Souriau has magnificently called *instauration,* or *l'œuvre à faire* (Souriau 1935, 1939). How come we account for construction, either from the side of the maker or from the side of the made, with a theory of action that any one of our own acts fully contradicts? Yes I know, the bad example comes from high above: the *ex nihilo* Creator playing with His dust, clay, and breath has given a bad name to all of us. But it is not because He was the first "social constructivist" inventing everything from the fancy of His own imagination that we have to follow His example. . . . Or maybe, when kicked out the Garden of Eden, we also lost the meaning of this Creation story. Not only would "we toil at the sweat of our brow" and "with pains give birth to children" but we would also be cursed with the impossibility of understanding what laboring and constructing and creating could mean. "Thou shall no longer grasp the meaning of God's agency." Will we live forever punished with the original sin of mistaking constructivism for "social" constructivism?

An Impossible Sentence: "The More Constructed The More Real"

To the Garden of Eden there is no trail back. It might be possible however to regain some of the lost powers of the original idiom of constructivism if only we could undo the curse that paralyzes our tongues every time we wish to use them. For that, it is not only necessary to delete the word "social," to redistribute agencies and to add some uncertainty concerning *what* is doing the making, as I just did. In order to salvage the constructivist manners of speech, another even more difficult move is requested of us since we also have to be able to stick to practice in just the way the sophisticated versions of constructivism forbids us to do.

Any architect, mason, city planner, tenant, in accounting for the reality of the building they designed, built, planned, or inhabit, will consider the amount of work done as one of the *reasons why* the building is well-designed, well-built, well-planned, or well-furnished. So, for them, working hard and having a building standing solidly and *independently* of their work is one and the same thing—provided it has been *well*-done. In their implicit accounting system, they have one *credit* column in which they enter their own work *as well* as the autonomous solidity of the building, and a *debit* column in which they enter what has been *badly* designed, planned, or built and what for this reason has been left dangerous, shaky, unfinished, ugly, inhabitable. How come then that they are asked by crooked constructivists to keep another book with an entirely different accounting practice? One in which all the items showing that the building *stands solidly and independently* are entered in the credit column while all the items tending to show that *work* has been done are noted in the debit column? Even Enron and Arthur Andersen would not dare massage their account books to that extent. And yet this is exactly what we do when we move from the practical language of construction to a theoretical one. We cheat, we lie, we enter into shabby double-dealing.

It is exactly such a betrayal of constructivism that science studies has contested. In the practical parlance of scientists at work, it is *because* they work and work *well* that facts are autonomous and stand independently of their (the scientists') own action (Latour 1996). And yet, as soon as they reflect back on what they have done—or as soon as they come under the influence of some sort of realist philosopher—they cook their book, doctor their accounts and begin to draw two opposite lines: one for the independent reality of the facts (the credit line) and another for the mundane, human, social, collective work they have done (the debit line).[6] Silly deal, first because the very *word* "fact" still retains traces of the other accounting system clumsily erased—*"les faits sont faits";* second, because in manipulating this new account, scientists lose any chance of gaining credit for their own hard work which now goes into the debit column!; and third, because they deprive themselves of any authority to ask for grant money, since it seems, by reading their massaged ledgers, that they will know even better, faster, and truer if they were not working, if they had no instruments, no collective undertaking, no construction site. . . . Independent reality stands alone and they are standing on the other side of a huge gap, unable to bridge it. But the fourth reason is really the one that exposes best the silliness of this double-dealing. The difference between *good* and *bad* science, *well*-designed and *badly* designed experiments, *well*-fabricated and *badly* fabricated facts has disappeared, whereas it was exactly this crucial difference that the other accounting system captured so well—and the one to which all the attention of scientists at work has been directed: the difference between a *good* and a *bad* scientist (Stengers 1993, 1997).

If it is clear, in the case of architects, that the only real interesting choice is between good and bad construction and not between construction and autonomous reality, why is this not the case for scientists and facts? Because of two added features that seem to condemn the language of constructivism for good. When we say of a building that it stands on its own weight *after* the work of engineers, planners, architects, and masons, and *because* of their *good* work, we don't have to engage ourselves in a tricky metaphysical question: everyone will agree that, whatever its autonomy, the building was not there before. No matter how elegant, coherent, necessary, adjusted the shape of a house in a landscape might end up being, no matter how "necessary" it appears to be, no matter how pleasing to the eye, it does not provide the sort of necessity requested from matters of fact. It still has a source and origin in some architecture studio signaled by a marble or brass plaque fixed somewhere on the wall—like all of us have the mark of our navel on our belly to humble our dream of self-construction. But it is precisely this navel that irritates (with good reason) scientists and philosophers when they see the word "fabrication" used in relation to "facts"—even though they might be painfully aware of the word's damning etymology. The autonomy they strive for is that of a building which has always stood erect on its own weight no matter what work has been necessary to discover its exact location, to measure its height and to visit or inhabit its interior. Such a degree of certainty, such an occupation of time and space, such an unquestionable autonomy, solidity, and durability no idiom of construction or architectural metaphor can provide—even if we stick as closely as possible to the confusing practice of really building real buildings—since construction, by definition, leaves exactly these traces that should be erased. If the double-book accounting system can be exposed for architects and engineers, it does not seem possible to do the same when hard facts are in question: autonomy and labor indeed seem contradictory. Is this then the last breath of constructivism?

Probably, especially when, to add insult to injury, critical sociology seizes this most difficult of all metaphysical questions and trivializes it into a Q & A at the end of a course in Continental Theory 101: "Is constructed reality constructed or real?" Answer: "Both." Commented with a mildly blasé smile: "Are we so naive as to think that we have to chose? Don't we know that even the maddest ideologies have real consequences? That we live in a world of our own construction and that it is no less real for that?"[7] How I despise this little "both" that obtains so cheaply a veneer of depth that passes nonetheless for the ultimate critical spirit. Never was critique less critical than when accepting as an obvious answer what should be, on the contrary, a source of utter bewilderment. "We" never build a world of "our own delusion" because there exists no such free creator in "us" and because there exists no material pliable enough to retain the marks of our playful ingenuity. "We" are never deluded by a "world of fancy" because there exists no force strong enough to transform us into the mere slaves of powerful illusions. On both accounts—as creations of our own imagination, or as what those creatures impose upon us in return—the critical spirit fails since it uses the least realistic definition possible of what it is to create, to construct, to be influenced, to be deluded. It transforms into a simple thing exactly what is most mysterious in the sharing of agencies with other actants, with *aliens*. The critical spirit slumbers just when it should be wide awake: no one was ever taken in by the return reality of a world of one's own making. Once again, constructivism is a victim of its own apparent friends, and the least probable version of what it is to "build a world of one's own" is used to render impossible any account of this very construction. This belief in naive belief is the only naive belief ever visible—only if you hold a Ph.D. in critical theory can you maintain this illusion against the constant disproof of practice.

So, in the end, things don't look very good. There seems to be no plausible way to say that *because* something has been constructed and *well*-constructed it is *thus* solid, durable, independent, autonomous, and necessary—even though this is what the manifold languages of practice obstinately belabor, and what science studies has tried to extract by staying as close to the bench as possible. The threat will be carried out, we will have to submit to the examination: "You have to choose: *either* it is real, *or* it is constructed," and if we dare answer "both" our own *positive* both will be confused with the weak, cheap, and blasé *negative* answer of our worst enemies, i.e., our dear friends the critical sociologists. . . . It seems that if deconstruction, more voraciously than termites, has been able to turn into dust all the claims to solidity, autonomy, durability, and necessity, it is because constructivism was too fragile a material to begin with. There seem to be no anti-termite treatments, no fumigation to protect constructivism against falling into ruins. Only what has *not* been constructed will stand the test of time.

A SCALE TO QUALIFY THE RIGHT AMOUNT OF CONSTRUCTIVISM

One solution would be to abstain from the word constructivism altogether.[8] But that would leave the field to whom? Naturalists on the one hand, deconstructionists on the other. There would be a place in the sun only for those who link reality with the *absence* of labor, and those who have the front of using labor to *debunk* claims to existence, solidity, necessity, and durability. Science studies will have no room for itself. A strange accounting system will render practice opaque to enquiry.

Fortunately, Ian Hacking has done good work on clarifying this most muddled topic in *The Social Construction of What?* Thanks to his attempt, I might succeed in offering a convincing inventory of what sentences such as "X should be taken as constructed," where X stand for "laws of nature," "divinities," "technologies," "political representations," "market organizations," "subjectivities," could mean. And we need such sentences to possess clear meaning since they designate all the ingredients which are up for grabs in the progressive definition of the common world—the name I now give to political process.[9] Could the curse on the theory of action implied by the many metaphors of construction be lifted?

Hacking understood that the reason these disputes around the right mix of reality and construction trigger so much passion is that they are political: they seem to talk about epistemology but they are really about how we should go about living together. To classify the various schools of "social constructivists" (only a branch of this family, as I will show), he offers a scale that goes from stage 0 (X is given by nature), then to stage 1 (X could have been otherwise), then to stage 2 (X is bad), then to stage 3 (X should be overthrown) (Hacking 1999, 6). In this view "social constructivists" can be ordered from the most innocuous (things have not always been the way they are, they have a history) to the more radical (they should be changed). And all the brands are opposed to a stage −1, which Hacking implies but does not define: X is the way it is, period.

Although it is an important step forward to reveal the inherently political nature of the argument, Hacking's gradient is too asymmetric. If it nicely orders the different brands of "social constructivists," he says nothing of the politics of those who should be called "naturalists," namely those who need this implied stage −1, which allows for X to be there as a permanent fixture of nature. To be able to use Hacking's scheme, it seems fairer to also include the politics of those who use this indisputable necessity of nature to define the common world: it is already made and remains off limits for any political process. Once this is done, constructivists and realists are all engaged in what I call "political epistemology," namely the organization of the arenas in which the various candidates that claim to inhabit the same shared world—humans and non-humans—are *represented* in all the many meanings of the word. Thus, the debate should not be seen as what pits scholars who object to the politicization of nature against militants who politicize everything, including the facts of nature for their various radical goals. Rather, it allows different factions, parties, leagues, to make *explicit* and *public* how they are supposed to distribute what is disputable and indisputable, what is contingent and necessary, what should be kept and what should be changed. To use a traditional set of metaphors, political epistemology is not an unfortunate distortion of good epistemology or good politics, but rather the necessary task of those who write a "Constitution" distributing powers in the various "branches" of this vast "government of things," looking for the best arrangement of "checks and balances" (Latour 1999b).

Once this common ground is recognized—once Hacking's asymmetric treatment of the various claims has been redressed—it might be possible to abandon, for a moment, the various labels given to the contending parties—realists, naturalists, constructivists, deconstructionists, etc.—to look instead at the list of *guarantees* they all wish to obtain from participants in the common world, although through different means. The list below appears to me to offer more generality, and maybe more clarity on ordering the sub-family of social constructivists, than the one offered by Hacking. It deals with his same "sticking points," but offers a different diplomatic opening.

First guarantee: once there, and no matter how it came about, discussion about X should stop for good. This is an essential assurance against endless controversies, heckling, superfluous doubts, excessive deconstruction. Such is one of the two meanings of the word "facts": once in place, reality should not be allowed to be disputed and should be used as the indisputable premise of other reasonings. This is the only way to assure a base of solid and stable facts to rest upon—if only to occasionally thumb a table in good spirit. . . . If this leverage is taken out, it seems that discussion is no longer possible (Hacking 1999, 84). If a party named "constructivists" appears to be jeopardizing this essential guarantee, then "that means war," and it is no surprise that the other factions will try and exclude it from any "parliament" (Stengers 1998). What went so wrong in the earlier debates around "social construction" was that such a guarantee went ignored—or rather was confused with the equally important one just to follow.

Second guarantee: in spite of the indisputability insured by the former, a revision process should be maintained, an appeal of some sort, to make sure that new claimants—which the former established order had not been able to take into account—will be able to have their voices heard. And "voice," of course, is not limited to humans. This is exactly what the crowd reviewed by Hacking requires when they attack the "naturalized," indisputable, taken-for-granted stage 0. Only what has been made can be unmade or remade; such is an indispensable source of energy. If all the means of revision are taken away, if we are simply faced with the indisputable matters of facts which have always been the way they are, an essential guarantee has been jeopardized and that, too, "means war." New candidates to existence will be forbidden access to the common world. If a party called "naturalists" appears to forestall all discussions, all revisions, because they use the state of nature to shortcut due process in the name of "law and order," then it is not surprising that the other factions will try to exclude it from the parliament.

The delicate checks and balances of political epistemology require both guarantees, there is no due process without them. But the discussion does not stop at these two.

Third guarantee: the common world is to be composed progressively; it is not already there once and for all. This guarantee is totally muddled when transformed into an argument for contingency against necessity—and on that account Hacking falls into the trap (his "sticking point" #1). To prove that matters of facts have been "constructed," it is argued, one has simply to show that they are contingent, that they could have been otherwise, that they are not necessary.[10] To disprove the constructivist account, it is counterargued, one has simply to show that there are no two ways for X to exist, only one. But such a debate is a profound misreading of the real argument in science studies, especially in the history of science. The point is not about demonstrating the existence of "alternative" physics, chemistry, or genetics, but about the impossibility of absorbing the world—in the singular—in one single chunk.[11] The unified world is a thing of the future, not of the past. In the meantime we are all in what James calls the "pluriverse," and those—scientists, philosophers, activists, commoners of all sorts—who strive to make it one are *taking risks* and they *could fail.* Danger, contingency, uncertainty, does not qualify the result—which might well be Necessity herself—but the process through which "the" world becomes progressively shared as one *same* world. The opposition is not between contingency and necessity, but between those who want to order the world once and for all on the cheap pretext that it is already "one," so that they can *subtract* everything else from it, and those who are ready to pay the price of its progressive *composition* into one because they cannot subtract anything.

Fourth guarantee: humans and non-humans are engaged in a history that should render their separation impossible. Again, this feature of constructivism is deeply misread when seen as a debate between realism and nominalism (Hacking 1999, 80). Words and worlds do not represent two statues facing one another and marking the respective territories of two kingdoms—only to one of them will loyalty be sworn. Rather, words and worlds mark possible and not very interesting extremities, end points of a complex set of practices, mediations, instruments, forms of life, engagements, involvements through which new associations are generated. To imagine that a choice has to be made between statements and matters of fact would be like pitting the two banks of a riverbed against one another while ignoring the huge and powerful river that streams in between. If philosophy has only registered the choice between realism and nominalism, this has nothing to do with the way we all deal with the truth content of matters of facts, but with a precise political order that has requested a strict separation between humans and non-humans (de Libera 1996). As soon as the political assembly is modified—and this is precisely what is registered by science studies—the guarantee is not to finally obtain a clear separation between words and worlds, nature and culture, facts and representation, but just the opposite: to ensure that there is no such separation.

Fifth guarantee: institutions assuring due process should be able to specify the quality of the "good common world" they have to monitor. As I have shown above, what is so crucial in the accounting proper to constructivism is to be able to differentiate good and bad construction—and not to be stuck forever in the absurd choice: is it or is it not constructed? Although the philosophical tradition has separated the moral question of the "good life" from the epistemological one of the "common world," it is just a question of which common world is *best* and how it can be shared as *one* which occupies the stage when the subtle discourse of practice is foregrounded.[12] This is where the *composition* of the common world takes its meaning and what has been expressed from the Greeks onward by the word *cosmos*—by opposition to *kakosmos*.[13] The quest of the common world cannot even begin to be raised when an opposition is drawn between an "unconstructed" world already there, already unified, devoid of values, on the one hand, and a "constructed" motley of conflicting social or subjective value claims on the other. Simply to "be there" is not enough for matters of fact to be absorbed, associated, digested, rendered compatible with other conflicting claims: they have to be composed, they have to become instead *states of affairs*.[14]

The idea of my (very rough) list is that it should now be possible to compare propositions entering the common arena—the new public space—to check if they lead toward a strengthening or a weakening of those five guarantees *taken together*. My claim is that this list allows a much more efficient classification than the scoring system proposed by Hacking (1999, 199).[15] For lack of a better term (I'd like to introduce "compositionism," but it has no pedigree), I wish to retain the word "constructivism" for the propositions that foot the bill and either "naturalism" or "deconstruction" for those that fail to fulfill them—the former because it maximizes the first guarantee while being indifferent to the others, the latter because it sticks to the second and fifth guarantee but minimizes the others. I am prepared to abandon the term completely as long as a new one is used to describe the constitutional order that I have wished to describe with this embarrassing word. Any term will do as long as it can allow me to designate something which (a) has not always been around, (b) which is of humble origin, (c) which is composed of heterogeneous parts, (d) which was never fully under the control of its makers, (e) which could have failed to come into existence, (f) which now provides occasions as well as obligations, and (g) which needs for this reason to be protected and maintained if it is to continue to exist. Too many traits, I confess, for one poor little word—and one ending with this rather damning postfix "-ism."

IF ONLY CONSTRUCTIONISM AND DECONSTRUCTION COULD PART COMPANY

The reason why my solution will most probably fail is not only because its usage raises the red flag for science warriors (I still think that they can be reassured),[16] but because of its much more dangerous association with *de*construction.[17] Even though the prefix "*de*" should be enough to indicate that it goes exactly in the opposite direction, the critical spirit will always hold back its ironical head and exclaim with glee: "If X is constructed, then I can easily 'deconstruct' it to dust." The relation seems as inevitable as the ecological one between prey and predator. When the word "construction" is uttered, instead of immediately looking for which tools and resources would assure its upkeep and maybe even restore the built structure, the Big Bad Wolf chomps his deconstructionist jaws in eager anticipation. The reason is that critical minds share at least one thing with fundamentalists, their harsh enemies: they too believe that if something is built, that alone is a proof that it is so weak that it should be deconstructed until one reaches the ultimate ideal they all share, namely what has not been built at all by any human hand (Galison forthcoming; Koerner forthcoming; Mondzain forthcoming).

Deconstruction meanders down a steep slope that constructionism—or compositionism—tries to ascend by painful zigzags. How strange that these two movements get confused when their goals are so different. It is true that viewed from above and afar they look alike since they both greatly diverge from the straight line fundamentalists always dream to trace. Both insist on the inevitable tropism of mediations, on the power of all those intermediaries that make impossible any *direct* access to objectivity, truth, morality, divinities, or beauty. Resemblance stops there, however. Deconstruction goes downhill to avoid the peril of presence, compositionism goes uphill to try to catch as much presence as possible. One behaves as if the main danger was for words to carry *too much* meaning, the other fights to wring out as much reality as possible from the fragile mediators it has painfully assembled. The former meanders so much it is because it has to constantly *delay* saying something, while the other strives for rectitude and is diverted only by the extreme steepness of the slope it tries to *ascend*. One tries to flee as far as possible from the face of the God it wishes to erase, the other knows there is no face of God, and thus nothing is to be erased. A face is to be produced instead, to be painted and repainted through as many non-mimetic re-productions and representations as possible (Koerner forthcoming).

Deconstructionists behave much like those illustrious French generals who were always one war late: they fight an old battle against naiveté, immediacy, naturalization, as if intellectuals still had to free the masses from too much belief. Have they not realized that critical minds have long died from an overdose of disbelief? The miniaturization of criticism, like that of computers, has cheapened doubt so much that now everyone, with no effort, can doubt the strongest and most entrenched certainty, deconstruct the most solid and high-standing building at no cost—any box cutter will do. Why are they so slow to realize that the diffusion of conspiracy theory has taken the place of the "naive confidence in authority"; that this expanded, popularized, and cheap revisionism has pushed criticism to mutate into its exact opposite, which one could call "naive diffidence in authority" or "critical barbarity."[18] By contrast, compositionists do not have to debunk belief, but rather to slowly produce confidence again. They don't see naiveté as the ultimate sin, but as a refreshing virtue to be regained with great pain. They don't jump to their gun when the word "certainty" is uttered, since they know what price has to be paid to produce a little bit of this most precious ware.

To convince the critically minded that constructivism means our only slow and progressive *access* to objectivity, morality, civil peace, and piety, and that, for this reason, all the subtle mediations of practice should be *protected* and cherished instead of being debunked and slowly destroyed would require such a deep alteration in our intellectual ecology that it is hard to see how it would come about.[19] And yet, this first move would be necessary if the next one, even more problematic, is to be attempted; namely, to convince fundamentalists that the idiom of constructivism might provide them with more solid and durable guarantees for preserving the values they all too quickly are ready to die for. How long will it be before the word "construction" does not sound either like an insult to be repaid in blood or like a confession of weakness inviting deconstruction? How long will it be before the word is heard not as a war cry to take up arms or hammers, but as an appeal for the extension of *care and caution,* a request to raise again the question: "How can it be built *better*?"

To finish with a quiz (in the spirit of Ian Hacking's scoring system), I propose the following test:

When you hear that something you cherish is a "construction," your first reaction is (check the right circle):

○ to take a gun
○ to seize a hammer
○ to erect a scaffold

Answer: If you checked the first, then you are a fundamentalist ready to annihilate those who appeal to the destruction of what remains strong only if it is unconstructed by human hands; if you checked the second, then you are a deconstructionist who sees construction as a proof of weakness in a building that should be pressed to ruins in order to give way to a better and firmer structure untouched by human hands; if you checked the third, then you are a constructivist, or, better, a compositionist engaged at once in the task of maintaining and nurturing those fragile habitations; if you ticked them all, then you are hopelessly muddled . . .

NOTES

My English was kindly corrected by Duana Fullwiley. I also thank Isabelle Stengers and Graham Harman for their suggestions.

1. For such a standard account, see Bourdieu (1986). For a powerful and definitive critique, see Favereau (2001).

2. In what follows I make no distinction between critical sociology and deconstruction: the first destroys in bulk, the other in detail; the first is sacrificing the present to the revolution, the second sacrifices everything, including the dreams of revolution, to the jealous god of presence.

3. Many rich examples can be found, for instance in Suchman (1987); MacKenzie (1990); McGrew, (1992); Lemonnier (1993); Bijker (1995); Petroski (1996).

4. Surface physics as it has been beautifully shown by Bensaude-Vincent (1998) could not hold a minute either in the poor materialist vocabulary, as Gaston Bachelard has shown earlier in many of his examples.

5. According to Jullien (1995) those thoughts would be much easier to conceptualize in Chinese.

6. Still inspired—or rather contaminated—by the anti-fetishism of critical theory, I misunderstood this shift in *Laboratory Life*. I thought that the product of their own hand—fabricated facts—became what no hand had produced—unfabricated facts—so that scientists, like good fetishists, were inverting causality by granting to what they had themselves done the reason why they had done it. But they were right . . . and so was I: in effect, there was indeed a shift, but from the first accounting system—the more hands the more autonomy—to the second—you have to choose between work and autonomy. To ferret this out, though, I had to dig at the heart of anti-fetishism, which remains to this day the main staple of critical theory . . .

7. For a typical example see Heinich (1993). For a "critique" of this critical position, see Koch (2002).

8. And delete the word "construction" from the subtitle of *Laboratory Life* after having deleted the word social—before facts, I am sure, go away too!

9. The necessary link between constructivism and diplomacy is explored in Latour (2002b), which is very much a companion paper to this one.

10. In technology studies, the same role is played by the tired old notion of "interpretive flexibility" or "pliability," as if being flexible and pliable were the only two states of matter worth registering.

11. Hacking himself, in the beautiful last chapter 7 on dolomite, shows how, even on such a simple case as rocks—the one Steven Weinberg liked to kick with his foot to prove that it was "there"!—the "oneness" of "the world" is hard to come by, because of the multi-realism any enquiry leads to. The author does not seem to be aware that this chapter renders his former analysis of the "sticking points" moot. My lists of guarantees simply tries to do justice to his empirical chapter better than he has been able to do.

12. Stages 2 and 3 of Hacking's list aims at this when they transform the contingent history of X, stage 1, into what "is bad" and "should be discarded," but they abandon the fourth guarantee as well as the third since *their* world, the one promised by "revolution," is exactly as uncomposed and as unnegotiable as the one they want to replace.

13. The conditions under which the fact/value distinction could be replaced by another set of two questions: what entity should we take into account? How can they be associated? (Latour 1999b).

14. To register the differences between two traditions of empiricism and the two stages in political epistemology they imply, I try to give a technical meaning to the difference in English between matters of fact and states of affairs.

15. With which I am simply unable to grade myself although I am one of the guinea pigs of his book—and with which it would be impossible, in my view, to score Hacking's own chapter on dolomites.

16. This is at least what I have attempted in Latour (1999b).

17. It is interesting to notice that there is one explicitly deconstructionist, even Derridian, architect, Daniel Liebeskind, but even a quick visit at his moving, claustrogene, and magnificent Jewish museum in Berlin is enough to show that he too is, first of all, a constructivist, and a master one at that.

18. I don't think it is a coincidence that these two critical barbarities have struck the World Trade Center one after the other: the first by destroying it to rubble, the second, adding insult to injury, by claiming that it was the deed of victims themselves, helped by the CIA or the Mossad. . . . But it is Baudrillard who has the honor of putting the last nail in the coffin of criticism: has he not claimed that the Towers, "icons of a self destroying capitalism" (Mr. bin Laden *dixit*), had deconstructed *themselves* by attracting passing planes to commit suicide? (Baudrillard 2002). One can only hope that this ultimate gesture, this ultimate self-destruction of nihilist thought about a nihilistic act of self-destruction, will be the last gasp of critical barbarity. . . . History shows, alas, that nihilism has no bottom.

19. The exhibition *Iconoclash* was, in my view, such a small effort at a local ecological alteration in the gardens of our prejudices.

Bibliography

Baudrillard, Jean. 2002. *L'esprit du terrorisme*. Paris: Galilée.

Bensaude-Vincent, Bernadette. 1998. *Eloge du mixte. Matériaux nouveaux et philosophie ancienne*. Paris: Hachette Littératures.

Bijker, Wiebe. 1995. *Of Bicycles, Bakelites, and Bulbs: Toward a Theory of Sociotechnical Change*. Cambridge, Mass.: MIT Press.

Bloor, David. 1999. "Anti-Latour." *Studies in History and Philosophy of Science* 30, no. 1: 81–112.

Bourdieu, Pierre. 1986. "La Force du droit." *Actes de la recherche en sciences socials* 64: 3–19.

De Libera, Alain. 1996. *La querelle des universaux. De Platon à la fin du Moyen Age*. Paris: Le Seuil.

Favereau, Olivier. 2001. "L'économie du sociologue ou penser (l'orthodoxie) à partir de Pierre Bourdieu." In *Le travail sociologique de Pierre Bourdieu. Dettes et critiques. Edition revue et augmentée*, edited by Bernard Lahire. Paris: La Découverte.

Galison, Peter. Forthcoming. "Images Scatter into Data, Data Gathers into Images." In *Iconoclash: Beyond the Image Wars in Science, Religion and Art*, edited by Bruno Latour and Peter Weibel. Cambridge, Mass.: MIT Press.

Geslin, Philippe. 1994. "Les salins du Bénin et de Guinée, ou comment l'ergonomie et l'ethnologie peuvent saisir le transfert de techniques et de sociétés." In *De la préhistoire aux missiles balistiques—l'intelligence sociale des techniques*, edited by Bruno Latour and Pierre Lemonnier. Paris: La Découverte.

Hacking, Ian. 1999. *The Social Construction of What?* Cambridge, Mass.: Harvard University Press.

Haraway, Donna. 1999. *Gender, Race, and Nature in the World of Modern Science*. London: Routledge and Kegan Paul.

Heinich, Nathalie. 1993. "Les objets-personnes. Fétiches, reliques et oeuvres d'art." *Sociologie de l'art* 6: 25–56.

Jullien, François. 1995. *The Propensity of Things: Toward a History of Efficacy in China*. Cambridge: Zone Books.

———. 1997. *Traité de l'efficacité*. Paris: Grasset.

Koch, Robert. "The Critical Gesture in Philosophy." In *Iconoclash: Beyond the Image Wars in Science, Religion and Art*, edited by Bruno Latour and Peter Weibel. 2002. Cambridge, Mass.: MIT Press.

Koerner, Joseph. Forthcoming. "The Icon as Iconoclash." In *Iconoclash: Beyond the Image Wars in Science, Religion and Art*, edited by Bruno Latour and Peter Weibel. Cambridge, Mass.: MIT Press.

Knorr-Cetina, Karin. 1999. *Epistemic Cultures: How the Sciences Make Knowledge*. Cambridge, Mass.: Harvard University Press.

Koolhas, Rem, and Bruce Mau. 1995. *Small, Medium, Large, Extra-Large*. Rotterdam: Office for Metropolitan Architecture.

Latour, Bruno, and Pierre Lemonnier, eds. 1994. *De la préhistoire aux missiles balistiques—l'intelligence sociale des techniques*. Paris: La Découverte.

Latour, Bruno. 1996. *Petite réflexion sur le culte moderne des dieux Faitiches*. Paris: Les Empêcheurs de penser en rond.

———. 1999a. *Pandora's Hope: Essays on the Reality of Science Studies*. Cambridge, Mass.: Harvard University Press.

———. 1999b. *Politiques de la nature. Comment faire entrer les sciences en démocratie*. Paris, La Découverte.

———. 2002a. "Gabriel Tarde and the End of the Social." In *The Social in Question: New Bearings in History and the Social Sciences*, edited by Patrick Joyce. London: Routledge.

———. 2002b. *War of the Worlds: What about Peace?* Chicago: Prickly Press Pamphlet.

Lemonnier, Pierre, ed. 1993. *Technological Choices: Transformation in Material Cultures since the Neolithic*. London: Routledge.

MacKenzie, Donald. 1990. *Inventing Accuracy: A Historical Sociology of Nuclear Missile Guidance*. Cambridge, Mass.: MIT Press.

McGrew, William. 1992. *Chimpanzee Material Culture: Implications for Human Evolution*. Cambridge: Cambridge University Press.

Mondzain, Marie-José. Forthcoming. "The Holy Shroud: How Invisible Hands Weave the Undecidable." In *Iconoclash: Beyond the Image Wars in Science, Religion and Art*, edited by Bruno Latour and Peter Weibel. Cambridge, Mass.: MIT Press.

Petroski, Henry. 1996. *Inventing by Design: How Engineers Get from Thought to Thing.* Cambridge, Mass.: Harvard University Press.

Pickering, Andrew. 1995. *The Mangle of Practice: Time, Agency and Science.* Chicago: University of Chicago Press.

Rheinberger, Hans-Jörg. 1997. *Toward a History of Epistemic Things: Synthetizing Proteins in the Test Tube.* Stanford, Calif.: Stanford University Press.

Souriau, Étienne. 1935. "L'oeuvre à faire." Paris: Félix Alcan.

———. 1939. *L'instauration philosophique.* Paris: Félix Alcan.

Stengers, Isabelle. 1993. *L'invention des sciences modernes.* Paris: La Découverte.

———. 1997. *Power and Invention.* Minneapolis: University of Minnesota Press.

———. 1998. "La guerre des sciences: et la paix?" In *Impostures scientifiques. Les malentendus de l'affaire Sokal,* edited by Baudouin Jurdant. Paris: La Découverte.

Suchman, Lucy. 1987. *Plans and Situated Actions: The Problem of the Human Machine.* Cambridge: Cambridge University Press.

Tarde, Gabriel. 1999. *Monadologie et sociologie.* Paris: Les empêcheurs de penser en rond.

Yaneva, Albena. 2002. "Scaling Up and Down: Models and Publics in Architecture—Case Study of the Extensions of Whitney Museum for American Art." Paper presented at the seminar of Max-Planck Institute for the History of Science in Berlin, Department II.

3. Interview with Donna Haraway

Participants: Randi Markussen, Finn Olesen, and Nina Lykke

Interviewer: Let us start with the "Cyborg Manifesto." Many women have been fascinated by the idea that the cyborg could be a woman. Why did you insist on the femaleness of the cyborg?

DH: For me the notion of the cyborg was female, and a woman, in complex ways. It was an act of resistance, an oppositional move of a pretty straightforward kind. The cyborg was, of course, part of a military project, part of an extraterrestrial man-in-space project. It was also a science fictional figure out of a largely male-defined science fiction. Then there was another dimension in which cyborgs were female: in popular culture, and in certain kinds of medical culture. Here cyborgs appeared as patients, or as objects of pornography, as "fem-bots," the iron maiden, the roboticized machinic, pornographic female. But the whole figure of the cyborg seemed to me potentially much more interesting than that. Moreover, an act of taking over a territory seemed like a fairly straightforward, political, symbolic technoscientific project. From my point of view, the cyborg was a figure that collected up many things, among them the way that post–World War II technoscientific cultures were deeply shaped by information sciences and biological sciences, by the implosion of informatics and biologics that was already well under way by the end of World War II, and that has only deepened in the last fifty years and transformed conditions of life very deeply. These are not matters of choice, neither are they matters of determinism. These are deep materializations of very complex sociotechnical relations. What interested me was the way of conceiving of us all as communication systems, whether we are animate or inanimate, whether we are animals or plants, human beings or the planet herself, Gaia, or machines of various kinds. This common coin of theorizing existence, this common ontology of everything as communication-control-system was what interested me. It made me very angry and anxious, but interested me in more positive ways, too. Among other things, I was attracted by an unconscious and dreamlike quality, and I was interested in affirming not simply the human-machine aspect of cyborgs, but also the degree to which human beings and other organisms have a kind of commonality to them in cyborg worlds.

It was the joint implosion of human and machine, on the one hand, and human and other organisms, on the other, within a kind of problematic subcommunication that interested me about the cyborg. There were many levels in this, for example, labor process issues: the particular ways that women (working-class women, women of color, women in Third World countries with export processing zones that would attract international capital for micro-electronics manufacture) were implicated in the labor process of cyborg production, as scientists, too, although in relative minorities. Women occupied many kinds of places in these worlds, in biomedicine, in information sciences, but also as a preferred workforce for trans-national capitals. Strategies of flexible accumulation involved the productions of various kinds of gender, for men and for women, that were historically specific. The cyborg became a figure for trying to understand women's place in the "integrated circuit," a phrase produced by feminist socialists. Moreover, the cyborg was a place to excavate and examine popular culture, including science fiction and, in particular, feminist science fiction. A novel like *Superluminal* by Vonda McIntyre made a strong use of cyborg imagery in complex, interesting ways that were quasi-feminist. Joanna Russ's clone sister fiction of the mid-1970s and, certainly, Octavia Butler's work intrigued me a lot. There was a great deal of feminist cultural production which was working with the cyborg in fascinating ways. Also, the cyborg seemed to me a figuration that was specifically anti-psychoanalytic. But in contrast to what a lot of people have argued, I do not think of the cyborg as without an unconscious. However, it is not a Freudian unconscious. There is a different kind of dreamwork going on here; it is not ethical, it is not edenic, it is not about origin stories in the garden. It is a different set of narrations, figurations, dreamwork, subject formations, and unconscious work. These sorts of figurations do not exclude ethical narrations or other kinds of psychoanalytic work, but they are not the same thing. It was important to me to have a way of dealing with figurations in technoscience that were not quite so hegemonized by psychoanalysis as I found it developed around me in really lively places of feminist cultural work such as film theory. Some marvelous work has been done with Freudian or post-Freudian tools here, but they did not seem right for the analysis of technoscience. So I turned to literature as well as biology and philosophy, and questions of figurations interested me a lot. Cyborgs are also places where the ambiguity between the literal and the figurative is always working. You are never sure whether to take something literally or figuratively. It is always both/and. It is this undecidability between the literal and the figurative that interests me about technoscience. It seems like a good place to think with. Moreover, it involves a physicality that is undeniable and deeply historically specific. It is possible to extend the cyborg image into other historical configurations, allegorically or analogically, but it seems to me that it had a privileged historical emergence. You can use it to inquire into other historical formations, but it has a specificity. In a way, you know, I am doing this analysis of the meanings attached to the cyborg retrospectively. I cannot imagine that I thought all these things in 1983 (laughter). It is a funny thing to look back at something I actually began writing seventeen years ago.

Interviewer: Please, tell us about the intriguing history of the "Cyborg Manifesto," which has taken on a life of its own in a way that academic papers seldom do.

DH: I began writing the manifesto in 1983. The *Socialist Review* in the United States wanted socialist feminists to write about the future of socialist feminism in the context of the early Reagan era and the retrenchment of the left that the 1980s was witnessing. Barbara Ehrenreich and I, and many other American socialist feminists were invited to contribute. Moreover, Frigga Haug and the feminist collective of the West German socialist journal *Das Argument* wanted me to write about reproductive technologies, and the cyborg is an obvious place for making reflections on the technologification of reproduction. Almost at the same time, a left democratic group in the former Yugoslavia was holding a conference and I was designated as one of the American representatives from *Socialist Review*. I wrote a version of the "Cyborg Manifesto" for this occasion, although I actually did not deliver my paper at the conference, because, instead, a small group of us made a demonstration about the division of labor at the conference, where the women were invisibly doing all the work, while the men were not so invisibly doing all the propounding! So in the beginning the "Cyborg Manifesto" had a very strong socialist and European connection.

Interviewer: Where did you read the word "cyborg" the first time? Do you remember that?

DH: I do not remember. I tried to remember it, and it felt like I made the word up, but I cannot have made it up. I read Norbert Wiener, but I do not think I got it there. I did not read Clynes and Kline until way after I had written the Cyborg Manifesto. I did not know about Clynes and Kline and that fabulous connection of the psychiatrist, the systems engineer, and the mental hospital. It was a graduate student of mine, Chris Gray, who told me about the cyborg article of Clynes and Kline from 1960.

Interviewer: How do you yourself look upon the remarkable history of the "Cyborg Manifesto"? How do you evaluate the reception, in terms both of positive and negative responses?

DH: I am astonished. But to answer your question, I can tell you that the reactions, right from the beginning, were very mixed. At *Socialist Review* the manifesto was considered very controversial. The Socialist Review East Coast Collective truly disapproved of it politically and did not want it published. But the Berkeley Socialist Review Collective did, and it was Jeff Escoffier, a very interesting gay theorist and historian, who was my editor at the Berkeley Collective, and he was very enthusiastic about the paper. So from the beginning the manifesto was very controversial. There were some who regarded it as tremendously anti-feminist, as a kind of blissed-out, techno-sublime euphoria. Those readers completely failed to see all the critique. They would read things that for me are highly ironic and angry, a kind of contained ironic fury; they would read these things as my literal position, as if I were embracing and affirming what I am describing with barely detained fury. The reading practices of the "Cyborg Manifesto" took me aback from the very beginning, and I learned that irony is a dangerous rhetorical strategy. Moreover, I found out that it is not a very kind rhetoric, because it does things to your audience that are not fair. When you use irony, you assume that your audience is reading out of much the same sort of experiences as you yourself, and they are not. You assume reading practices that you have to finally admit are highly privileged and often private. The manifesto put together literacies that are the result of literary studies, biology, information sciences, political economy, and a very privileged and expensive travel and education. It was a paper that was built on privilege, and the reading practices that it asks from people are hard. I learned something about that from certain receptions of the manifesto. On the other hand, most of my readers shared the same privileges (laughter).

There were also readers who would take the "Cyborg Manifesto" for its technological analysis, but drop the feminism. Many science studies people, who still seem tone-deaf to feminism, have done this. It is generally my experience that very few people are taking what I consider all of its parts. I have had people, like *Wired* magazine readers, interviewing and writing about the "Cyborg Manifesto" from what I see as a very blissed-out, techno-sublime position. But I have also had this really interesting reception from young feminists—a reception which I love. They embrace and use the cyborg of the manifesto to do what they want for their own purposes. They have completely different histories from mine, from this particular moment of democratic socialism and socialist feminism, the transition of the 1980s of which I just narrated. This is not their history at all. They have a totally different relationship to cultural production, to access to media, to use of computers for performance art and other purposes, to technomusic, and they have, to my pleasure and astonishment, found the "Cyborg Manifesto" useful for queer sexuality work, and for certain kinds of queer theory that take in technoscience. I found myself to be an audience here. In this context, I am one of the readers of the manifesto, not one of the writers. I did not write that manifesto, but I love reading it (laughter). These young feminists have truly rewritten the manifesto in ways that were not part of my intention, but I can see what they are doing. I think it is a legitimate reading, and I like it, but it really wasn't what I wrote. So sometimes people read the manifesto in ways which are very pleasant surprises to me, and sometimes it is really distressing to be confronted with the reading practices. But, anyway, it is a hard paper to read. Difficulty is an issue. On the other hand, I swear, I meet people without academic training who read the manifesto and who do not give up. They read it for what they want, and they just do not care about the difficulty issue.

Interviewer: I have been teaching gender and technoculture to registered nurses, and for many of them, the manifesto was a revelation. It helped them to see their practice as nurses in a new light and to avoid being caught in the dilemma between a humanistic and partly technophobic concept of care on the one hand, and on the other the powerful and uncritically self-glorifying visions of progress, embedded in the discourses of medical science. Your cyborg was for them a critical tool, a position from which they could think their professional identity differently.

DH: This is very interesting. I think that part of the feminist argument of the manifesto is exactly in line with this. It is neither technophobic, nor technophilic, but about trying to inquire critically into the worldliness of technoscience. It is about exploring where real people are in the material semiotic systems of technoscience and what kinds of accountability, responsibility, pleasure, work, play, are engaged, and should be engaged.

Interviewer: Another aspect of the cyborg which I would like to ask you about is how you evaluate the danger that it might lose its critical potential and become a mainstream figure, closed within a certain mainstream narrative, since it today—much more than when you started writing about it in 1983—has become a so obvious and inescapable part of society and culture.

DH: I think that as an oppositional figure the cyborg has a rather short half-life (laughter), and indeed for the most part, cyborg figurations, both in technical and popular culture, are not and have never been oppositional, or liberatory, or had a critical dimension in the sense that I use critique, i.e., in the sense that things might be otherwise. It is a sense of critique that is not negative, necessarily, except in the particular way that the Frankfurt School understood negativity—a way which I think is really worth remembering and holding on to. It is critique in the deep sense that things might be otherwise. There is much of the Frankfurt School that I have never embraced, but that sense of critique as a freedom project is important. There was a certain amount of work, and there even still is a certain amount of work in that freedom project that oppositional, or critical cyborgs can do, but I agree that it is much less true now than it was in 1983. Precisely because of the kind of tightening of the Internet around us all; precisely because we are now in the matrix in such a relentlessly literal way that there is some really new tropic work that has to be done in this figure. I take figurations and the question of how they work very seriously, as a practice trying to understand what collects up the life-and-death concerns of people. It seems to me that we need a whole kinship system of figurations as critical figures and in that sense I think cyborg figurations can continue to do critical work. But it can quickly become banal, and mainstream, and comforting. The cyborg may be an alibi that makes the technoscientific bourgeois figure comfortable, or it may be a critical figure.

Interviewer: You pointed out that a whole kinship of figurations is needed.

DH: Yes (laughter), littermates, a kennel, a breed.

Interviewer: So I would like to leave the cyborg and look at another figuration that has emerged in your work: the coyote. I read the coyote figure in your texts as a figuration that becomes necessary because your complex approach to the deconstruction of the dichotomy between "nature" and "culture" implies a refusal to consider non-human "nature" as nothing but stupid, soulless matter. To me your coyote figure is a figuration in which the search for alternative understandings of the phenomena we are used to call "nature" is embedded. But why did you choose this particular figuration?

DH: It is partly a regional issue. You know, I am a Westerner, not just in the sense of inheriting Western traditions, but I am from the western United States.

Coyote figures are important to Native Americans in many places in North America, including various groups in the southwestern United States. When I use the coyote figure, a double issue is at stake. First of all, my use of the coyote is marked by the middle-class, white feminist appropriation of Native American symbols, about which one must be very suspicious. There is a particular way in which feminist spirituality has operated in a rather colonial way to Native American religion. I have a certain criticism of my own use of the coyote figuration on this background. However, saying that I do not mean to dismiss or to forbid what I and others have been doing in terms of using Native American symbols. What I want, is to add a certain caution, because figures do travel, and they travel outside of their places of emergence in various ways, and certain figures like the raven and the coyote do work in Anglo culture as well as in Native culture. We do live in a world that is made up of complexly webbed layers of locals and globals, and who is to say that Native American symbols are to be less global than those produced by Anglo-Americans? Or who is to say that one set of symbols has got to stay local, while all the other ones get to figure in so-called globalization? So I think there is a way in which this cross-talk between figurations is politically interesting, although certainly not innocent.

Thus, the coyote is a specific figuration. It is not nature in a Euro-American sense and not about resources to the makings of culture. Moreover, the coyote is not a very nice figure. It is a trickster figure, and, particularly in Navajo figurations, the coyote is often associated with quite distressing kinds of trickster work. The coyote is about the world as a place that is active in terms that are not particularly under human control, but it is not about the human on the one side and the natural on the other. There is a communication between what we would call "nature" and "culture," but in a world where "coyote" is a relevant category, "nature" and "culture" are not the relevant categories. The coyote disturbs nature/culture ontologies. I chose the coyote and not, for example, Spider-woman, because of the already overdetermined feminist appropriations of the latter, and for one thing the coyote is not female, particularly.

Interviewer: Is it post-gender?

DH: No! I have no patience with the term "post-gender." I have never liked it.

Interviewer: But you used it in the manifesto.

DH: Yes, I did. But I had no idea that it would become this "ism"! (Laughter) You know, I have never used it since! Because post-gender ends up meaning a very strange array of things. Gender is a verb, not a noun. Gender is always about the production of subjects in relation to other subjects, and in relation to artifacts. Gender is about material-semiotic production of these assemblages, these human–artifact assemblages that are people. People are always already in assemblage with worlds. Humans are already congeries of things that are not us. We are not self-identical. Gender is specifically a production of men and women. It is an obligatory distribution of subjects in unequal relationships, where some have more property than others. Gender is a specific production of subjects in sexualized forms where some have rights to reproductivity, and sexuality, and other modes of being in the world. So gender is specifically a system of that kind, but not continuous across history, which means that things need not be this way, and in this particular sense that puts focus on a critical relationship to gender along the lines of critical theory's "things need not be this way"; in this sense of blasting gender I approve of the term "post-gender." But this is not "post-gender" in a utopian, beyond-masculine-and-feminine sense, which it often is taken to mean. It is the blasting of necessity, the non-necessity of this way of doing the world.

Interviewer: Going back to the coyote and your choice to include that in your kinship of potentially critical figurations instead of such explicitly female figures as Spiderwoman or the goddess. . . . Did that have something to do with coyote being post-gender in the sense that you just defined?

DH: Oh yes! It has much to do with "post-gender" in the sense of blasting the truth scandal of gender and with a feminism that does not embrace Woman, but is for women, and which involves the particular powerful theories of intersection that came out of post-colonial theory, and women of color feminist theory, and that came overwhelmingly, though not only, from people who had been oppressed in colonial and racial ways. They insisted on a kind of relentless intersectionality, that refused any gender analysis standing on its own, and in this context, I find that the term "post-gender" makes sense. Here it can be understood as a kind of intensified critical understanding of these many threads of production of inequality.

Interviewer: To go a bit further into your deconstruction of the nature/culture dichotomy, I will ask you to comment on your concept of the "apparatus of bodily production." Like the cyborg and coyote figurations, this concept is a useful tool when you want to shift the traditional nature/culture boundaries and create new ways of understanding bodies as well as the sex/gender dichotomy. How do you yourself look upon the link between the concept of "apparatus of bodily production" and the breaking down of the "sex/gender" dichotomy?

DH: Sex and gender is an analytical device that is clearly indebted to a way of doing the world that works through matter/form categories. It is a deeply Aristotelian dichotomy. It works on the cultural appropriation of nature for the teleological ends of mind. It has terribly contaminated roots. Nonetheless it has been a useful tool for analyzing the sex/gender system. In that sense, it was a radical achievement at a certain moment. But the analytical work was mistaken for the thing itself, and people truly believed, and believe, in sex and gender as things. It is the mistake of misplaced concreteness. Instead it is important to remember the contaminated philosophical tradition that gives us tools of that kind. In order to do the world in other than Platonist and Aristotelian ways, in order to do ontology otherwise, in order to get out a world that is done by notions of matter/form, or production/raw material, I feel aligned with ways of getting at the world as a verb, which throws us into categories like practices, worlds in the making, and apparatuses of bodily production without the categories of form and matter, and sex and gender.

Interviewer: And without reducing everything either to purely social constructions or purely natural things?

DH: Absolutely. I am neither a naturalist nor a social constructionist. Neither-nor. This is not social constructionism, and it is not technoscientific, or biological determinism. It is not nature. It is not culture. It is truly about a serious historical effort to get elsewhere.

Interviewer: You have recently included a new member in your kinship of potential critical figurations: the dog. Why?

DH: Dogs are many things. They occupy many kinds of categories, breeds, populations, vermin, figures, research animals, sources of rabies, the New Guinea singing dog, the dingoes, etc. Dogs are very many kinds of entities. The ontology of dogs turns out to be quite big, and there are all those names for dogs that are about various kinds of relationalities. Dogs have many kinds of relationality, but one kind that is practically obligatory is with humans. It is almost part of the definition of a dog to be in relationship with humans, although not necessarily around the word "domestication." Though "domestication" is a very powerful word, it is not altogether clear. In fact, it is probably not true that humans domesticated dogs. Conversely, it is probably true from an evolutionary and historical point of view that dogs took the first steps in producing this symbiosis.

There are a lot of interesting biological-behavioral stories that have a certain evidential quality. These are partly testable stories, partly not testable stories. So dogs have this large array of possible ontologies that are all about relationship and very heavily about relationships with humans in different historical forms. And dogs then for people do a tremendous amount of semiotic work. They work for us not only when they are herding sheep, they also work as figures, and dogs figure back very important kinds of human investments. For me, there are many, many ways in which I am interested in dogs. I am interested in the fact that dogs are not us. So they figure not-us. They are not just cute projections. Dogs do not figure mirror-of-me. Dogs figure another species, but another species living in very close relationship, another species in relation to which the nature/culture divide is more of a problem than a help when we try to understand it. Because dogs are neither nature nor culture, not both/and, not neither/nor, but something else.

Interviewer: The notion of companionship becomes important here, I assume?

DH: Yes, although the notion of companionship is a very modern way of seeing the dogs. The notion of the companion animal is a quite recent invention. Seeing dogs as companion animals, but not pets, is a rather recent contestation. We have necessarily to be in an ethical relationship with dogs, because they are vulnerable to human cruelty in very particular ways, or to carelessness, or to stupidity. So dogs become sites of meaning making and sites of inquiry: ethical inquiry, ontological inquiry, inquiry about the nature of sociality, inquiry about pedagogy and training and control, inquiry about sadism, about authoritarianism, about war (the relationship between the infantry and the war dog as tools in military history). Dogs become good figures to think with, in all sorts of circumstances. There is the development of service dogs, for example, the seeing-eye dogs. There are all the different ways that dogs are brought into relationship with human need, or human desire. There are dogs as toys, toy dogs, dogs as livestock guardians in charge of protecting sheep against wolves, bears, coyotes, and so an. Working dogs interest me a lot and so does the relationship of a human being and a dog in the sports world. There are also dependency issues, but dogs are not surrogate children. Dogs are adult. Adult dogs should not be permanently infantilized! When you live with a dog you live with another adult who is not your species. I find this cross-species companionship and the questions of otherness that are involved really interesting. Dogs confront us with a particular kind of otherness that raises many questions, ethical, ontological, political, questions about pleasure, about embodiment etc.

Interviewer: How does the dog relate to the cyborg and the coyote? Is it an in-between figure in the kinship of figurations?

DH: It is, and in that sense, you know, I feel like I have written about many sorts of entities that are neither nature nor culture. The cyborg is such an entity, and the coyote, and the genetically engineered laboratory research animal OncoMouse is also in this odd family—this queer family that is neither nature nor culture, but an interface. The family includes, for me, in terms of what I have written about personally, the cyborg, the coyote, the OncoMouse, the FemaleMan, the feminists, the history of women within feminist analysis, the dogs in my new project, and, of course, the non-human primates. All these are entities that require one to be confused about nature and culture.

Interviewer: Are they all on the same level, or do you consider the cyborg to be a kind of meta-category?

DH: Well, sometimes the cyborg functions as a meta-category, but I am actually much happier to demote it to one of the litter. Sometimes I do end up saying these are all cyborg figures, but I think that is a bad idea. I like to think the cyborg as one of the litter, the one that requires an awful lot of intervention in order to survive (laughter). It has to be technically enhanced in order to survive in this world.

NOTE

This interview took place when Donna Haraway visited Denmark as keynote speaker at the conference "Cyborg Identities—The Humanities in Technical Light," October 21–22, 1999, arranged by Randi Markussen and Finn Olesen, Institute of Information and Media Sciences, Aarhus University, as part of the initiative "The Humanities at the Turn of the Millennium," Centre for Cultural Studies, Aarhus University. The interview was taken as part of a special event with Donna Haraway, organized by the FREJA research project "Cyborgs and Cyberspace—Between Narration and Sociotechnical Reality"; the three interviewers are all members of the FREJA research group. First published in *Kvinder, køn & forskning* [Women, Gender and Research] 9, no. 2 (2000): 6–15. Reprinted by permission.

4. Cyborgs to Companion Species: Reconfiguring Kinship in Technoscience

Donna Haraway

for my father, fifty years a sportswriter at the Denver *Post*

EXCERPTS FROM "NOTES OF A SPORTSWRITER'S DAUGHTER," SPRING–FALL 2000

(1) Cayenne, our year-old Australian Shepherd bitch, is in full "teenage mode," popping like drops of Leyden frost on a hot stove. Things she did on cue yesterday without question today fail to engage her roving mind. Back to basics! I have written "shut up and train" across my forehead. Peace reigns in her lusty soul if she gets at least five miles a day of running and a few other bouts of vigorous activity. Cheap to a good home. . . .

(2) Ms. Cayenne Pepper continues to colonize all my cells—a sure case of what the biologist Lynn Margulis calls symbiogenesis. I bet if you checked our DNA, you'd find some odd transfections between us. Her saliva must have the viral vectors; her darter-tongue kisses are irresistible. Co-evolution in the naturecultures of companion species has as many punctuated equilibria as Stephen J. Gould could ever have wished. Margulis and Gould, opponents in evolutionary theory in their lives, are fused in Cayenne and me.

(3) Roland Dog, our Aussie-Chow six-year-old, was beautiful at the agility trials Saturday. He had speed, drive, heart, and he was paying attention. We would have gotten two legs out of our three runs if I hadn't literally gotten a mental

white-out at a jump choice in mid-course each time. He was great; I was middle-aged and unused to even novice high functioning after getting up at 4 A.M. to drive a hundred miles to spend time with my dogs!

(4) Dear Vicki,[1]

Watching Roland with you lurking inside my head over the last week made me remember that such things are multi-dimensional and situational, and describing a dog's temperament takes more precision than I achieved. We go to an off-leash, large, cliff-enclosed beach in Santa Cruz almost every day. There are two main classes of dogs there: retrievers and meta-retrievers. Roland is a meta-retriever. (My partner points out there is really a third class of dogs too—the "nons"—not in the game at issue here.) Roland'll play ball with us once in a while (or anytime we couple the sport with a liver cookie or two), but his heart's not in it. The activity is not really self-rewarding to him, and his lack of style there shows it. But meta-retrieving is another matter entirely. The retrievers watch whoever is about to throw a ball or stick as if their lives depended on the next few seconds. The meta-retrievers watch the retrievers with an exquisite sensitivity to directional cues and micro-second of spring. These meta-dogs do not watch the ball or the human; they watch the ruminant-surrogates-in-dog's-clothing. Roland in meta-mode looks like an Aussie–Border Collie mockup for a lesson in Platonism. His forequarters are lowered, forelegs slightly apart with one in front of the other in hair-trigger balance, his hackles in mid-rise, his eyes focused, his whole body ready to spring into hard, directed action. When the retrievers sail out after the projectile, the meta-retrievers move out of their intense eye and stalk into heading, heeling, bunching, and cutting their charges with joy and skill. The good meta-retrievers can even handle more than one retriever at a time. The good retrievers can dodge the metas and still make their catch in eye-amazing leaps—or surges into the waves, if things have gone to sea. Since we have no ducks or other surrogate sheep or cattle on the beach, the retrievers have to do duty for the metas. Some retriever people take exception to this multitasking of their dogs (I can hardly blame them), so those of us with metas try to distract our dogs once in a while with some game they inevitably find much less satisfying. I drew a mental Larson cartoon on Thursday watching Roland, an ancient and arthritic Old English Sheepdog, a lovely red tricolor Aussie, and a Border Collie mix of some kind form an intense ring around a shepherd-lab mix, a plethora of motley Goldens, and a game pointer who hovered around a human who—liberal individualist in Amerika to the end—was trying to throw his stick to his dog only. Meanwhile, in the distance, a rescue whippet was eating up sand in road-runner fashion, pursued by a ponderous, slope-hipped German Shepherd dog.

Why do I feel all of this is about the extended, cross-species family of a sportswriter's daughter?

PREAMBLE

This is a chapter of fragments, of work-in-progress, of dog-eaten props and half-trained arguments. But I offer this set of notes toward a future work as a training diary for reshaping some stories I care about a great deal, as a scholar and as a person in my time and place. Telling a story of co-habitation, co-evolution, Whiteheadian concrescence, and embodied cross-species sociality, "Kinship in Technoscience" compares two cobbled together figures—cyborgs and companion species—to ask which might more fruitfully inform livable politics and ontologies in current life worlds. These figures are hardly polar opposites. Cyborgs and companion species each bring together the human and non-human, the organic and technological, carbon and silicon, freedom and structure, history and myth, the rich and the poor, the state and the subject, diversity and depletion, modernity and post-modernity, and nature and culture in unexpected ways. Besides all that, neither a cyborg nor a companion animal pleases the pure of heart who long for better protected species boundaries and sterilization of category deviants. Nonetheless, the differences between even the most politically correct cyborg and an ordinary dog matter.

I begin with stories, histories, ecologies, and technologies of the space-faring NASA machine-organism hybrids named cyborg in 1960. Those cyborgs were appropriated to do feminist work in Reagan's Star Wars times of the mid-1980s. By the end of the millennium, however, cyborgs could no longer do the work of a proper herding dog to gather up the threads needed for serious critical inquiry. So I go happily to the dogs to explore the birth of the kennel in order to help craft tools for science studies in the present time, when secondary Bushes threaten to replace the old growth of more livable naturecultures in the carbon budget politics of all water-based life on earth. Having worn the scarlet letters, "Cyborgs for earthly survival!" long enough, I now sport a slogan only Schutzhund women could have come up with, when even a first nip can result in a death sentence: "Run fast; bite hard!"[2]

This is a story of biopower and biosociality, as well as of technoscience. Like any good Darwinian, I tell a story of evolution. In the mode of (nucleic) acidic millennialism, I tell a tale of molecular differences, but one less rooted in Mitochondrial Eve in a neocolonial Out of Africa and more rooted in those first mitochondrial canine bitches who got in the way of man making himself yet again in the Greatest Story Ever Told. Instead, those bitches insisted on the history of companion species, a mundane and ongoing sort of tale, one full of misunderstandings, achievements, crimes, and renewable hopes. And so, mine is a story told by a student of the sciences and a feminist of a certain generation who has gone utterly to the dogs, literally. Dogs, in all their historical complexity, matter here. Dogs are not just an alibi for other themes; dogs are fleshly material-semiotic presences in the body of technoscience. Dogs are not surrogates for theory here; they are not here just to think with. They are here to live with. Partners in the crime of human evolution, they are in the garden from the get-go, wily as Coyote.

Whitehead (1948, 1969) talks about "the concrete" as "an actual entity as a concrescence of prehensions"—there are no pre-constituted subjects and objects in his world. Stressing the processual character of reality, he called actual entities "actual occasions." His philosophy is one among many resources for figuring "aliberal" subjects and objects, which/who are constituted in relational process. Subjects and objects (and kinds, genres, genders) are the products of their own relating, through many kinds of "emergent ontologies" (Verran 2001); or "ontological choreographies" (Cussins 1996); or "scale-making" in space and time (Tsing 2000). For Whitehead, "objectifications" had to do with the way "the potentiality of one actual entity is realized in another actual entity." This is very promising philosophical bait for training science studies folk to understand companion species in both storied deep time, which is chemically etched in the DNA of every cell, and in very recent doings, which leave more odoriferous traces.

And like a decadent gardener who can't keep good distinctions between natures and cultures straight, the shape of my kin networks looks more like a trellis, an esplanade, than a tree. You can't tell up from down, and everything seems to go sidewise. Such snake-like, sidewinding traffic is one of my themes. My garden is full of snakes, full of trellises, full of indirection. Instructed by evolutionary population biologists and bioanthropologists, I know that multi-directional gene flow—multi-directional flows of bodies and values—is and has always been the name of the game of life on earth. In that spirit, it is certainly the way into the kennel. Unfairly, I will risk alienating my old doppelganger, the cyborg, in order to try to convince my colleagues and comrades that dogs might be better guides through the thickets of technobiopolitics in the Third Millennium of the Current Era.

I. CYBORGS

An Evolutionary Cartoon of Enhanced Man in Space

Most Western narratives of humanism and technology require each other constitutively: How else could man make himself? Man births himself through the realization of his intentions in his objects; that is the quest story of masculinist, single-parent, self-birthing. Those objects—those realized intentions—return in the form of the threat of the instrument's surpassing the maker; thus emerges the dialectic of technophilic, technophobic apocalypse. The myth system is simple and old; cyborg practices are much less simple and much more recent.[3]

The term "cyborg" was coined by Manfred Clynes and Nathan Kline in 1960 to refer to the enhanced man who could survive in extraterrestrial environments. They imagined the cyborgian man-machine hybrid would be needed in the next great technohumanist challenge—space flight. The travel tale is a birth narrative. A designer of physiological instrumentation and electronic data-processing systems, the Australian-Austrian Clynes was the chief research scientist in the Dynamic Simulation Laboratory at Rockland State Hospital in New York. Director of research at Rockland State, Kline was a clinical psychiatrist. Their article was based on a paper the authors gave at the Psychophysiological Aspects of Space Flight Symposium sponsored by the U.S. Air Force School of Aviation Medicine in San Antonio, Texas. Enraptured with cybernetics, Clynes and Kline (1960, 27) thought of cyborgs as "self-regulating man-machine systems." That paper featured a white lab rat implanted with an osmotic pump under its skin to permit the continuous injection of chemicals to regulate basic physiological parameters. The join of pump/machine and organism, effected through the engineering of feedback-controlled communication circuits, produced an ontologically new, historically specific entity: the cyborg, the enhanced command-control-communication-intelligence system (C3I). Here, the machine is not other to the organism, nor is it a simple instrument for effecting the purposes of the organism. Rather the machine and the organism are each communication systems joined in a symbiosis that transforms both.

This cyborg is a technohumanist figure of the Cold War and the heyday of the space race. Escape from the earth, from the body, from the limits of merely biological evolution is the message and the plot. Man is his own invention; biological evolution fulfills itself in the evolution of technology. Any emergent ethics of care for the hybrid machine-organism resolves into blissed-out, jacked-in terror of the communications-machinic self. A plethora of actors and a motley of agencies reduce to One, at least in the myth. Co-evolution and mutual co-constitution in this story resolve into the figure of transcendent self-surpassing, not into a tale of mundane and mortal co-inhabiting, where the struggle for a practice of co-flourishing across categories might be sought. And, naturally, rats go first where no man has gone before.

Plainly, not all cyborgs have agreed to abide by this birth contract. In my own "Cyborg Manifesto" in the mid-1980s, I tried to write another surrogacy agreement, another trope, another figure for living within and honoring the skills and practices of contemporary technoculture without losing touch with the permanent war apparatus of a non-optional post-nuclear world and its transcendent, very material lives. Cyborgs can be figures for living within contradictions, attentive to the naturecultures of mundane practices, in opposition to the dire myths of self-birthing, embracing mortality as the condition for life, and alert to the emergent historical hybridities actually populating the world at all its contingent scales.[4]

However, cyborg refigurations hardly exhaust the tropic work required for ontological choreography in technoscience. Indeed, I have come to see cyborgs as junior siblings in the much bigger, queer family of companion species, in which reproductive biotechnopolitics are generally a surprise, sometimes even a nice surprise. I know perfectly well that a U.S. middle-aged white woman with a dog playing the sport of agility is no match for Man in Space or Bladerunner and their trans-genic kin in the annals of philosophical inquiry or the ethnography of naturecultures. Besides, (1) self-figuration is not my task; (2) transgenics are not the enemy; and (3) contrary to lots of dangerous and unethical projection in the Western world that makes domestic canines into furry children, dogs are not about oneself. Indeed, that is the beauty of dogs. They are not a projection, nor the realization of an intention, nor the telos of anything. They are dogs; i.e. . . . , a species in an obligatory, constitutive, protean relationship with human beings.

There cannot be just one companion species; there must be at least two to make one. It is in the syntax; it is in the flesh. Dogs are about the inescapable, contradictory story of relationships—co-constitutive relationships in which none of the partners pre-exist the relating, and the relating is never done once and for all. Historical specificity and contingent mutability rule all the way down, into nature and culture, into naturecultures. There is no foundation; there are only elephants supporting elephants supporting elephants all the way down. Dogs might be better guides to what Karen Barad (1995) calls intra-action than Niels Bohr's troubling quantum phenomena at the scale of wave forms and elementary particles. Inter-action implies that already existing actors get together and act. Intra-action implies something much messier, much less determinate, ontologically speaking. Whitehead knew that; he must have had a dog. Famously, Freud certainly did. No wonder he knew something about subject making.

I am certain that, in addition to composing "Notes of a Sportswriter's Daughter," I will soon write a "Companion Species Manifesto." For now my task is more modest. It has three parts; to wit, (1) establishing that companion animals are only one kind of companion species and that neither category is very old in American English, (2) appropriating molecular biologists to affirm an origin story good enough for dogs and humans to get on together, and (3) turning to cats, in the guise of tigers, to suggest how the technocultural apparatus of biodiversity practices and discourses in dogland torques the origin story toward a more salubrious complexity. I'll finish with a tangled cat's cradle figure for doing technoscience studies among companion species.

2. COMPANION SPECIES

Dramatis Personae

In United States English, "companion animal" is a recent category, linked to the medical and psycho-sociological work done in veterinary schools and related sites from the middle 1970s (Beck and Katcher 1996). This is the research that told us that, except for non-dog-loving New Yorkers who worry to excess about unscooped dog shit in the streets, having a dog (or, *in extremis,* a cat or even a hamster) lowers one's blood pressure and ups one's chances of surviving childhood, surgery, and divorce. Certainly, written references in European languages to animals serving as companions, rather than as working or sporting dogs, for example, predates this biomedical, technoscientific literature by centuries. However, "companion animal" enters technoculture through the land-grant academic institutions housing the vet schools. That is, "companion animal" has the pedigree of the mating between technoscientific expertise and late industrial pet-keeping practices, with their democratic masses in love with their domestic partners, or at least with the non-human ones. Companion animals can be horses, dogs, cats, or a range of other beings willing to make the leap from pet or lab beast to the biosociality of service dogs, family members, or team members in cross-species sports. Generally speaking, one does not eat one's companion animals (nor get eaten by them); and one has a hard time shaking colonialist, ethnocentric, ahistorical attitudes from those who do.

"Companion species" is a much bigger and more heterogeneous category than companion animal, and not just because one must start including such organic beings as rice, bees, tulips, and intestinal flora, all of whom make life for humans what it is—and vice versa. I want to rewrite the keyword entry for "companion species" to insist on four tones simultaneously resonating in the linguistic, historical voice box that makes uttering this term possible. First, as a dutiful daughter of Darwin, I insist on the tones of the history of evolutionary biology, with its key categories of populations, rates of gene flow, variation, selection, and biological species. All of the debates in the last 150 years about whether the category denotes a real biological entity or merely provides a convenient taxonomic box provide the over- and undertones. Species is about biological kind, and scientific expertise is necessary to that kind of reality. Post-cyborg, what counts as biological kind troubles any previous category of organism.

The machinic is internal to the organic and vice versa in irreversible ways. Second, schooled by Thomas Aquinas and other Aristotelians, I remain alert to species as generic philosophical kind and category. Species is about defining difference, rooted in polyvocal fugues of doctrines of cause. Third, with an indelible mark on my soul from a Catholic formation, I hear in species the doctrine of the Real Presence under both species, bread and wine, the transubstantiated signs of the flesh. Species is about the corporeal join of the material and the semiotic in ways unacceptable to the secular Protestant sensibilities of the American academy and to most versions of the human sciences of semiotics. Fourth, converted by Marx and Freud, I hear in species filthy lucre, specie, gold, shit, filth, wealth. In *Love's Body*, Norman O. Brown taught me about the join of Marx and Freud in shit and gold, in specie. I met this join again in modern U.S. dog culture, with its exuberant commodity culture, its vibrant practices of love and desire, its mongrel technologies of purebred subject and object making. Pooper scoopers for me is quite a joke. In sum, "companion species" is about a four-part composition, in which co-constitution, finitude, impurity, and complexity are what is.

A. Who's on First? Account of Co-Evolution[5]

Pleasures and anxieties over beginnings and endings abound in contemporary dog worlds. This should not be surprising when we are awash in millennial discourses. Why shouldn't dogs get in an apocalyptic bark or two? Dog tales demand a serious hearing; they concern the basic *dramatis personae* in the ecological theater and the evolutionary play of rescripted naturecultures in technonatural, biosocial modernity (Hutchinson 1965; Rabinow 1992). This modernity is a living fictional territory; it is always here and now, in the technopresent. With reference to anthropology's late and little-lamented "ethnographic present," the technopresent names the kind of time I experience inside the *New York Times* Science Tuesday section and on the front pages and business pages so attuned to the animation and cessation of NASDAQ. History in the technopresent is Whig time enterprised up (Strathern 1992); i.e., this history is reduced to the vehicle for getting to the technopresent. In the technopresent, beginnings and endings implode, such that the eternal here and now energetically emerges as a gravity well to warp all subjects and objects in its domain. I write this paper suspended in this odd, millennial, American chronicity; but in this dimensionally challenged medium, I sense some code fusions promising another and better story about animals, machines, and people. I sense the emergence of companion species after the departure of possessive individuals and hermetically sealed objects, who will have finally succumbed to their own alien invasion of the earth. In this paper, I want to tell the story of companion species in the context of diversity discourses in U.S. dog worlds.

Evolutionary origin stories are always a good place in U.S. technoscientific worlds to check for the moves of nature and culture on the board game of widely disseminated Western metaphysics and for the players in the current versions of the game. In recent years, the long-running dog-wolf romance has a stirring new series. The origin of dogs might be a humbling chapter in the story of *Homo sapiens*, one that allows for a deeper sense of co-evolution and co-habitation and a reduced exercise of hominid hubris in shaping canine natureculture.

Accounts of the relations of dogs and wolves proliferate, and molecular biologists tell some of the most convincing versions. Robert Wayne and his colleagues at UCLA studied mitochondrial DNA (mtDNA) from 162 North American, European, Asian, and Arabian wolves and from 140 dogs representing 67 breeds, plus a few jackals and coyotes (Vilá, et al 1997). Their analysis of mtDNA control regions concluded that dogs emerged uniquely from wolves—and did so much earlier than scenarios based on archaeological data permit. The amount of sequence divergence and the organization of the data into clades support the emergence of dogs more than 100,000 years ago, with very few separate domestication events. Three-quarters of modern dogs belong to one clade; i.e., they belong to a single maternal lineage. The early dates give *Canis familiaris*[6] and *Homo sapiens* roughly the same calendar, so folks walking out of Africa soon met a wolf bitch who would give birth to man's best friends. And, building a genetic trellis—not a tree—as they went, both dogs and people walked back into Africa (Templeton 1999). These have been species more given to multi-directional traveling and consorting than to conquering and replacing, never to return to their old haunts again. No wonder dogs and people share the distinction of being the most well-mixed and globally geographically distributed large-bodied mammals. They shaped each over a long time. Their pedigrees are a proper mess.

Further—in a story familiar from the post–World War II studies of human population gene frequencies that were so important to the early 1950s antiracist UNESCO statements and to subsequent reforms of physical anthropology and genetics teaching—dog mtDNA haplotypes do not sort out by breed, indicating that breeds have diverse doggish ancestries. "Pure" breeds are an institutional fiction, even if it threatens the health of animals regulated by the story. Variations of many genes and markers within breeds exceed variations between populations of dogs and wolves. And, in another lab's study, "greater mtDNA differences appeared within the single breeds of Doberman pinscher or poodle than between dogs and wolves," even while "there is less mtDNA difference between dogs, wolves and coyotes than there is between various ethnic groups of human beings" (Coppinger and Schneider 1995, 33). Genetic difference studies are a high-stakes game, and emphases on similarity or divergence shift with the theoretical bets laid.

Findings from Wayne's lab have been controversial, partly because the mtDNA clock doesn't measure up to the accuracy demanded by Swiss watchmakers. At an International Council for Archaeozoology symposium in 1998 at the University of Victoria, controversy waxed over Wayne's arguments. Relevant to this paper are implications for thinking about agency in dog-human interactions. Wayne argued that to domesticate dogs took a lot of skill, or it would have happened more often. His story bears the scent of the anatomically wolfish hunting dog, and this dog is a man-made hunting tool/weapon. In this version, morphologically differentiated dogs did not show up in the fossil or archaeology record until 12,000–14,000 years ago because their jobs in settled post–hunter-gatherer, paleoagricultural communities did not develop until then; so they got physically reshaped late in the relationship. People call the shots in both chapters of a story that makes "domestication" a one-sided human "social invention." But archaeozoological expert Susan Crockford, who organized the Victoria symposium, disagreed. She argued that human settlements provided a species-making resource for would-be dogs in the form of garbage middens and—my addition—concentrations of human bodily waste. If wolves could just calm their well-justified fear of *Homo sapiens,* they could feast in ways all too familiar to modern dog people. "Crockford theorizes that in a sense, wild canids domesticated themselves" (Weidensaul 1999, 57; Crockford 2000).

Crockford's argument turns on genes that control rates in early development and on consequent paedomorphogenesis. Both the anatomical and psychological changes in domesticated animals compared to their wild relatives can be tied to a single potent molecule with stunning effects in early development and in adult life—thyroxine. Those wolves with lower rates of thyroxine production, and so lower titers of the fright/flight adrenaline cocktail regulated by thyroid secretions, could get a good meal near human habitations. If they were really calm, they might even den nearby. The resulting pups who were the most tolerant of their two-legged neighbors might themselves make use of the caloric bonanza and have their own puppies nearby as well. A few generations of this could produce a being remarkably like current dogs, complete with curled tails, a range of jaw types, considerable size variation, doggish coat patterns, floppy ears, and—above all—the capacity to stick around people and forgive almost anything. People would surely figure out how to relate to these handy sanitary engineers and encourage them to join in useful tasks, like herding, hunting, watching kids, and comforting people. In a few decades, wolves-become-dogs would have changed, and that interval is too short for archaeologists to find intermediate forms.

Crockford made use of the forty-year continuing studies of Russian fur foxes, beginning in the 1950s, which have been much in the recent popular science news (Weidensaul 1999; Trut 1999; Belyaev 1969). Unlike domesticated animals, wild farmed foxes vigorously object to their captivity, including their slaughter. In what were originally experiments designed to select tamer foxes for the convenience of the Soviet fur industry, geneticists at the Siberian Institute of Cytology and Genetics found that by breeding the tamest kits from each fox generation—and selecting for nothing else—they quickly got dog-like animals, complete with non-fox attitudes like preferential affectional bonding with human beings and phenotypes like those of Border Collies.[7] By analogy, wolves on their way to becoming dogs might have selected themselves for tameness. People got in the act when they saw a good thing.

With a wink and a nod to problems with my argument, I think it is possible to hybridize Wayne's and Crockford's evolutionary accounts and so shamelessly save my favorite parts of each—an early co-evolution, human-canine accommodation at more than one point in the story, and lots of dog agency in the drama of genetics and co-habitation. First, I imagine that many domestication sequences left no progeny, or offspring blended back into wolf populations outside the range of current scientific sensors. Marginally fearless wolfish dogs could have accompanied hunter-gatherers on their rounds and gotten more than one good meal for their troubles. Denning near seasonally moving humans who follow regular food-getting migration routes seems no odder than denning near year-round settlements. People might have gotten their own fear/aggression endocrine systems to quell murderous impulses toward the nearby canine predators who did garbage detail and refrained from threatening. Paleolithic people stayed in one place longer than wolf litters need to mature, and both humans and wolves reuse their seasonal sites. People might have learned to take things further than the canines bargained for and bring wolf-dog reproduction under considerable human sway. This radical switch in the biopolitics of reproduction might have been in the interests of raising some lineages to accompany humans on group hunts or perform useful tasks for hunter-gatherers besides eating the shit. Paleoagricultural settlement could have been the occasion for much more radical accommodation between the canids and hominids on the questions of tameness, mutual trust, and trainability.

And, above all, on the question of reproduction. It's on this matter that the distinction between dogs and wolves really hinges; molecular genetics may never show enough species-defining DNA differences. Rather, the subtle genetic and developmental biobehavioral changes through which dogs got people to provision their pups might be the heart of the drama of co-habitation. Human baby-sitters, not Man-the-Hunter, are the heroes from doggish points of view. Wolves can reproduce independently of humans; dogs cannot. Even Italian feral dogs still need at least a garbage dump (Boitani et al. 1995). As Coppinger and Schneider summarized the case: "In canids with a long maturation period, growth and development are limited by the provisioning capacity of the mother. . . . Wolves and African hunting dogs solved the pup-feeding problem with packing behavior, in coyotes the male helps, and jackal pairs are assisted by the 'maiden aunt.' The tremendous success of the domestic dog is based on its ability to get people to raise its pups" (1995, 36). People are part of dogs' extended phenotype in their Darwinian, behavioral ecological, reproductive strategies. Pacé Richard Dawkins.

Two points emerge from this evolutionary origin story: (1) co-evolution makes humans and dogs companion species from "the beginning," but with historically changing and specific sets of inter-species biotechnosocial relations and with agency a mobile and distributed matter; and (2) the fine arts of molecular genetics and hormone biochemistry are indispensable for this account of the agency of nature in the person of dog-wannabe wolves. The latest in sequencing machinery, sampling protocols, and DNA comparison software are crucial to the tale of "nature" making the first moves in a "social" invention. But this nature does not have the shape of the specters from the recent U.S. science and culture wars, where unruly science studies people were accused of arguing that scientists invented nature rather than reported on her in a mood of humble truth-telling. Here, with those worried realist warriors, I am also arguing that hominids did not "invent" nature or culture (wolves become dogs), then or now, but that all of the players emerge in a kind of Whiteheadian concrescence, where none of the actors precede, finished, their interaction. Companion species take shape in interaction. They more than change each other; they co-constitute each other, at least partly. That's the nature of this cat's cradle game. And the ontology of companion species makes room for odd bedfellows—machines; molecules; scientists; hunter-gatherers; garbage dumps; puppies; fox farmers; and randy bitches of all breeds, genders, and species.

I want to use the figure of companion species to do a lot of analytical and associative work. Figures are powerful attractors that collect up the hopes, fears, and interests of collectives. Figures promise to fulfill hopes in a sense related to Christian realism (Auerbach 1953). Companion species are figures of a relational ontology, in which histories matter; i.e., are material, meaningful, processual, emergent, and constitutive. In the past, I have written about cyborgs, and cyborgs are a kind of companion species congeries of organisms and machines located firmly in the Cold War and its offspring. Equally on my mind have been genetically engineered laboratory organisms like OncoMouse™, also companion species tying together many kinds of actors and practices. Dogs and humans as companion species suggest quite different histories and lives, compared to cyborgs and engineered mice, emergent over the whole time of species being for the participants. In much of my own work, I have tried to figure out the conse-

quences for biology and for cultural theory and politics of the implosion of biologics and informatics in post–World War II life sciences. In this implosion, organisms lost their ontological privilege to genomes, those wonderful generators
of new wealth, new knowledge, and mutated ways of living and dying. While I
take for granted many of the consequences of the implosion of biologics and informatics in shaping ways of being and knowing in the technopresent, I am here
attending to a related but different sort of implosion—that of the utterly "natural" and the wholly "technical," where, for example, endangered species in the
necessarily managed wilderness wear electronic sensors and live in habitats
monitored by satellites as a crucial part of their biological reproductive apparatus. It remains to be seen if this arrangement will be an Evolutionary Stable
Strategy (Dawkins 1982), but it has surely become a figure of biosocial modernity. Simply put, biodiversity has become dependent upon high technology in
many parts of the world. The physical implosion of the "natural" and the "technical," materially-semiotically speaking, is a normal, everyday, earthly fact in the
most biophilic, diversity-committed communities every bit as much as in the
most technophilic worlds. And none of it is innocent—or guilty.

Is there a moral to this story? Dogs invented themselves; they are not an invention of humans? Or dogs and people shaped each other in a long and complicated history, where the story of the wannabe dogs taking the first steps is
more convincing than its opposite? If dogs are a human technology, so also is
the reverse true, as part of an extended phenotype in a canine sociobiological
tale. I like the co-evolution story better than either the version that the dogs did
it or the people did it. It redoes the story of the human place in nature in homely
ways that also impact on fortifications between categories of nature and culture.

There are stakes here beyond what we think about dog evolution. The stakes
are how we think about liveliness and agency in different worlds. We require a
multi-species and a multi-expertise way of doing/thinking worlds and ways of
life, and that requires muting the command/communication/control/intelligence
idiom of cyborgs.

Companion species are, among other things, a serious feminist matter, right
at the heart of the ongoing Western feminist effort to do better than recycling
idioms of liberalism and their benefits-maximizing, bounded, and independent
selves as archetypes of freedom. Companion species offer a kind of bypass surgery
for liberal idioms of both individuals and of diversity. Companion species do
this right in the belly of the monster—inside biotechnology and the New World
Order, Inc. Genders, breeds, races, lines, species—all the kinds are in play in these
narrative morphings, with material-semiotic consequences. This is concrescence
from the point of view of the birth of the kennel, in ongoing, relentlessly historical layers of practice, where all the actors and agencies are not human.

B. Biodiversity Goes to the Dogs[8]

Genetic disease is not news to dog people, and perhaps especially purebred dog people. Many breeders and owners—some willingly, some not—have become used to thinking about the genetic difficulties common to their breeds and even about polygenic traits with unknown modes of inheritance and strong environmental and developmental components affecting expression, like canine hip dysplasia. In myriad ways, genetic disease discourse shapes communities of practice for owners, breeders, researchers, dog rescue activists, breed clubs, kennel clubs, journalists, shelter workers, veterinarians, dog sports competitors, and trainers. There is much to say about the fascinating cultures of genetic disease in dogs, but in this paper I want to focus on a much more unsettling topic in purebred dog land: genetic diversity in small populations. First, let us look at why genetic diversity concerns are news—and hard-to-digest news—for most dog people, in spite of the long history of population genetics and its importance for the modern theory of natural section and the neo-Darwinian synthesis and its offspring.

Genetic culture for both professionals and non-professionals, especially but not only in the United States, has been strongly shaped by medical genetics. Human genetic disease is the moral, technoscientific, ideological, and financial center of the medical genetic universe. Typological thinking reigns almost unchecked in this universe; nuanced views of developmental biology, behavioral ecology, and genes as nodes in dynamic and multi-vectorial fields of vital interactions are only some of the crash victims of high-octane medical genetic fuels and gene-jockey racing careers. For my taste, genomes are too much made up of investment opportunities of the "one region–one product" sort, a kind of enterprised-up descendant of the "one gene–one enzyme" principle that proved so fruitful in research. Taken one at a time, genes, especially disease-related genes, induce brain damage in those trying to come to grips with genetic diversity issues and their consequences.

Evolutionary biology, biosocial ecology, population biology, and population genetics (not to mention history of science, political economy, and cultural anthropology) have played a woefully small role in shaping public and professional genetic imaginations, and all too small a role in drawing the big money for genetic research. Considering only dog worlds, my preliminary research turns up millions of dollars in grants going into genetic disease research (even though peanuts compared to dollars for genetic research in organisms like mice, who are conventionally models for human disease; dog genetics gets more money as it is shown that genome homologies across taxonomic divisions make canines ideal for understanding lots of human conditions, e.g., narcolepsy, bleeding disorders, and retinal degeneration), and only a few thousand dollars (and lots of volunteer time from both professionals and lay collaborators) going into canine genetic diversity research.

The emergence since the 1980s of biodiversity discourses, environmentalisms, and sustainability doctrines of every political color on the agendas of myriad NGOs and of First World institutions like the World Bank, the International Union for the Conservation of Nature and Natural Resources (IUCN), and the Organization for Economic Cooperation and Development (OECD), as well as in the Third World, has made a difference in this situation.[9] The notoriously problematic politics and also the compelling naturecultural complexity of diversity discourses requires a shelf of books, some of which have been written. I think the emergence of genetic diversity concerns in dog worlds only makes sense historically as a wavelet in the set of breakers constituting transnational, globalizing, biological, and cultural diversity discourses, in which genes and genomes (and immune systems) are major players. Noticing some of the conditions of emergence of a discourse is not the same thing as reducing its value to ideological stepchild status. Quite the opposite: I am compelled by the irreducible complexity—morally, politically, culturally, and scientifically—of diversity discourses, including those leashed to the genomes and gene pools of purebred dogs and their canine relatives in and out of "nature."

The last few paragraphs are preparation for logging onto the Canine Diversity Project website, www.magma.ca/~kaitlin/diverse.html, owned by Dr. John Armstrong, a lover of Standard and Miniature Poodles and a faculty member in the department of biology at the University of Ottawa until his death in the summer of 2001. Armstrong wrote and distributed as widely as possible his analyses of the effects of a popular sire and a particular kennel in Standard Poodles. Also the owner of CANGEN-L, Armstrong conducted collaborative research with dog health and genetics activists to study whether longevity is correlated to the degree of inbreeding. Aiming in its introductory sentence to draw the attention of dog breeders to "the dangers of inbreeding and the overuse of popular sires," the Diversity Project website started in 1997. Used by at least several hundred dog people of several nationalities, the site registered 4,500 logons in the first three and a half months of 2000. I have myself learned a tremendous amount from this website; I appreciate the quality of information, the controversies engaged, the evident care for dogs and people, the range of material, and the commitments to issues I am concerned with. I am also professionally acutely alert to the semiotics—the meaning-making machinery—of the Canine Diversity Project website.

Animated by a mission, the site draws its users into its reform agenda at every turn.[10] Some of the rhetorical devices are classical American tropes rooted in old popular self-help practices and evangelical Protestant witness, devices so ingrained in U.S. culture that few users would be conscious of their history. For example, right after the introductory paragraph with the initial link terms, the Diversity Project website leads its users into a section called "How You Can Help." The question the visitor confronts is like that used in advertising and in preaching: Have you been saved? Have you taken the Immune Power pledge? (slogan from an ad for a vitamin formulation in the 1980s) Or, as the Diversity Project puts the query, "Ask the Question—Do you need a '*Breed Survival Plan*'?" This is the stuff of subject-reconstituting, conversion and conviction discourse (Harding 1999).

The first four highlighted linkage words in the opening paragraphs of the website are "popular sires," a common term for many years in purebred dog talk about the overuse of certain stud dogs and the consequent spreading of genetic disease; "Species Survival Plans," a term that makes a new link for dog breeders to zoos and the preservation of endangered species; "wild cousins," which places dogs with their taxonomic kin and reinforces considering purebreds within the family of natural (in the sense of "wild"), and frequently endangered, species; and "inherited disease," firmly in last place on the list and of concern primarily because a high incidence of double autosomal recessives for particular diseases is an index of lots of homozygosity in purebred dog genomes. Such high incidences of double recessives are certainly related to excessive in- and line breeding, which are diversity-depleting practices. But, as I read it, the soul of the website is the value of diversity for itself in the semiotic framework of evolutionary biology, biodiversity, and biophilia (Wilson 1988, 1992), not diversity as an instrument for solving the problem of genetic disease. Of course, these two values are not mutually exclusive; indeed, they are complementary. But priority matters. In that sense, "breeds" become like endangered species, inviting all the wonderful apparatus we have become familiar with in wildlife biology at the turn of the millennium.

The website is constructed as a teaching instrument; it constructs its principal audience as engaged lay breeders and other committed dog people. These are the subjects invited to declare for a breed survival plan. Secondarily, scientists of whatever specialty might learn from using the site, but scientists are more teachers here than they are researchers or students. Nonetheless, there are plenty of trading zones and boundary objects linking lay and professional communities of practice in this inviting site. Further, the nature of a website, as opposed to many other writing technologies (King forthcoming), resists reduction to single purposes and dominating tropes. Links lead many places, and these paths are explored by users, within the webs initially spun by designers, to be sure, but rapidly spiraling out of the control of any designer, no matter how broad-minded. The Internet is hardly infinitely open, but its degrees of semiotic freedom are many.

"Popular sires" is sufficiently recognized that the linking term would appeal to the tender-footed neophyte thinking about genetic diversity. For one thing, the link stays with dogs as the principle focus of attention, and does not launch the user into a universe of marvelous creatures in exotic habitats whose utility as models for dogs is hard to swallow for many breeders, even those interested in such non-dog organisms and ecologies in other contexts. "Species Survival Plans," on the other hand, open up controversial metaphoric and practical universes for breeders of purebred dogs and, if taken seriously, would require major changes in ways of thinking and acting.[11] The first obvious point is that "survival plans" connotes that something is endangered. The line between a secular crisis and a sacred apocalypse is a thin one in U.S. American discourse, where millennial matters are written into the fabric of the national imagination from the first Puritan City on a Hill to Star Trek and its sequelae. The second obvious point is that the prominent role given to species survival plans on the Canine Diversity Project website invites a reproductive tie between natural species and purebred dogs. This is one of those ties where the natural and the technical keep close company, semiotically and materially.

To illustrate this point, I will dwell on the material on my screen after I click on "Species Survival Plan" and follow up with a click on "Introduction to a Species Survival Plan." I am teleported to the website for the Tiger Information Center, and, appreciating a face-front photo of two imposing tigers crossing a stream, I am presented with a paper on "Regional and Global Management of Tigers," by R. Tilson, K. Taylor-Holzer, and G. Brady. Now, I know lots of dog people love cats, contrary to popular stereotypes about folks being either canine or feline in their affections. But tigers in zoos around the world and in shrunken "forest patches spread from India across China to the Russian Far East and south to Indonesia" is a leap out of the kennel and the show ring or herding trials. I learn that three of the eight recognized subspecies of tigers are already extinct, a fourth on the brink, and all the wild populations stressed. Ideally, the goal of a SSP master plan for an endangered species is to create, out of existing animals in zoos and some new "founders" brought in from "nature," viable, managed, captive populations to maintain as much of the genetic diversity for all the extant taxa of the species as possible. The purpose is to provide a genetic reservoir for the reinforcement or reconstitution of wild populations where necessary and possible. A practical SSP, "because of space limitations generally targets 90% of genetic diversity of the wild populations for 100–200 years as a reasonable goal." I am in love with the hopefulness of that kind of reasonableness. The "Zoo Ark" for the tigers, lamentably, has to be more modest because the resources are too few and the needs too great. A SSP is a complex, cooperative management program of the American Zoo and Aquarium Association (AZA).

What does developing and implementing a SSP involve? The short answer is—a long list of companion species of organic, organizational, and technological kinds. A minimum account of such companion species must include these: the World Conservation Union's specialist groups who make assessments of endangerment; member zoos, with their scientists, keepers, and boards of governors; a small management group under the AZA; a database maintained as a regional studbook, using specialized software like SPARKS (Single Population and Records Keeping System) and its companion programs for demographic and genetic analysis, produced by the International Species Information System; funders; national governments; international bodies; and, hardly least, the animals in danger. Crucial operations within a SSP are measurements of diversity and relatedness. One wants to know Founder Importance Coefficients (FICs) as a tool for equalizing relative founder contributions and minimizing inbreeding. Full and accurate pedigrees are precious objects for an SSP. Mean Kinship (MK) and Kinship Values (KV) rule mate choice in this sociobiological system. "Reinforcing" wild species requires a global apparatus of technoscientific production, where the natural and the technical have very high coefficients of semiotic and practical inbreeding.[12]

Purebred dog breeders also value deep pedigrees, and they are accustomed to evaluating matings with regard to breed standards, which is a complex, nonformulaic art. Inbreeding is not a new concern. So what is so challenging about a SSP as a universe of reference? The definition of populations and founders is perhaps first. Discussions among engaged breeders on CANGEN—i.e., people sufficiently interested in questions of genetic diversity to sign on and post to a specialized Internet mailing list—show that dog people's "lines" and "breeds" are not equivalent terms to wildlife biologists' and geneticists' "populations." The behavior properly associated with these different words is quite different. A dog breeder educated in the traditional mentoring practices of the fancy will attempt through line breeding, with variable frequencies of outcrosses, to maximize the genetic/blood contribution of the truly "great dogs," who are rare and special. The great dogs are the individuals who best embody the type of the breed. The type is not a fixed thing, but a living, imaginative hope and memory. Kennels often are recognized for the distinctiveness of their dogs, and breeders point proudly to their kennel's own founders, and breed club documents to the breed's founders. The notion of working to equalize the contribution of all of the founders in the population geneticists' sense is truly odd in traditional dog breeders' discourse. Of course, a SSP, unlike nature and unlike dog breeders, is not operating with adaptational selectional criteria; the point of a SSP is to preserve diversity as such as a reservoir. Small populations are subject to intense extinction pressures—loss of habitat, fragmented sub-populations no longer able to exchange genetic material, loss of genes through the random process called genetic drift, crisis events causing population crashes like famines or diseases, and on and on.

The SSP is a conservation management plan, not nature, however conceptualized, and not a breed's written standard or an individual breeder's interpretation of that standard. Like a SSP, a breed standard is also a kind of large-scale action blueprint, but for other purposes. Some breeders talk of those purposes in capital letters, as the Original Purpose of a given breed. Others are not typological in that sense and are attuned to dynamic histories and evolving goals within a partly shared sense of breed history, structure, and function. These breeders are keenly aware of the need for selection on the basis of many criteria as holistically as possible to maintain and improve a breed's overall quality and to achieve the rare special dogs. They take these responsibilities very seriously; and they are not virgins to controversy, contradiction, and failure. They are not against learning about genetic diversity in the context of the problems they know or suspect their dogs face. Some breeders—a very few, I think—embrace genetic diversity discourse and population genetics. They worry that the foundation of their breeds might be too narrow and getting narrower. But the breeder's art does not easily entertain adopting the heavily mathematical and software-driven mating systems of a SSP. I witness in my research several courageous breeders insisting on deeper pedigrees and regular calculations of coefficients of inbreeding, with efforts to hold them down where possible. But the breeders I overhear are loathe to cede decisions to anything like a master plan. In my judgment, they do not see their own dogs or their breed primarily as biological populations. The dominance of specialists over local and lay communities in the SSP world does not escape dog breeders' attention. Most of the breeders I overhear squirm if the discussion stays on a theoretical population genetics level and if few if any of the data come from dogs, rather than, say, a Malagasy lemur population or lab-bound mouse strain. In short, breeders' discourse and genetic diversity discourse do not hybridize smoothly, at least in the F1 generation. This mating is what I hear breeders call a "cold outcross" that they worry risks importing as many problems as it solves.

There is much more to the Canine Diversity Project website than the SSP links, and if I had the space to examine the rich texture of the whole website, many more sorts of openings, repulsions, inclusions, attractions, and possibilities would be evident for seeing the ways dog breeders, health activists, veterinarians, and geneticists relate to the question of diversity. At the very least, the serious visitor to the website could get a decent elementary education in genetics, including Mendelian, medical, and population genetics. Fascinating collaborations between individual scientists and breed club health and genetics activists would emerge. The differences within dog people's ways of thinking about genetic diversity and inbreeding would be inescapable, as the apocalyptic and controversial Jeffrey Bragg's "evolving breeds" and Seppala Siberian Sled Dogs meet John Armstrong's more modest Standard Poodles (and his more moderate action plan, "Genetics for Breeders: How to Produce Healthier Dogs") or Leos Kral's and C. A. Sharp's ways of working in Australian Shepherd worlds. Links would take the visitor to the extraordinary Code of Ethics of the Coton de Tulear Club of America and this breed's alpha-male geneticist activist, Robert Jay Russell, as well as to the online documents with which the Border Collie website teaches genetics relevant to that fascinating breed. The visitor could follow links to the molecular evolution of the dog family, updated lists of current DNA gene tests in dogs, discussions of wolf conservation and wolf taxonomic debates, accounts of a cross-breeding (to a Pointer) and back-cross project in Dalmatians to eliminate a common genetic disease, and of importing new African stock in Basenjis to deal with genetic dilemmas. One could click one's way to discussions of infertility, stress, and herpes infections, or follow links to endocrine disrupter discourse for thinking about how environmental degradation might be affecting dogs, as well as frogs and people, globally. Right in the middle of the Diversity Project website is a bold-type invitation to join the mailing list Armstrong ran until his death, the Canine Genetics Discussion Group (CANGEN-L), where a sometimes rough-and-tumble exchange among heterogeneous lay and professional dog people stirred up the pedagogical order of the website.

So dogs, not tigers—and breeds, not endangered species—actually dominate on the Canine Diversity Project website. But the metaphoric, political, and practical possibilities of those first links to Species Survival Plans attach themselves like well-positioned ticks on a nice blade of grass, waiting for a passing visitor from purebred dog land. Frontline defenses are not always enough.[13] We are in the fiercely local and linked global zones of technobiopolitics, where few species are more than a click away. Naturecultural survival is the prize.

3. CAT'S CRADLE: A CONCLUSION IN TANGLES

What I Like about the Material-Semiotic Know, the Literalized Figure, of Companion Species

1. Networks of co-constitution, co-evolution, communication, collaboration, abound to help us rethink issues of communication and control at the heart of the cyborg figure.
2. Humans, other organisms, artifacts, and technologies are all players, a requirement of an aliberal approach. The relationship is the smallest possible unit of analysis.

3. Likewise, scientists, lay people, and dogs are all on the playbill in this evolutionary drama.

4. Companion species are not involved in another Hegelian confrontation of self-other, culture-nature, or similar dualisms.[14]

5. Companion species are not another version of a Marxist humanist dialectic of nature remade by labor. The making goes in too many directions.

6. The story is more Whiteheadian, full of his kind of objectifications.

7. This story provokes finding non-anthropomorphic ways to figure agencies and actors.

8. Companion species throw comparative methods into crisis because the norm stabilizing comparison wobbles; e.g., consciousness will not do for considering animal well-being. Companion species discourse does not produce an animal rights or human rights agenda, but does insist on complex ethical discourse

9. Here we have situated co-constitution, with inherited pasts of many kinds, rather than dialectical unity; i.e., situatedness displaces teleology analytically and morally. This is all about origin stories. How we might live and flourish is a permanent, finite, mundane question; there is no way out, especially in terms of extraterrestrial projects of man (species) evolving toward bodylessness.

10. Companion species worlds are at home with the non-heroic dailiness of epistemological/ontological/ethical action; the birth of the kennel is a homely story.

11. Susan Leigh Star's question (1991) cannot be evaded: *cui bono*? Who lives, and lives well, and who dies and why, in companion species relations?

12. We have real histories of dogs and people; not The Dog and The Human; in co-constitution there are layers of practices and many chronicities. Scale is made, not given (Tsing 2000).

13. There is always a necessary weave of narrative and other material-semiotic practices.

14. Full of cross talk and questions about locations of expertise and authority, this story is not cynical about telling the truth. Practices must be relentlessly situated inside truth telling, and vice versa.

15. The story requires considering seriously "companion animals" and complex moral-scientific action outside the straitjackets of much animal rights discourse, feminist and otherwise. "Companion species" is not a friendly notion for those "animal rights" perspectives that rely on a scale of similarity to human mentality for assigning value. Both people and their partners are co-constructed in the history of companion species, and the issues of hierarchy and cruelty, as well as colleagueship and responsibility, are open and polyvalent, both historically and morally. Also, "companion species" does not prejudge the category of the

"species"; they could be artifacts, organisms, technologies, other humans, etc. The simple and obvious point is that nothing is self-made, autocthonous, or self-sufficient. Origin stories have to be about fraught histories of consequential relationships. The point is to engage "ontological choreography" in the yearning for more livable and lively relationships across kinds, human and non-human.

16. Dog worlds become a place to work through idioms and practices around diversity, including in environmental politics and human-animal relationship politics, both of which are areas of major feminist concern.

17. The literalized figure of companion species addresses the long history of feminist critique of possessive individualism. By "literalized," I mean materially-semiotically engaged, fleshly and significant all the way down.

18. The literalized figure of companion species does semiotic-material work on idioms of breed, species, sex, reproduction, behavior, genome.

19. The literalized figure of companion species foregrounds relations of communities of practice in relation to intersectionally (Crenshaw 1993; gender, race, nation, and species are only a start). Attention to differentiated expertise and differentiated literacies—whether called "lay" or "professional"—lay and professional, is required.

20. The literalized figure of companion species invites "intersectional analysis" of key themes: breeds and the history of eugenics; technology and the organic body; histories of class, race, gender, and nation.

21. A key question is: who cleans up the shit in a companion species relationship?

NOTES

Portions of pp. 66–69 are adapted from Donna Haraway, "For the Love of a Good Dog: Webs of Action in the World of Dog Genetics," in Donald Moore, ed., *Race, Nature, and the Politics of Difference* (Durham, N.C.: Duke University Press, forthcoming 2003), also published in shortened form in Alan Goodman, Susan Lindee, and Deborah Heath, eds., *Genetic Nature/Culture: Anthropology and Science beyond the Two Culture Divide* (Berkeley: University of California Press, 2003).

Portions of pp. 65 and 71–79 are reprinted, by permission, from *Remaking Life and Death: Toward an Anthropology of the Biosciences*, edited by Sarah Franklin and Margaret Lock. © 2003 by the School of American Research, Santa Fe.

1. Vicki Hearne is a dog writer, philosopher, and e-mail correspondent, who died in the summer of 2001. See Hearne (1986).

2. This slogan can be found on T-shirts and windshield stickers among enthusiasts of the dog sport called Schutzhund, which involves competition in tracking, protection work, and obedience.

3. See Gray (1995) for a rich set of documents and accounts of cyborg worlds. See Tofts, Jonson, and Cavallaro (2002) for a striking intellectual history of cyberculture.

4. See Haraway (1985) for my effort to live in the naturecultures of Marxist feminism conjugated with technoscience studies in the time of Reagan's Star Wars. See Sofoulis (2002) for in incisive account of the fate of that cyborg material-semiotic doppelganger. See also Goodeve (2000).

5. The dog-human co-evolution story below is slightly revised from "For the Love of a Good Dog: Webs of Action in the World of Dog Genetics" (Haraway forthcoming a).

6. Recent taxonomic revisions make dogs into a subspecies of wolves, *Canis lupens familiaris,* rather than into a species of their own, *Canis familiaris.* This technical issue has multiple consequences beyond the scope of this paper. See Coppinger and Coppinger (2001, 273–282). For a critique of Villá, et al's dating of dog evolution from mtDNA data, see Coppinger and Coppinger (2001, 283–294).

7. Like much in the former USSR, this trickster drama of worker safety, industrial efficiency, and evolutionary theory and genetics in the far north devolved in the post–Cold War economic order. Since the salaries of the scientists at the Genetics Institute have not been paid, much of the breeding stock of tame foxes has been destroyed. The scientists scramble to save the rest—and fund their research—by marketing them in the West as pets with characteristics between dogs and cats. A sad irony is that if the geneticists and their foxes succeed in surviving in this enterprise culture, the population of remaining animals bred for the international pet trade will have been genetically depleted by the slaughter necessitated by the rigors of post-Soviet capitalism and commercializing the animals not for fur coats but as pets. Note also the tones of the Lysenko affair in the story of the evolution of tame Soviet foxes.

8. The section on biodiversity in dogland below is drawn from an earlier version of parts of "Cloning Mutts, Saving Tigers: Ethical Emergents in Technocultural Dogland" (Haraway forthcoming b).

9. See, for example, *World Conservation Strategy,* IUCN, 1980; the Bruntland Report, *Our Common Future,* WECD, 1987; Agenda 21; Convention on Biodiversity, 1992; Guiding Principles on Forests; *Valuing Nature's Services,* World Watch Institute Report of Progress toward a Sustainable Society, 1997; *Investing in Biological Diversity,* Cairns Conference, OECD, 1997; *Saving Biological Diversity: Economic Incentives,* OECD, 1996.

10. I am using a version of the website online in 2000.

11. The Rare Breed Survival Trust in the UK (mainly for poultry, sheep, pigs, cattle, and other "farm livestock heritage" animals not usually thought of as either companion animals—especially not as "pets"—or wild animals, including the working collie dogs that the Trust attends to), and its journal *The Ark,* would repay close attention in relation to action in dog worlds. Thanks to Sarah Franklin and Thelma Rowell for handing me into *The Ark.*

12. SSP is a North American term. Europeans have European Endangered Species Programs (EESPs), Australasians have Australasian Species Management Programs, and China, Japan, India, Thailand, Malaysia, and Indonesia all have their own equivalents. This is global science of indigenous species.

13. Information for those whose lives are not ruled by real ticks and real dogs: Frontline(tm) is a new-generation tick and flea control product that has made dogs' and dog peoples' lives much less irritable.

14. I am in obvious and deep alliance with Bruno Latour on these matters. See Latour (1993).

Bibliography

Auerbach, Eric. 1953.*Mimesis: The Representation of Reality in Western Literature*. Princeton, N.J.: Princeton University Press.

Barad, Karen. 1995. "Meeting the Universe Halfway: Ambiguities, Discontinuities, Quantum Subjects, and Multiple Positionings in Feminism and Physics." In *Feminism, Science, and the Philosophy of Science: A Dialog*, edited by L. H. Nelson and J. Nelson. Norwell: Kluwer Press.

Beck, Alan, and Aaron Katcher. 1996. *Between Pets and People: The Importance of Animal Companionship*. 2nd ed. West Lafayette, Ind.: Purdue University Press.

Belyaev, D. K. 1969. "Domestication of Animals." *Science Journal*, UK 5: 47–52.

Boitani, L., F. Francisci, P. Ciucci, and G. Andreoli. 1995. "Population Biology and Ecology of Feral Dogs in Central Italy." In Serpell, ed., pp. 217–244.

Brown, Norman O. 1966. *Love's Body*. New York: Random House.

Clynes, Manfred E., and Nathan S. Kline. 1960. "Cyborgs and Space." *Astronautics*, September 26–27, 1960, pp. 75–76.

Coppinger, Raymond, and Lorna Coppinger. 2001. *Dogs: A Startling New Understanding of Canine Origin, Behavior, and Evolution*. New York: Scribner.

Coppinger, Raymond, and Richard Schneider. 1995. "Evolution of Working Dogs." In Serpell, pp. 21–47.

Crenshaw, Kimberle. 1993. "Demarginalizing the Intersection of Race and Sex: A Black Feminist Critique of Antidiscrimination Doctrine, Feminist Theory, and Antiracist Politics." In *Feminist Legal Theory: Foundations*, edited by D. Kelly Weisberg, pp. 383–395. Philadelphia: Temple University Press.

Crockford, Susan J. 2000. "Dog Evolution: A Role for Thyroid Hormone Physiology in Domestication Changes." In *Dogs through Time: An Archaeological Perspective*, edited by S. Crockford, pp. 11–20. Oxford, England: BAR International Series 889.

Cussins, Charis Thompson. 1996. "Ontological Choreography: Agency through Objectification in Infertility Clinics." *Social Studies of Science* 26: 575–610.

Dawkins, Richard. 1982. *The Extended Phenotype: The Gene as a Unit of Selection*. London: Oxford University Press.

Franklin, Sarah, and Margaret Lock, eds. 2003. *Remaking Life and Death: Toward an Anthropology of the Biosciences*. Santa Fe: SAR Press

Goodeve, Thyrza. 2000. *How Like a Leaf: An Interview with Donna Haraway*. New York: Routledge.

Gray, Chris Hables, ed. 1995. *The Cyborg Handbook*. New York: Routledge.

Haraway, Donna. 1985. "A Manifesto for Cyborgs," *Socialist Review*, no. 80, pp. 65–108.

———. Forthcoming a. "For the Love of a Good Dog: Webs of Action in the World of Dog Genetics." In Donald Moore, ed. *Race, Nature, and the Politics of Difference*. Durham, N.C.: Duke University Press.

———. Forthcoming b. "Cloning Mutts, Saving Tigers: Ethical Emergents in Technocultural Dog Worlds." In Franklin and Lock.

Harding, Susan. 1999. *The Book of Jerry Farwell*. Princeton, N.J.: Princeton University Press.

Hearne, Vicki. 1986. *Adam's Task: Calling Animals by Name*. New York: Knopf.

Hutchinson, George Evelyn. 1965. *The Ecological Theater and the Evolutionary Play.* New Haven, Conn.: Yale University Press.

King, Katie. Forthcoming. "Feminism and Writing Technologies." Manuscript, University of Maryland at College Park.

Latour, Bruno. 1993. *We Have Never Been Modern.* Translated by Catherine Porter. Cambridge, Mass.: Harvard University Press.

Rabinow, Paul. 1992. "Artificiality and Enlightenment: From Sociobiology to Biosociality." In *Incorporations,* edited by J. Crary and S. Qwinter, pp. 234–252. New York: Zone Books.

Serpell, James, ed. 1995. *The Domestic Dog: Its Evolution, Behaviour, and Interactions with People.* Cambridge: Cambridge University Press,

Sofoulis, Zoe. 2002. "Cyberquake: Haraway's Manifesto." In Tofts et al.

Star, Susan Leigh. 1991. "Power, Technology and the Phenomenology of Conventions: On Being Allergic to Onions." In *A Sociology of Monsters: Power, Technology, and the Modern World,* edited by John Law, pp. 26–56. Oxford: Basil Blackwell.

Strathern, Marilyn. 1992. *Reproducing the Future: Anthropology, Kinship, and the New Reproductive Technologies.* New York: Routledge.

Templeton, Alan. 1999. "Human Race in the Context of Human Evolution: A Molecular Perspective." Paper for the Wenner Gren Foundation Conference on Anthropology in the Age of Genetics, June 11–19, Teresopolis, Brazil.

Tofts, Darren, Annemarie Jonson, and Alessio Cavallaro, eds. Forthcoming 2002. *Prefiguring Cyberculture: An Intellectual History.* Cambridge, Mass.: MIT Press.

Trut, Lyudamila N. 1999. "Early Canid Domestication: The Fox-Farm Experiment." *American Scientist* 87 (March–April): 160–169.

Tsing, Anna. 2000. "Inside the Economy of Appearances." *Public Culture* 12, no. 1: 115–144.

Verran, Helen. 2001. *Science and an African Logic.* Chicago: University of Chicago Press.

Vilá, Carles, Peter Savolainen, Jesús E. Maldonado, Isabel R. Amorim, John E. Rice, Rodney L. Honeycutt, Keith A. Crandall, Joakim Lundeberg, and Robert K. Wayne. 1997. "Multiple and Ancient Origins of the Domestic Dog." *Science* 276 (June 13): 1687–1689.

Weidensaul, Scott. 1999. "Tracking America's First Dogs." *Smithsonian Magazine,* March 1, pp. 44–57.

Whitehead, Alfred North. 1948. *Science and the Modern World.* New York: Mentor; orig. 1925.

———. 1969. *Process and Reality.* New York: Free Press; orig. 1929.

Wilson, E. O. 1992. *The Diversity of Life.* New York and London: W. W. Norton.

———, ed. 1988. *Biodiversity.* Washington, D.C.: National Academy Press.

5. Interview with Andrew Pickering

Participant: Casper Bruun Jensen

CBJ: First, I would like to ask a background question about your peculiar scholarly trajectory or perhaps production as a theorist. As I have understood it, you were trained as a physicist, and maybe even worked as one? How did you get into contact with science studies, and with what purposes in mind? How did the "identity change" from physicist to a sort of SSK constructivist take place? Was it a drawn-out process? Do you consider yourself to be marked by your training in physics or natural sciences in general at this point in time?

AP: Yes, Casper, peculiar. In my first incarnation I was a physicist. I did a Ph.D. at University College London and a couple of years as a postdoc in elementary particle theory. Then I drifted around London for a wonderful year and, through some improbable but fortunate coincidences, returned to the academic life at the Science Studies Unit in Edinburgh. I had met Harry Collins (in Bath) along the way and was intrigued by his constructivist stories about gravitational waves. At the same time, I thought there was something missing from them. My early work in Edinburgh was an attempt to find out what that was—and eventually, of course, the answer was a positive account of what scientific practice looked like. My earlier work in particle physics formed the bridge to science studies; all of my work at the Unit focused on particle physics, culminating in my book *Constructing Quarks* in 1984. I felt that supplied answers to the questions that Collins had raised, though he was cruel enough to describe it as "product differentiation," i.e., nothing new. There is a second connection between incarnations that becomes increasingly obvious in retrospect. Elementary particle physics is, as it name states, a predominantly reductive field, concerned with (a) identifying the fundamental constituents of matter, and (b) exploring calculable, time-reversible interactions between them. Technically, particle theory is good at weak-coupling regimes, in which interactions between particles can be calculated perturbatively. In contrast, I was fascinated as a physicist by the mysteries of strong coupling and emergent properties. I tried to solve the problem of quark confinement, the inextricable binding of quarks to form non-quark-like objects: hadrons-protons and neutrons, etc. (Needless to say, I failed.) Much later, in 1995 in *The Mangle of Practice,* I found myself writing about "temporal emergence." I think of gravity's rainbow—the arc of the V2 rocket in Thomas Pynchon's novel. In science studies, I have returned to the same mysteries that drew me into science as a schoolboy, but now the object is different.

CBJ: You anticipated my next question by invoking your theoretical development from SSK, what Collins called "product differentiation," to your work in the mid-90s on *The Mangle of Practice.* How did this further development take place? There seems to be a connection here to your idea about certain mysteries of emergence that has fascinated you. Did you experience a dissatisfaction with SSK's abilities to handle such problems? How do you understand the relationship between your earlier work on *Constructing Quarks* and your new work on *The Mangle of Practice,* as a natural development or as incompatible?

AP: 1983–84 was an interesting year. Our first child, Lucy, was born in July 1983, a week before I handed over the final manuscript of *Constructing Quarks.* I was on the dole again, this time in Edinburgh, and had to sell my Triumph Spitfire (which was unspeakably rusty anyway). I was rescued from unemployment by the offer of an Exxon Fellowship in the STS Program at MIT. I (well, we—me, Jane, and Lucy) went there in September 1984 and I started meeting occasionally with Thomas Kuhn, who pressed me along the following lines. "Andy," he would say, "you Strong Programmers are good on negotiations between scientists; what about their negotiations with nature?" Back home we had held this question at arm's length, fearing that once we started talking positively about nature the battle with traditional philosophers of science would be lost. (Barry Barnes and David Bloor were clear that nature was the source of "causal inputs" to knowledge production, but liked to speak as if they could be "factored out.") At MIT, Leo Marx helped me to begin answering Kuhn's question by insisting that it was time I read pragmatism. Harvard University Press had William James's *Pragmatism and the Meaning of Truth* on sale, and I was instantly taken by it. Not only was James a great writer, but he had found a way of talking about knowledge as engaged with our doings in a non-human world without slipping into the kind of naive realism which my earlier studies had convinced me was nothing more than a block to serious thought. In the summer of 1985, I messed around, trying to translate what I got from James into what I knew about science. Then I joined the Sociology Department at the University of Illinois, where I enjoyed having a real job for the first time in my life. Then I spent 1986–87 on leave at the Institute for Advanced Study in Princeton. There I returned to thinking about a study of quark-search experiments that I had begun in the late 1970s and started to see the production of scientific facts as a delicate, reciprocal, and uncertain process of alignment of the material and the conceptual, of experimental setups and their performances on the one hand, and theories and models on the other. Simon Schaffer passed through Princeton at that time and seduced me into promising an essay for a volume on *The Uses of Experiment* that he was putting together with David Gooding and Trevor Pinch, so I wrote up my thoughts as "Living in the Material World" (stolen from Madonna's hit single). That essay was a key point of transition for me, and led more or less directly to *The Mangle*. It answered Kuhn's question about negotiations with nature, but in a "pragmatic realist," rather than naive or correspondence realist, fashion. Everything I had learned about the social construction of knowledge could continue to stand (hence a continuity with *Constructing Quarks*), but now one could appreciate in detail the constitutive engagement of knowledge with the material world too (hence what I regard as a productive elaboration). At the same time, I could see how the analysis I set out there could be a model for an understanding of scientific practice in general—a topic that was beginning to interest many people. But, still, I was intensely puzzled by what I found myself saying. I was talking about an essentially temporal process whose course and end-point emerged in real time, rather than being "explained" by anything that endured through it. I had never seen anything like that in the theoretical literature I knew. I only started to feel confident about it in writing *The Mangle*. So "Material World" was part of the loop back to the mysteries of emergence, but I didn't recognize that at the time.

CBJ: As a follow-up on these questions on your theoretical developments I would like to ask a sort of two-pronged question on earlier and current affiliations. The first has to do with hard scientists, the ones you have worked on, such as Morpurgo, as well as other readers. So the question is: How have your works been received among such people? Has the reception changed and in what sense? If there have indeed been changes, how much have they related to your own changes in conceptualizing science from socially constructed to "mangled" and how much have they changed due to the recent "science wars"?

AP: I think scientists generally accept my empirical, historical writing as accurate and perspicuous. They don't like the arguments that I base upon them. The reaction to *Constructing Quarks* was typical: read chapters 2 to 13 (the history); don't even look at chapters 1 and 14 (the theory and conclusions). In a sense I asked for that; the last page or so sums up the argument in a rather provocative fashion. On the other hand, when my book took on a new life in the "science wars," I was unpleasantly struck by the fact the spokespersons for "evidence and argument" were content to mock a couple of decontextualized sentences from the end of a 400-page book while completely ignoring the evidence and argument that led up to and put me in a position to utter those sentences. Nothing in my thinking has changed as result of "epistemological" critiques of my work; we in science studies are the serious scholars on that terrain; even Nobel laureates in physics can be complete amateurs, recycling their unexamined prejudices. I also note that as much as I have figured in the "science wars," it has been as the author of *Constructing Quarks,* not *The Mangle of Practice.* The "science wars" operates a kind of binary opposition: naive realism vs. its presumed opposite, social constructivism. The *Mangle* fits even less well into that binary space than *Constructing Quarks,* so the "science warriors" are even less capable of demonizing it.

CBJ: And then I would like to redo this question, only emphasizing the changes in relations and alliances you have found in and outside science studies. Originally I guess, the entire English social constructivist milieu must have strongly influenced you, whereas now it is hardly noticeable in your writings. Instead there is an increased engagement with Latour and ANT, not to mention people like Gilles Deleuze and Manuel De Landa. How and when did such changes take place?

AP: In Edinburgh, Latour's work was looked upon as a thinly disguised version of Barry Barnes's "interest model"; knowledge is understood as a scientific construct, and social interests are the relevant explanatory variables. There is, indeed, much in Latour's early writings that will bear that construal. In 1988, however, I taught a seminar on the sociology of scientific knowledge, and I recall we began to go through Kuhn's *Structure of Scientific Revolutions.* Having at that stage taught the *Structure* a couple of times already, I changed course in midstream to look at Latour's then new book *Science in Action.* Whereas as a researcher I felt at liberty to be as negative about the work of others as I liked, as a teacher it seemed incumbent upon me to make the readings sound as interesting as I could. I therefore went through *Science in Action* in class looking for novelty and originality, rather than for traces of what I already understood. I certainly found it. I was most struck by Latour's idea that the social is not a stable explanatory variable; that whatever human or social variables one cares to appeal to—interests, say—are just as much at stake and liable to transformation in the production of knowledge as knowledge is itself. The social is thus itself part of the delicate and uncertain business of making alignments in practice as the material and the conceptual. This was another key step, for me, leading from "Material World" to *The Mangle*. I have continued to admire and learn from Latour ever since.

Deleuze and De Landa. These are both post-*Mangle*. Writing that book, I had still found little outside theoretical inspiration in thinking about the temporality of practice and emergence more generally (though I took Latour to be interested in this too). Only in the last couple of years have I realized that what I experienced as solitude was actually just ignorance. We could talk more about that; now or later.

CBJ: What I want to do now is take your clue seriously and ask some questions about your newfound inspiration in places ordinarily marginal to science studies scholars. After this series, I would like to ask some questions from a more philosophical point of view, and I want to end asking you about your current development of something of a normative position, and in what directions your current work is taking you. Let's start off with a few related critical questions. You mention Latour and ANT as main inspirations in *The Mangle of Practice*. It is certainly feasible to see your work as intimately related. But from a "strict" ANT point of view it seems as if you withdraw from the most radical ontological conclusion: a symmetry or monism between non-humans and humans. In its place you put a kind of dualism dependent on a vague notion of human intentionality as goal-directedness. It could seem that this is a very loose way of differentiating humans from non-humans as ontological entities?

AP: I'm against the idea of an exact symmetry or identity between humans and non-humans, or between cats and dogs, or mathematical equations and love letters. I think monism is the wrong way to go, and I think the metaphor of the "seamless web" should be stamped out. I like the Latour of *Irreductions,* and I like Deleuze and Guattari's emphasis on irreducible multiplicity. To talk about multiplicity is to talk about differences, an open-ended list of differences. The important thing is to stay on the level of specific visible differences, and not disappear into the realm of hidden differences that define once and for all the essence of this or that. My claim is that to understand some passages of human practice it is important to recognize that we sometimes have future goals in view. To understand others, such as repetitive practices (and their drift in time) it is not. When speaking of goals, it is important to realize that they themselves are situated and liable to mangling, just like, say, the configuration and performance of laboratory apparatus or bodies of knowledge; they don't run the whole show. I don't think we need to make a special big deal about goals. If I was talking about cats, I might find it relevant sometimes to point out that they have fur and that, say, snakes don't. So what?

CBJ: The second question of this series also has to do with your investigation into sciences and ontologies of becoming. You propose that the concept of the mangle of practice could work as a TOE (theory of everything) and as you well know this is an extremely provocative suggestion. In "On Becoming," you qualify this statement in the following way: ". . . there is a hole in the middle of the metaphysics; it does not tell us what the entities are, how they relate to each other, or how they come together in assemblages." So, the provocative question back to you would be: What does it offer, aside from a loose idea of perpetual change? Where, when, or why does it benefit us to think of becoming?

AP: It wasn't a qualification. I made the remark about the hole because I realized the mangle-as-TOE wasn't quite the same kind of TOE as the physicists typically have in mind. Theirs is reductive: a TOE identifies hidden building blocks of the universe and their relations, and imagines that it can theoretically construct the visible universe in its entirety from them. The mangle refers to a visible ontology (whatever it might be in any specific situation) and a universal pattern of becoming in time. What's the benefit of thinking about becoming? Well, if the world continually becomes, shouldn't we be able to think, talk, and reason about that? Shouldn't we worry that so many academic discourses instead make it impossible to conceptualize becoming?

CBJ: In direct continuation of the last question, I would like to return to another passage from the appendix to "On Becoming." You write that "I believe therefore, that one should not take any specific science of becoming literally; the effect of doing so seems inevitably to be a) a narrowing of the imagination—the impulse to pick out just those becomings that fit in with the theory in question and to ignore others, and b) to take us away from the world again—one begins to see all sorts of amazing happenings and performances in the world as exemplifications of one or a few 'abstract diagrams' or whatever." I take this to be a critical comment on any sort of hopes for general typologies or patterns (as you also criticize Peter Galison for in *The Mangle*). More explicitly, I take the criticism of abstract diagrams to be a comment on Manuel De Landa's use of this Deleuzian concept. But my question would have to do with reversal. Why is it imperative, or at least prioritized, to always think of change? Is nothing ever to be gained by, like De Landa, exploring patterns of stability as well as change? Wouldn't he counter your argument by claiming that the mangle of practice, as you analyze it, is just one particular "abstract diagram" which is especially unlikely to stabilize, but that there are many others. He could even claim that it is through his Deleuzian ability to find many more abstract diagrams that he gains some purchase on *The Mangle,* since he is trying to fill out the hole in metaphysics that you refuse to try to do. How do you understand such arguments, and how do you explain your rigorous focus on emergence against stability?

AP: Well, first, I stick by the passage you quoted. I think De Landa and Deleuze's abstract diagrams narrow our imaginations and take us away from the visible world into some invisible, behind-the-scenes realm. I repeat, I think we should stay with the visible. But still, they take us behind the scenes in a different way from the reductive sciences; they offer us simple models of a degree of emergence that might otherwise be hard to grasp and imagine. I certainly find that attractive in their writings. The second answer is more tentative. I note that all the sciences I know have their own specific exemplary objects in the realm of the visible: thermodynamics and steam engines, organic chemistry and synthetic dyes, cybernetics and autonomous weapons systems (and other monstrous objects too). It seems possible to me that one can arrange these objects on a spectrum marked out by the violence of their becoming. A dilute gas is a pretty good exemplar for a time-reversible physics; a self-guided anti-aircraft gun for early cybernetics; biological morphogenesis for newer wave theories of self-organization; and so on. But still, even morphogenesis has a repetitive aspect. Intricate processes of self-organization produce a pretty predictable product, traveling from a simple embryo to an adult organism. My argument in *The Mangle* was that the development of scientific culture lacks even that kind of repetitivity. It just becomes. So I want to draw attention to that end of the spectrum which the sciences of self-organization have yet to approach (and which perhaps they cannot approach and still call themselves "sciences"). Coming from my angle, visibly repetitive phenomena invite further thought, but I'm not sure where to take that idea. . . . Another point worth making here is that much of the scientific and mathematical work that Manuel draws upon has to do with emergent properties of large numbers of simple and identical objects. I have not yet found it useful to think about culture in that way. In my studies of Giacomo Morpurgo's quark-search experiments, for example, it seemed to me that one needed to think about open-ended extensions of material and conceptual models and their alignment in the real time of practice. I argued that the trajectory of such extensions and alignment was a temporally emergent phenomenon, but

I can see no point in imagining some abstract diagram in phase space complete with attractors and basins of attraction behind the history as I documented it. In fact, I can't see any point of purchase for that analogy. In still unpublished work on the nineteenth-century history of the organic chemistry and the synthetic dye industry, I claimed that the emergence of mauve, the first synthetic dye, from a specific chemical recipe was an emergent phenomenon. After the fact, of course, the chemists eventually came up with a behind-the-scenes explanation of what was going on, but it was a traditional reductive explanation, nothing to do with Manuel's abstract diagrams.

CBJ: Finally, I would like to ask one more question on the relation between your theories and those of Manuel De Landa, since you are both so influenced by what you call sciences of becoming, such as artificial life, cybernetics, far-from equilibrium chemistry, etc. Whereas you are interested in emergence you are wary of "taking any specific science of becoming" literally, for the reasons discussed above. De Landa on the other hand is quite happy with an analysis based on a sort of scientific reading of Deleuze, in which highly abstract notions such as "attractors" or "phase-spaces" are used to specify an ontology. I know you (and I) are inspired by the types of analyses De Landa is making, but how do you respond to the sort of taken-for-grantedness with which he appropriates scientific concepts? This sounds about as far from a skepticist SSK background as one can get! Where are the lines of convergence and divergence?

AP: Manuel is faithful to what I call the representational idiom. He thinks the point of knowledge is to mirror the world. And in this sense he is a very traditional realist. He thinks these abstract diagrams really capture the hidden truth of the world. I am not a correspondence realist. I think that contemplating such structures is at best an aid to the imagination, a kind of mental gymnastics that can help some people to think becoming. And I think imagination is important because how we imagine the world to be and how we act in it hang together. That goes with my performative story of knowledge in relation to practice.

CBJ: There's no doubt that Manuel is a realist, albeit of a particular (Deleuzian) kind. But the way he understands realism and representation also seems to get him a certain purchase (which you don't like). He is able to propose mechanisms on a high level of abstraction as "virtual but real" and use these in an explanatory sense. Contrarily, one of the problems with the notion of the mangle as it has been perceived is that, used as a TOE, it may capture everything (such as theoretical, material, and social aspects of reality) but in a very vague sense; the vocabulary is limited to notions such as dialectics of resistance and accommodation, tuning, etc. Do you see any ways of making the conceptual vocabulary more specific and powerful? I guess this is a sort of retake on the discussion about temporal patterns and abstract diagrams earlier. But there seems to be a certain tension between achieving a conceptual fit that is neither so loose as to explain everything and nothing, or one that is too rigid.

AP: It's not a choice, Casper. My analysis of the mangle of practice didn't come before my empirical studies of practice. I worked through various case studies trying to understand them in as much detail as I could, and the mangle was what I ended up with—this in a positive sense, as a compact and graspable account of how the new grows out of the old without being at all reducible to it. But also in a negative sense. It seems to me that my studies undermine many explanatory schemas that are often taken for granted in academic life. In the book (*The Mangle*), for instance, I showed at probably excessive length how all sorts of stories that give explanatory priority to the social fail in relation to the examples I discussed. But the same goes for Manuel's abstract diagrams. They don't, actually, achieve any purchase on my examples. I can't see that they have anything to do with my empirical studies (see my earlier remark on analyses of systems made up of many identical elements vs. the cases I discuss). Neither, it must be said, has Manuel ever indicated to me that he can see any connections. So one has two options. Either ignore my examples and focus on others that can be made out as, say, the workings behind the scenes of strange attractors or whatever. This is the usual strategy followed in making a science. Or refuse to be dazzled by conceptual structures and stay with the visible, which is my path. The traditional view of "theory," which De Landa shares, I think, is as a kind of labor-saving device. Theory tells us what there is in the world, so one doesn't have to look very carefully. The mangle, in contrast, beyond serving to develop a certain sensitivity to becoming in time in fields of multiplicity, tells us nothing about ontological substance. It returns us to specifics: What is there in this situation? How does it go? It throws us back on the empirical world, into the thick of things—unlike traditional theory, which takes us away.

CBJ: The next question also relates to your understanding of concepts, this is from Evan Selinger. One thing that enrages some philosophers is your handling of concepts (agency, say). How do you understand the relationship between concepts and the history of concepts? You seem to pick conceptual names at will without considering how, for instance, the concepts of "time" or "real" are deeply sedimented in long metaphysical histories that mediate how "entities" are understood. My own addition is that this concern could be applicable, for example, to your loose understanding of human agency as "goal-directed."

AP: Oh, I'm fed up with questions like that. It's like trying to have a conversation with Pavlov's dogs. Some branches of the humanities and social sciences have elevated certain definitions of words like "agency" to ridiculous heights and inscribed them into their very essence. Agency goes with will, therefore only humans can have it (and hence a pure humanist philosophy and social science). Therefore my references to material agency must be simple conceptual mistakes, therefore end of any thought of post-humanist de-centering. And it turns out that all the key terms one might want to use in thinking about people and things, their interrelation and their becoming, are poisoned like that. The question then is, what to do about it? Since one cannot, as far as I can see, just make up new non-poisoned words, my strategy is to develop everyday (not academic) language in a different way. As it happens, for example, people have long been capable of talking about the agency of things as well as people; I give examples of such usage in the book. It is, as a matter of fact, only the Pavlovian philosophers and social scientists (which, I insist, does not mean all philosophers and social scientists) who have any difficulty with this. And then, to pin down my sense of words like "agency," I give examples of how I would apply the word in relation to detailed empirical studies. I think this is the primary way in which words get their sense. I do not think one can tie them down with definitions. This is one important thing I learned at the Science Studies Unit in Edinburgh—they call it "finitism"; I think of it as an example of the general phenomenon that I call "open-endedness" or "openness" for short. Of course, to get even clearer for the benefit of overconditioned academics, I suppose I could start writing a history of philosophy and the social sciences, noting when and how words like "agency" started to acquire the peculiar senses that I want to get away from, and seeing how the disciplines might have taken a different turn. But that would be a major enterprise in itself and, at the moment, I find myself more interested in the world than in the history of philosophy.

CBJ: Another thing that "enrages" some philosophers is your relativistic stance on "big questions," not least moral, ethical, political, normative ones. People such as Andrew Feenberg are concerned because the focus on difference and specificity prevents normative conclusions of any broad kinds to be made. For example, he fully supports David Noble's analysis which you criticize; he suggests that while accommodations and tunings might have taken place in this organization, stepping back a bit one can clearly see repressive capitalist mechanisms at play. Since these relate to the larger societal picture, they should be foregrounded and evaluated, not hidden behind a cloak of minor site-specific differences. Again, this seems to me to be a rehash of our pattern talk, but translated into a normative register. How do you understand such accusations?

AP: So much rage. . . . Again, I say that it's not a choice. I admire David Noble's work enormously. I have long been fascinated by his book *Forces of Production*. As history, it's just great. But we come back to the negative aspect of *The Mangle*. There I showed that Noble's theoretical analysis of the "limits" of capitalism was hot air. I did not reject it on principle; I demonstrated that Noble's analysis amounted to empty (but seductive) retrospection on his empirical material. If Feenberg wants to defend hot air on principle, I can't stop him, although I don't think that's what academics should do. If he wants to engage with my arguments, let him do so, and we'll see where it takes us. In this connection, I always think of Stephen Turner's wonderful book *The Social Theory of Practices*. Turner quite straightforwardly portrays great swathes of behind-the-scenes social theorizing as "an opaque end to thought and reflection."

CBJ: Nevertheless you have approached the normative lately, from a peculiar angle. You use the styles of the painters Mondrian and de Kooning as exemplars of, respectively, stasis and becoming. In recent provocative analyses of, for instance, the Mississippi delta you use this as a demarcation criteria for thinking of the future of New Orleans. You go as far as to suggest that one might consider "letting go" of New Orleans in order to let beautiful new waterscape emerge. A first "enraged" position might claim that this was a very unfortunate aesthetization of politics. But even going along with your idea, it seems that Mondrian and de Kooning are extremely slippery markers of a politics of becoming. For instance one could make analyses to show the co-production of stasis and becoming and how this foregrounds change and stability depending on the level of abstraction at which one is analyzing. Normative issues seem to be involved even in deciding at which level to approach phenomena. How could a performative-normative analysis be strengthened?

AP: You Danes always push me on this. I'm grateful for it. I think it's a fascinating and important issue. But I can't give you a straight answer. I'm still trying to think through the issues, as, I think, are many people. I also don't suppose I should rehearse the entire conference paper which has provoked you to mention Mondrian, de Kooning, the Mississippi, and New Orleans. But I could say a couple of things. First, I don't think one should be too quick to buy the idea that one can make a clean split between aesthetics and politics. Do we really want a politics that ignores desire and pleasure, pain and fear? What would it be? Free-market economics? And again, have we got a choice? Your colleague, our friend, Randi Markussen tells me that there is a real example of the situation I only imagined with respect to New Orleans happening right now in Mårup in the north of Denmark. An ancient church is slowly slipping into the sea as the coastline erodes, and people are really arguing about what should be done about this—try to fortify the church and the coast? Let the church go? One could say that this is, at once, a political argument, an aesthetic argument, an economic argument (think of tourism), and a philosophical argument (hinging on whether we should affirm or deny becoming). Or one could say that it is simply a political argument in the best sense of that phrase, as encompassing dimensions that are usually abstracted from one another (politics, aesthetics, economics, engineering, ontology). Perhaps the key contribution of a politics of becoming might be to encourage such an enrichment of our sense of what "politics" is. Second, traditional politics depends on this "abstraction" you keep going on about. It depends on stepping out of the thick of things, finding some structure behind the scenes and projecting it into the future. Think of Marxism, class struggle, and the coming revolution. Perhaps it is inevitable that we conduct our affairs like that. But I think that we should be much more suspicious of our abstractions than we are in routine politics. Think of the horrors perpetrated in the last few years in the name of free markets and competition. And, on the other hand, perhaps we should try, some of the time at least, staying in the thick of things. A politics of becoming would be a politics of experiment, desperately interested in the visible world, material and social, continually trying this and that without pretending to know the outcomes in advance. It would also be a politics of the imagination, continually searching for other ways to imagine the space in which such trials take place (beyond, for example, the grim field marked out by terms like capital, markets, and risks).

CBJ: I am happy you should mention the Danish church, since this is actually a project Randi is doing with me! I am going to wrap this up with two short ones. First, there is no doubt you are struggling with redefining academic analyses in a way that is compatible with your views of the world as becoming. You often mock the disciplines for their inability to cope with such changes. How could they cope? How could, say, the universities align themselves to match the complexity of a world of becoming? How can one be post-disciplinary? Is there a way of creating disciplines of becoming? Second, insofar as you are a representative of this way of working, can you tell us a bit about your current projects (I think there is something about cybernetics) and where you think of them as going? Do you work to provide more examples of the mangle of practice (à la Collins product differentiation?) or do you have something else up your sleeves?

AP: The shorter your questions get, Casper, the longer the answers they invite. But to keep things finite: yes, I think the world is a good place to look for inspiration, even for those of us interested in theory, and the place I'm looking now is the history of cybernetics, concentrating on the work of a fascinating bunch of Englishmen from the 1940s onwards—especially Ross Ashby, Stafford Beer, Gordon Pask, and Grey Walter. (I'm also interested in later work on related themes like self-organization, as discussed earlier.) No, I'm not primarily interested in the history of cybernetics as another process of open-ended mangling, though I'm sure it is one. It's more that I'm drawn to mangle-ishness of cybernetics. Conceptually these people have inhabited a space very similar to the mangle (did I talk about the two big paradigms earlier?) and I'm interested in understanding their ideas and exploring their relation to my own. I can find theoretical inspiration in that. But unlike desk jockeys like myself, the cyberneticians did things in the real world. They built, or tried to build, real cybernetic machines (artificial self-organizing neurons and brains!); they tried to reorganize management and even entire economies. I'm extraordinarily impressed by that (my earlier incarnation as a physicist reasserting itself, no doubt). What would a mangle-ish engineering look like? Situated robotics à la Rodney Brooks, perhaps. I'm also very impressed by the social configuration of cybernetics. People have said that cybernetics was a "universal discipline" in that it could provide a framework for all the traditional disciplines. It was more radical. Cybernetics did not float above the disciplines like a kind of umbrella; it rather implied a substantive reconstruction from below (centered on specific cybernetic exemplars or "monsters" as I like to call them) that effectively dissolved the boundaries between disciplines. One can, of course, see this sort of convergence happening in the universities today, within the second big paradigm I think I talked about. Worse than that, however, cybernetics was not centered in the universities at all. The cyberneticians wandered with ease through all sorts of institutions that we tend to think of as completely different—the universities, certainly, but also business, the military, the arts, politics, religion. Exploring the history of cybernetics is a way, then, of stretching my own imagination. I could never have invented such a striking conceptual, material, and social formation. It might be a model for the third millennium—open-endedly extended, of course.

CBJ: Andy, thank you very much for your interesting discussions and clarifications.

AP: Casper, thank you; talking to you always makes me think.

NOTE

The interview with Andy Pickering was carried out over email from November 10, 2000 to January 23, 2001. The exchange was carried out between Pickering and Casper Bruun Jensen, while Evan Selinger was instrumental and inspirational in formulating many of the questions.

6. On Becoming: Imagination, Metaphysics, and the Mangle

Andrew Pickering

> "Qual" is a philosophical play on words. Qual literally means torture, a pain which drives to action of some kind; at the same time the mystic Böhme puts into the German word something of the meaning of the Latin qualitas; his "qual" was the activating principle arising from, and promoting in its turn, the spontaneous development of the thing, relation, or person subject to it, in contradistinction to a pain inflicted from without.
>
> —FREDERICK ENGELS

> [We thus arrive at] an overall emergent and posthumanist vision of mangle-ish human practice as happening in one corner of a world that is itself a mangle-ish place, a vision in which everything becomes in relation to everything else and nothing is fixed. It is a nice picture to meditate upon—the dance of agency as the dance of Shiva . . .

Thus the exit line to my book *The Mangle of Practice* (Pickering 1995a, 252). In this essay I continue the meditation on time and becoming.[1] In the main text of *The Mangle* I developed a strongly historicist account of practice and culture in science, mathematics, technology, and society, while in the "Postscript" just quoted I toyed with the idea that much the same analysis might be carried through for nature itself. In this essay, I take that idea more seriously and try to develop a metaphysical image that can embrace the becoming of both the human and the non-human. We seem to have considerable difficulty in recognizing the emergence of real, irreducible novelty in the world, and I want to get that process into focus. The metaphysics helps me, at least, to do that, and my hope is that it is consistent with both what we know and how, historically, we have come to know it.

In section 1, I lay out a basic metaphysical model of becoming. Section 2 draws upon ideas about biological evolution to enliven the model. Section 3 turns to inanimate technologies. Section 4 is about articulated knowledge and theory—which is where the real problems lie in thinking about becoming.[2] The essay then takes a reflexive turn. In section 5 I discuss the question of realism, and I argue that the metaphysics developed here should be seen as an aid to the imagination. Section 6 discusses some scholarly implications of that, and section 7 tries to suggest that a reconfigured imaginary can have real-world implications, too. Finally, an appendix very tentatively picks up a line of thought on the becoming of inanimate matter, which was allowed to drop in section 3.

I. METAPHYSICS

Authors like Bruno Latour (1995) and Niels Viggo Hansen (n.d., 1997) have found resources for thinking about becoming in the process-metaphysics of Alfred North Whitehead (1929). I find the work of Gilles Deleuze and Felix Guattari (1987) and Manuel De Landa (1991, 1997a) easier to get to grips with, and I want to begin by describing what I take to be a Deleuzian picture of being and becoming.

The image is one of multiplicity. Imagine a set of entities. Imagine each of them sporting endlessly, changing their nature open-endedly, first this way then that, in indefinite spaces of possibility. Imagine that subsets of these sportings occasionally come into alignment and reciprocally sustain or interactively stabilize one another, forming a new entity that sports anew. Imagine that the original entities formed in the same way, so that all entities are assemblages. Iterate.

This is the simple image that I will elaborate on in various ways in what follows. First, it enables me to clarify or define two key terms. It is an image of *being:* an image of what exists at any given time. In "being" one should also include whatever relations there are between existents. The image is thus a *relational* one, though I would not attempt to reduce entities to relations.[3] At the same time it is an image of *becoming,* inasmuch as the present state of the set of entities does not determine its future. There is a pattern to what happens in time, but it is a pattern to which chance is endemic—in specific sportings at specific times, and in the interrelation of those sportings, whether they together form an assemblage or not. And it is a pattern from which genuine novelty can appear in the world—new assemblages themselves. The state of the set of entities at any given time is a function both of the initial set of entities (*relativity; situatedness*) and of the temporal path taken by them up to that time (*path-dependence*). Viewing this process as moving into the future, one can speak of *temporal emergence;* looking the other way, of *historicity.*

Two questions arise at this point. One is, just what is an assemblage? What is it that determines whether two or more entities come together to form a new unity? I can find no general answer to that question. I do not think there is any general principle of assemblage and interactive stabilization. The unity (temporary, fragile) of any given assemblage seems to lie in its specifics: *this* hangs together with *that* in *that particular way.*[4] And, second, just what are these entities that sport so? The answer I want to give is that they might be anything. In the main text of *The Mangle* they appeared as the "made things" of human culture (including material culture), but now I want to see what happens if these entities span the space of all that exists in the world (including human culture). That is why I have spoken of metaphysics—why I spoke at the end of *The Mangle* of a theory of everything, a TOE, as the scientists like to call it. But anyone can say things like that. The difficult thing is to see how the theory might bear on real examples. We should leave the realm of abstraction.

2. EVOLUTIONARY BIOLOGY

Evolutionary biology is the body of established knowledge that most straightforwardly exemplifies the metaphysics of becoming. The entities in question are biological species, open-endedly mutating and playing into each others' dynamics. Evolutionary theory is a science of temporal emergence and historicity. I cannot go into the details of biology, but I doubt whether I should. I want instead to appeal to some simple ideas and examples from biology to put more flesh on the metaphysics.

(1) Most biological mutations lead nowhere. They find no resonance; they are unproductive; they die out. One should imagine the same is true more generally. Thus the metaphysics of becoming is also a metaphysics of stasis, though the converse is not true: one cannot understand change if one thinks only of reproduction.

(2) Within the field of becoming, evolutionary examples suggest what might be a useful if not absolute distinction. Many becomings, one might say, are only *weakly coupled* to one another. Finches' beaks become a bit larger, affecting their access to some food supply, which changes slightly the space of becoming for other species, and so on. The ontological "basis states" remain largely the same, though the precise contours of those states drift in time. *Here we have a relatively smooth notion of becoming that needs to be added to the image of emergence sketched out in section 1.*

(3) On the other hand, trajectories of becoming sometimes become *strongly coupled* to one another. Symbiosis: the bees that evolve into total dependence on orchids that have evolved into total dependence on those bees, for example. This amounts to a change in the basis states of evolution—the appearance of the bee-orchid couple as a new evolutionary entity. In the terms of section 1, this is the formation of a new assemblage, and it points to a kind of bumpiness, lumpiness, almost discontinuity in the field of becoming. A very strong sense of

emergence and historicity attaches to such processes, *punctuating*, one might say, the more continuous processes conjured up under heading (2).[5]

(4) Another sense of discontinuity also arises in connection with biological evolution. I think, for example, of birds, wings, and flight. Flight, I want to say, is an *emergent phenomenon*. It just turned out that wings worked for aerial travel. They constituted a new grip of the animate on the inanimate (the air). Such emergent phenomena again punctuate the more continuous processes mentioned under heading (2). They are just as relational as the symbiosis of biological species, but now exist at the interface with the inorganic.[6]

3. MACHINES AND US

Biology is the easy case for thinking about becoming. Since Darwin most of us have been taught to believe in the historicity of species. Now for a harder case. What about machines, like the steam engine? Do inanimate machines display the same sort of historicity as biological organisms?

This is a point of some delicacy, and I am going to let the discussion bifurcate here. Following on from section 2, one is inclined to ask oneself questions like: Did the inner sporting of inanimate matter lead up to and into the steam engine? Did the inner sporting of the steam engine in turn produce steam turbines and internal combustion engines? The answer to such questions must be no—and that is the line I will take in this section. One can note, though, that the machinic evolutionary trajectory just sketched out is a trajectory seen from the human standpoint. And one might wonder why inanimate matter should sport *like that*—fortunate coincidence indeed. I therefore return in an appendix to reconsider the sporting of inanimate matter from a different angle.

In the sense just described, I find it impossible to think of any inner sporting in connection with inanimate machines. However, if we introduce human beings into the picture and think about the sweep of technological history, a Deleuzian metaphysics starts to become more plausible. In *The Mangle* I argued that machinic development should be understood as entailing a process of modeling: scientists and engineers try out new machines which are modeled on old machines, and—this is a key point—modeling is an *open-ended process:* nothing in the model determines what extension of the model should be tried or how it will perform.

Here, then, there is a precise equivalence between the sporting of biological species and the extension of the machinic field. Both become open-endedly and unpredictably into the future. A further equivalence concerns the possibility of making a distinction between the relatively continuous and discontinuous aspects of such becoming. The sporting of machines traverses a space of material performativity, which is sometimes smooth and sometimes lumpy. In *The Mangle*, for example, I discussed Giacomo Morpurgo's fine-tuning of the material apparatus that he used to search for free quarks. No great discontinuities surfaced there: his apparatus looked much the same within each of the various stages of his experiment; its performances did not change much—though they did change in their details, and that was crucial to the production of knowledge. In contrast, Donald Glaser's attempts to produce a new kind of particle detector modeled on the cloud chamber eventually arrived at the bubble chamber, which constituted, I would say, a quite new material grip on the world, a new emergent power. The appearance of bubble chambers in particle physics was, in just this sense, like the appearance of wings in the field of biological species.[7]

But still, we have this disanalogy: the inner sporting of the biological realm versus the humanly assisted sporting of the machinic band. What are we to make of this? The interesting move is to symmetrize the picture. In *The Mangle* I argued that just as the becoming of machines depends upon us, so our becoming—of our goals and intentions, social roles and relations, disciplines and subject positions—depends upon machines. Sometimes this is true in a relatively continuous fashion, sometimes less so, and I can dwell briefly on the latter. In *The Mangle*, and later more extensively elsewhere, I argued that human history, too, is punctuated by the emergent powers of machines—specific sportings of the human and social are interactively stabilized by specific sportings of machines and the performativities they reveal.[8]

In World War II, for example, the becoming of radar sets hung together with new ways of fighting battles ("technowar"), new ways of doing science ("big science"), and new social relations between science and the military (new linking institutions like the OSRD; the "enfolding" of science by the military) (Pickering 1995b). In much the same way, no doubt, though writ even larger, the coming into being and technological refinement of steam engines hung together with the massive social changes of the Industrial Revolution: the factory, the division of labor, the growth of industrial towns and industrial architecture, new social classes, and class struggle. One cannot understand the specific trajectory of evolution of the steam engine without reference to the human and social space in which it appeared; but, reciprocally, that human and social space evolved in a way that was itself structured by the emergent powers of steam.

The upshot of this phase of the discussion is, then, that while it may be hard to think the historicity of the machinic "band" taken alone, one can readily conceive of the historicity and becoming of machine-human couples. Industrial capitalism, like the post-war military-industrial complex, has to be seen as one of those emergent assemblages I began by talking about in section 1. Here we should speak of the being and becoming not purely of the machinic or human bands but of *cyborg* being and becoming, the intertwined evolution of the human and the non-human.[9]

4. KNOWLEDGE

So far, so good. We have cleared the first hurdle—understanding how inanimate machines might be included in an overall picture of becoming. Now for the next obstacle: knowledge! Birds just flap their wings and fly, but we think about it. How, then, might thought and knowledge fit into an overall story of becoming? Oddly enough, this is where the trouble starts in thinking about becoming.

At first glance, there is no problem. The discussion can go along the same lines as that in section 3. I cannot see any point in talking about the inner sporting of knowledge itself, but if one thinks of ideas and representations as engaged in human practice, then one is back into the analysis of open-ended extensions of conceptual culture, from which particular vectors are selected in interactive stabilizations against sportings of material culture, social formations, and so on. I have argued and exemplified this point many times in *The Mangle* and elsewhere—most recently in connection with the production of knowledge in nineteenth-century organic chemistry (Pickering forthcoming a)—and it encourages us simply to see knowledge as itself becoming as part of cyborg assemblages even wider than those discussed in section 3—assemblages that are material, social, *and conceptual.*

At this level, the temporal emergence and historicity of knowledge is clear. But a real difficulty does arise when we think about the *form and content* of our knowledge. Knowledge—both everyday and scientific/technological—often has, as I will say, an *atemporal* form and content. Much of our knowledge is a kind of statics, in which no reference to time appears at all; and even when time does appear in scientific theories, say, it is as an abstract time-variable figuring in stories of how things happen in time, whatever time it happens to be. In this sense, then, much of our knowledge seems to deny becoming. What can we make of that?

The first move would be to say that this paradox—a recognition of the historicity of knowledge juxtaposed with the denial of historicity by the knowledge itself—is no paradox at all. One can reasonably say that atemporal knowledge is knowledge of *being, not becoming*—it is about relations between parts of assemblages as they presently exist. One finds out about specific assemblages by pulling and pushing their components and seeing what happens, how their constituent entities are, in this instance, interlinked—by subjecting them to trials, as Latour says. If we stoke the fire more furiously, can we get more power out of a steam engine? What if we operate with high-pressure instead of atmospheric-pressure steam? Thermodynamics emerged out of investigations like those.

So atemporal knowledges are of being not becoming. They do not speak of becoming, but why should they? No paradox arises, therefore, in their simultaneous embeddedness in history and their lack of recognition of the fact. But we are not quite out of the woods yet. The problem is that, as a matter of fact, we *use* atemporal knowledge in our travels through becoming. When we set out to design a new machine or instrument, for example, we draw upon our knowledge of the being of existing machines. And this is what generates the trickiest paradox: our habit of treating atemporal knowledge as extending through time—not just backwards into the past, but forwards into the future too. Hence such commonly encountered locutions as "knowledge made it possible for us," or "permitted us," to build lasers and CD players, send men to the moon, and so on. This extrapolation is the point at which ideas about being clash seriously with any metaphysics of becoming.

So how should we proceed? We should, I think, consider what happens in practice when we make such extrapolations of atemporal knowledge into the future, and an example discussed by Latour (1987, 104–106) comes to mind. Drawing upon his knowledge of classical thermodynamics, Rudolf Diesel set out around 1887 to build a new kind of internal combustion engine, a constant-temperature engine, and it did not work. There followed a period in which, "by modifying the whole design of the engine many times, Diesel drifted away from the original patent and from the principles presented in his book" (Latour 1987, 105). Other engineers also took up the struggle, and in 1908, twenty-one years down the road (and after Diesel had gone bankrupt, suffered a nervous breakdown, and committed suicide) what we retrospectively recognize as prototypical Diesel engines went into common use—now understood as constant-pressure (not constant-temperature) engines.

The moral of this story, which could be multiplied and elaborated indefinitely with further examples from the history of science and technology, is the following. First, we do indeed use atemporal knowledges in our trips through material performativity. But such knowledge does not have the magical quality of "allowing us" to accomplish any particular objective. When we depart from our base models we are liable to find ourselves left in the lurch by the emergent performances of the material world, and we then wallow around, open-endedly tinkering with our atemporal ideas, material setups, and social relations until, if we are lucky, some new assemblage appears before us and for us, along with a suitably retuned atemporal understanding of how it works. This I believe to be a general pattern of the intertwining of knowledge and practice in time.[10]

And now we can see more clearly, I hope, how to resolve the paradox of atemporal knowledge vs. becoming. Atemporal knowledge is marked by the processes of its emergent becoming, but it cannot itself explicitly register the existence of truly emergent phenomena, nor can it thematize the shocks and the struggles that their emergence precipitates. Becoming is actively obscured by the way we use atemporal knowledge in the world. The price to pay for a metaphysics of becoming is recognition of this fact.[11]

With the exception of an appendix, that is as far as I propose to take the constructive development of the metaphysics of becoming. The remaining sections take a reflexive turn.

5. REALISM, SYMMETRY, AND IMAGINATION

> One can only study what one has already dreamed.
> —GASTON BACHELARD

> Gentlemen, let us learn to dream, and perhaps then we will find
> the truth . . . but let us also beware not to publish our dreams until
> they have been examined by the wakened mind.
> —AUGUST KEKULÉ

In *The Mangle* I argued that in order to think straight about science and technology we needed to "thicken up" our image of the material world (relative to the exceptionally thin image prevalent in history, philosophy, and sociology of science through much of the twentieth century). The metaphysics of becoming is one way of continuing along that line. But there is a well-known objection to this tactic, set out in Collins and Yearley's (1992) critique of the Actor-Network approach to science and technology studies. The critique is that by attributing properties (such as agency) to the material world one effectively surrenders to scientists' accounts of the world. I think this is wrong, but it is worth setting out why.

I have been pursuing the idea that there is no limit to the applicability of the Deleuzian scheme; that wherever one looks—in the material, social, and conceptual worlds, and in hybrid, cyborg intertwinings thereof—one can find entities sporting, interacting weakly or strongly, forming assemblages with emergent powers and generally becoming in time. In that sense, the metaphysics is, indeed, a theory of everything. A strong claim, but perhaps not as strong as it might appear. There is a hole in the middle of the metaphysics: it does not tell us what the entities are, how they relate to one another, or how they come together to form assemblages. Which means, of course, that *the work remains to be done* of knowing the world in its specifics—which is nothing less than what the sciences (as well as common sense, history, and so on) do for us.[12] And I argued in the previous section that that work of knowing is embedded in history, and should be understood, appreciated, and analyzed as such. So it is not the case that the present metaphysics commits us to any specific scientific account of the world. It does draw our attention to the engagement of, say, the atemporal sciences with the material world, but without entailing a correspondence realism—to mention a common accusation—about any of them.[13]

On the other hand, the metaphysics does seem to violate the venerable principle of symmetry and impartiality of the Strong Program in the sociology of scientific knowledge. It certainly *does not* require us to give different kinds of accounts of different bodies of knowledge (e.g., true vs. caused); but it nevertheless fosters a degree of *partiality*. Having written this essay, I feel like thanking Charles Darwin for helping us to become aware of becoming, and I feel like criticizing the pretensions (not the substance) of the atemporal sciences that obscure becoming. What is happening here?

I have no idea whether Darwin was right about the evolution of species—and, actually, the specific idea of natural selection by competition does little to illuminate any historical episode that I have studied—but it is undeniable that Darwin helped us to *imagine*, and hence explore, becoming. He gave us a spectacular set of examples of the becoming of real novelty in the world—species and their attributes arranged in time—and some simple concepts with which to think about that. In the present context, his specifically biological ideas were less important than the kind of blueprint he presented for thinking about becoming in general. He showed that, in a very down-to-earth way, it is possible to think becoming.

My judgment is that this is an important but difficult task in which still more help is needed, and I hope that my metaphysics counts as that, to some small degree. In this sense, the metaphysics of becoming is intended as a constructive contribution to a tradition of thought that goes back to Darwin (and, of course, a long way beyond him). I conclude that one does not have to choose between the positions of detached observer of the world of knowledge and engaged participant in it.

6. MATTERS ACADEMIC

> The teaching of Being, of things, and of all those constant entities, is a *hundred times more easy* than the teaching of *Becoming* and of evolution. . . .
>
> —FRIEDRICH NIETZSCHE

There is no point in metaphysical thought unless it is somehow consequential, and the last two sections of this essay seek to speak to that point. In this section I point to some consequences of my Deleuzian metaphysics for academic writing and research; in the next I think about, well, life as we live it.

I noted above that from the metaphysical perspective the work of knowing the world remains to be done, but I also suggested a role for the imagination in structuring how we go about knowing it. What follows consists of notes on how thinking about becoming might intersect with research and writing in various fields and disciplines. Remarks under one heading are often readily transferable to others.

Social Science

The social sciences in general are remarkably weak in the analysis of change. I have made this point at some length elsewhere (e.g., Pickering 1993, forthcoming a), and I mention it here only to note that the present analysis has helped me to understand this weakness better.[14] In self-conscious emulation of the natural sciences, the social sciences often aim at an analysis of being, not becoming. The exploration of correlations between social variables in quantitative sociology is precisely analogous to similar explorations concerning temperatures, pressures, and the performance of steam engines. One cannot object in principle to such approaches in the social sciences. But many people have noticed that the natural sciences have often enjoyed much more productive relations with their objects than have the social sciences, and one could make a suggestion as to why that might be: the social world is much more fluid and labile than the aspects of the natural world seized upon by physics and so on.[15] A steam engine turns out to be a wonderful object on which to found a science of being; there is no reason to assume that there are human equivalents. I suspect that the analysis of becoming is much of the analysis of the social *in toto.*[16]

There is a second aspect of the mimicry of the natural sciences by the social sciences. The latter frequently do not rest content by measuring correlations; they seek also to go behind the scenes, postulating invisible entities to explain visible social phenomena. The nicest example is Durkheim's suicidogenetic current, considered as a social analogue of natural forces like gravity, but one could cite many more.[17] This explanatory strategy has been very productive in the natural sciences, but much less so in the social sciences, where it simply redoubles the difficulty of thinking becoming.

History

Here I will concentrate on the question of units of analysis. I should not generalize too much, but much of the historical writing with which I am familiar (history of science, technology, and society) treats the units of analysis as given and enshrined in sub-disciplinary genres: history of ideas, histories of science and of specific sciences, histories of technology and of specific technologies, business history, and so on. When these genre-histories intersect, the sophisticated response is *contextualism;* the historian of science might, for instance, appeal to industrial history to fill explanatory gaps in the history of science proper.

Of course, one has to start somewhere—one has to have some idea of one's objects in order to begin historical research. But the metaphysics of becoming suggests a rather different historical methodology than that just described. The "entities" of the metaphysics become in history; they are not fixed things. And they therefore have to be *found* in any particular instance; one cannot know in advance what they will turn out to be. But how, then, should we go about looking for them?

The point to note is that an entity is an assemblage which is only weakly coupled to its surroundings, that does, in fact, retain its integrity over some period of time. Sometimes, say, academic physics might have that character, in which case it makes sense to write a self-contained or appropriately contextualized history of physics; other times it might not. Conversely—and conceivably more importantly—when entities become strongly coupled as members of new assemblages—when the set of basis-states changes—it makes little sense to stick to the old set of historical categories. One cannot understand the history of organic chemistry in the second half of the nineteenth century without thinking about the history of the synthetic dye industry in the same period, and vice versa (Pickering forthcoming a). Or, to be more precise, one can stick to the old set of categories and contextualize them, but the price of this is (a) a paradoxical view of history in which it sometimes appears that the object of analysis is the vanguard of progress, but then, in a shift of gestalt, a mere symptom of its context, and (b) the elision of major historical discontinuities—the formation of new assemblages.[18]

So the metaphysics of becoming has important methodological, historiographic implications. I cannot make the key terms, weak- and strong-coupling, more precise because I lack a reductive and general principle of assemblage. But I can note this. In practice, it is not hard to identify what is weakly or strongly coupled to what. There is nothing subtle or mysterious at stake here. The coupling I have in mind is not buried beneath the surface of appearances, needing clever analysts to bring it to light. It is more like the visible flows of money, materials, knowledge, methods, and personnel that linked organic chemistry and the dye industry together in the nineteenth century. Such couplings are historically manifest; they are what one has to *explain away* if one wants to maintain the purity of traditional historiographic genres.[19]

Philosophy

I have one specific topic in mind here, and I can be very brief. For most of the twentieth century, philosophers have sought to discern a fundamental unity of the sciences, as individual exemplifications of a unitary science. The metaphysics of becoming sorts ill with this image. It fits much better with recent thinking on the "disunity of science."[20] The idea is to see each of the sciences as, as it were, the science of being of a particular emergent phenomenon—thermodynamics and the steam engine, etc. The complication, of course, is the crisscrossing that goes on: the alignments that are produced between different sciences, the extension of sciences from one emergent phenomenon to the next, and so on. I have already indicated in section 6 how we might think about such moves in relation to a metaphysics of becoming.

These remarks about the philosophy of science, and the world of which science speaks, can be generalized, taking us back to one of our starting points. The significance of the title of Deleuze and Guattari's book *A Thousand Plateaus* is that the many specific topics treated there (not quite a thousand of them) each requires its own specific philosophical analysis—a disunity of philosophy in general goes with a disunity of the world in general.

7. HIGHWAY 61 REVISITED

So much for scholarship. What about the consequences of the metaphysics for life in general? Again, I want to dwell upon the relationship between the metaphysics and the faculty of imagination. Simply being able to think about and grasp the becoming of genuine novelty in the world can help to reconfigure our mental horizons, not just along scholarly axes but in general. Dazed by repetition, under the sway of atemporal categories, conceptualizations, and explanations, the world loses its flavor for us, and we move leadenly through it. The metaphysics of becoming might be an antidote to that.

Addressing the same point somewhat differently, the metaphysics can help us to imagine the world *before our knowledge of it*. On the one hand, the metaphysics serves to put knowledge in its place, as just one part of an evolving cyborg assemblage, rather than as some kind of aetherial simulacrum of the whole thing. On the other hand, though not at all rich or detailed, the metaphysics helps us to imagine the thing itself, the world itself that knowledge is about: entities sporting, coupling, forming temporary unities, and so on. It helps us to get back to the world and wonder at it. It helps me, at least, to see that the flight of birds, the material agency of steam engines—the emergent powers of assemblages—are spectacular and amazing worldly performances. I should really say that it helps me remember this fact. I knew it at an early age, but familiarity breeds a contempt that is only reinforced by the atemporal sciences—flight as so many instances of aerodynamics, steam engines as textbook examples of thermodynamics . . .

The general idea is, then, that the metaphysics of becoming can expand our mental horizons, enabling us to recognized and grasp aspects of the world that seem otherwise to have become, for whatever reason, unimaginable and unrecognizable. This, I think, is important, not just for how and what we experience and think, but for how we act in the world. And I will close the main text of this essay with a final example that can illustrate what is at stake.

Consider the 1960s. Many of us who lived through that decade regret its passing. We recall life as being not just quantitatively better then—we had more fun and less stuff—but qualitatively too—as if there were something special in the air, that started leaking away around 1973. I have often struggled to express what that specialness was, and here is an idea that came to me as I was writing this essay.

I recently saw part of a TV documentary—I think it was a BBC history of rock. One of the Pink Floyd was talking about how the band's singular style of music came about. "We wanted to play the guitar," he said, "but in those days everyone was playing like this"—and here he mimed someone playing with the guitar held high to their chest, strumming it in conventional fashion, an image that immediately conjured up the early Beatles. A grimace of disgust. "I picked my guitar up like this"—in one hand—"and I started banging it as hard as I could. And it sounded *like this* . . ."—whereupon the documentary cut to the highly distinctive sound of some early Floyd classic. Now think of the *differently* weird and wonderful sounds that Jimi Hendrix could get from a guitar with his teeth, Neil Young's feats of feedback and the Who's habit of progressively destroying their instruments on stage. What should we make of this?

First, we can note that these musical developments map exactly onto the present metaphysics—cyborg sportings of human/instrument couples that happened to cut interestingly across the space of emergent powers, the production of new sounds in this case. Second, note that hardly any knowledge was involved in these sportings. The spirit was: let's try banging, kicking, and biting musical instruments, let's smash them on each other's heads, let's make the noise the signal, let's see what happens—and it worked. The singularity of the music of the high sixties was a practical and wonderful vindication of such exploration.

In retrospect, of course, the inclination is to dwell on the new music itself. Why not? It is still playing at my local bar and nobody complains. But I want to emphasize the exploration as well as the end-point, the willingness to experiment, the sense of open-ended possibilities. This willingness, I suggest, was an index of a *conscious recognition of strong temporal emergence*, a recognition that, beyond incremental becoming, real novelty is there to be found—emergent phenomena, new powers, new worlds. This awareness was almost a commonplace in the 1960s, and it was, I am now inclined to argue, what gave the 1960s their special quality—in music, but also in fashion, drugs, sex, social arrangements, and what have you, not to mention science, technology, and the arts in general—all of those things together, in fact.

Not all of the 1960s experiments ended as well as some of the musical ones, which must be a part of the historical explanation of the ending of the sixties. But whatever the reasons one might give, that ending marked the beginning of a kind of material, social, and conceptual heat-death of the universe. Relics of the time (the LPs, the drugs) linger on, but retro is not enough. The self-consciousness of openness, becoming, and emergence has faded away. The 1960s have gone; one cannot rewind history. But the example of the sixties shows that awareness of becoming can really make a difference in the world. This essay has tried to make a difference in our awareness.

APPENDIX: THE INANIMATE

Our terrestrial world is grossly bimodal in its forms: either the forms in it are extremely simple, like the run-down clock, so that we dismiss them contemptuously, or they are extremely complex, so that we think of them as being quite different, and say they have Life. . . . Today we can see that the two forms are simply at the extremes of a single scale.

—W. Ross Ashby

In section 3 I noted a point of bifurcation in my discussion, conceding that from one, distinctly human, perspective it makes no sense to think about the sporting of inanimate matter, while reserving the right to return to the topic here. What follows are some very preliminary and open-ended thoughts (hence their exile to an appendix). Do we have to think of inanimate matter as "dead"? Does it just sit there? I want to approach this question from several angles.

First, we can perhaps gain some inspiration from the atemporal sciences themselves. The atemporality of those sciences typically resides at the level of laws or equations that bear no reference to historical time. My remarks in section 4 on knowledge bear precisely on that aspect of the sciences. But if we think about those sciences at the level of ontology, their image of their objects, one can find a much more lively picture. At the most "fundamental" level we have quantum mechanics (and quantum field theory). And ontologically, quantum mechanics is all about the sporting of matter—the wave function of an electron is a description of all sorts of things the electron might be doing. Feynman's path-integral formulation of quantum mechanics sums all possible paths a system might take between one state and the next. And, connecting straight back to section 2 above, Geoff Bowker notes that Niels Bohr saw precise equivalences between quantum processes and biological evolution: "the result of any interaction between atomic systems is the outcome of a competition between individual processes" (Bohr 1960, 4, quoted in Bowker 1993, 119).

Further, one does not have to delve into the mysteries of quantum mechanics to find such images of the sporting of matter. Think of statistical thermodynamics with its image of endless fluctuation at the level of aggregates of atoms and molecules. And think even of the use of variational methods in physics, beginning in classical physics. I dimly recall from my school days a variational method for calculating the forces acting in static mechanical structures, bridges, for example: one gets the forces by imagining all possible deformations of the structure. Suppose bridges are like that: continually fluctuating in their precise contours, and that their stability is really fluctuation temporarily held in check.

At the ontological level, then, even the hard atemporal sciences sometimes point us toward a sporting and becoming (in potentia, at least) of inanimate matter—of all matter. The laws and equations of the atemporal sciences might therefore be seen not so much as laws of being, but as laws of *becoming held in check*. I think that the metaphysics of becoming might find inspiration in this idea. It recurs below, though I may as well admit that much still puzzles me about it.

Thinking along the same lines, but leaving the realm of scientific knowledge for that of material powers and performances, we can go back to steam engines. A practical problem with early steam engines was that their cycling rate and power output fluctuated, increasing and decreasing unpredictably. Steam engines *were* given to sporting. And a practical solution to that problem was the "governor," a mechanical device that sensed the cycling rate and acted back on the working conditions so as to counteract tendencies to deviate from the desired rate. Here again we have an example which speaks not of the timeless being of an assemblage but of an engineered frustration of becoming. And even such engineered frustration is never guaranteed. Massive explosions marked the history of steam engines, and I imagine that enquiries into the causes of explosions must themselves have led into specific path-dependent histories of metal: how this bolt was loosened in the repeated working of the engine, or why that weld had lost its strength. Perhaps we should recognize, then, that even the inanimate realm continually confronts us with sportings, temporal emergence, and becoming. Perhaps we typically ignore that because the sportings are not *for us*—from our point of view, machines tend to degrade; steam engines do not turn into nuclear power stations.[21]

One last thought on the steam engine. The governor as a mechanical device gave rise to a great deal of scientific and mathematical work on control devices and feedback systems, which in turn, around World War II, fed into the new science of cybernetics.[22] Seen from this historical angle, cybernetics is a science of becoming, albeit of frustrated becoming, as manifest in its obsession with control, homeostasis, and biological models. But related sciences of becoming have also flourished since the war that are not similarly restricted. Phrases like "self-organization" come to mind (likewise autopoiesis, chaos theory, attractors, complexity, cellular automata, autocatalysis, artificial life, non-equilibrium thermodynamics, etc.—and these, of course, often fold back into my starting point, evolutionary biology: Depew and Weber 1997). I can thus observe that there exists a class of sciences that, unlike the atemporal sciences, actively thematizes becoming over the entire range of the inanimate and the animate, and which therefore have close affinities with the metaphysics of becoming—as is evident in the use by Deleuze and Guattari and De Landa of imagery drawn from such sciences.[23] But how far should we go in incorporating the sciences of becoming into our metaphysics? Should we, to go back to the topic of section 5, interpret them realistically?

My feeling is that inasmuch as the sciences in question deserve to be called sciences, it must be that they somehow contain within themselves some general principle of assemblage and emergence. And I have already stated my conclusion, based on the instances I know from my own studies, that no such principle exists. I believe, therefore, that one should not take any specific science of becoming literally; the effect of doing so seems inevitably to be (a) a narrowing of the imagination—the impulse to pick out just those becomings that fit in with the theory in question and to ignore others, and (b) to take us away from the world again—one begins to see all sorts of amazing happenings and performances in the world as exemplifications of one or a few "abstract diagrams" or whatever.[24] Conversely, of course, I can see every reason to espouse the sciences of becoming as aids to the imagination. As I said before, becoming is a terribly difficult concept to get hold of. Repeated iteration of a simple set of coupled equations can lead to amazingly complex behaviors of the variables, behaviors that display extreme sensitivity to initial conditions. If seeing that helps anyone to imagine becoming, I am all in favor of it.

NOTES

1. My thanks to Bruce Lambert, Manuel De Landa, Niels Viggo Hansen, Finn Olesen, Randi Markussen, Malcolm Nicolson, and Isabelle Stengers for very stimulating discussions on topics addressed here. My original inspiration for thinking further about becoming was the highly imaginative and unusual meeting on "Time, Heat and Order" organized by Niels Viggo Hansen at the University of Aarhus in September 1997. I am grateful for the hospitality in spring 1998 of the departments of philosophy and information and media science, Aarhus University, where much of the thinking for this essay

was done, and I gratefully acknowledge a fellowship from the John Simon Guggenheim Memorial Foundation, which made the work of writing possible.

2. My idea that one should think about the becoming of knowledge derives from my earlier work in science and technology studies, and to a degree differentiates what follows from related thought on the becoming of the material and social worlds. It feeds into the discussion of realism and imagination that begins in section 5.

3. Such a reduction was once the ambition of the physics of fields; the idea was to see the sources of electric and magnetic fields (moving charges) as field-singularities (rather than entities in themselves). This program did not succeed; these days fields are regarded as effects of the exchange of entities (though this is still a relational image). On the recent resurgence of pure relationism in social theory, see Emirbayer (1997).

4. Latour's thoughts on "irreduction" point toward a similar conclusion (Latour 1988, part 2). One can, however, perhaps discern a rule of *locality* or adjacency in the formation of assemblages: literally or metaphorically, entities have to be adjacent to one another if they are to form assemblages. The set of entities, one could say, maps out a space, and places within that space are important. Besides inner sportings, *displacements* can thus be important markers in the flow of becoming. For an exemplification of this idea, see Pickering (forthcoming a). A principle of locality lies, I think, behind Hansen's (1998) Whiteheadian discussion of special relativity.

5. I borrow the idea of weak- and strong-coupling from old elementary-particle theory. There one finds the idea that one can understand weakly coupled systems of entities (charged particles, say) as composites of free entities that retain their integrity and only disturb one another a little. In contrast, it makes no sense to consider strongly coupled systems in terms of the dynamics of the primitive constituents; one has to describe such systems in terms of the collective properties of the whole. Hence the idea that the basis states change between weak- and strong-coupling regimes.

6. A certain asymmetry becomes evident here. Growing wings was a big deal for birds, but probably not for the air. Flight was an emergent phenomenon for the bird-air couple as it engaged with the being of birds.

7. So the appearance of the bubble chamber punctuated the history of physics. But I should emphasize that to punctuate history is not to arrest it. Glaser's early bubble chambers constituted a "bridgehead" (Pickering 1995a) to be further explored and elaborated in the history of physics.

8. Pickering (1995b, 1997, 2001a, forthcoming a, b). These all contribute to a project that I call the history of agency, organized around the kinds of punctuation just mentioned.

9. I often find it helpful to think of the space of entities as partitioned into different "bands"—"human," "non-human," "animate," "inanimate," and so on. Thus section 2 was about the organic band (including humans only as one more biological species), this section is about the machinic band and the human band, section 6 concerns the conceptual band, and the appendix is about the inanimate band. One can also think of "crossovers" between bands: errant flows of materials—"pollution"—around, say, steam engines and plutonium reactors that can feed into the becoming of local and global non-human ecologies (and that can later cross back into the becoming of the human). The problem with this style of thought is that interactions between bands can erode the clarity of such distinctions, as in the text. Hence the proliferation of terms like "cyborg," "Actor-Network," "hybrid," "imbroglios" and "post-human."

10. I argue, for instance, along precisely these lines in my analysis of the relation between organic chemistry and the synthetic dye industry (Pickering forthcoming a). To give a parallel example from the social world, think of the collapse of the Soviet Union. For most of my lifetime, Kremlinologists assured inhabitants of the West that no such thing could ever happen, backing the assurances up with data and arguments. After the collapse, they explain its inevitability in terms of new data and new arguments.

11. To return to my personal bête noir, I can perhaps now clarify my objection to "constraint" as an analytical concept. I can see no objection to "constraint" as a term of art in the atemporal sciences where it has a precise sense, but one should never suppose that it has any use in thinking about becoming.

12. So there is a difference here between the metaphysics and the usual sense of "theory of everything" as used by contemporary scientists. The scientists think they know the basic entities and their interactions—the universe is made of quantized strings or whatever.

13. Hence the philosophical position that I called "pragmatic realism" in *The Mangle*.

14. Another weakness of the social sciences that I have often addressed concerns the coupling of the social to the non-social (section 3). The present metaphysics also helps us to think further about the de-centering of the human in social theory, but I want to concentrate on time in this essay.

15. Thus I remarked in *The Mangle* that we humans often imagine new and different futures and then try to bring them into existence (without any guarantee of success); this distinguishes us from inanimate matter, machines, and most, if not all, animals.

16. It might help to rephrase this paragraph by reversing its logic. Thinking through this essay has helped me to see what I had not seen clearly before: that my own work on change in science and technology is in a different space, so to speak, from the social science of correlations and its cognates. For further development of this idea, see Pickering (2001b).

17. James Naughton (1998, 16) says of recent work by Pierre Bourdieu that his "central idea is that journalism has to be understood as a 'field'—a structured social space in which various forces operate. It is, in a way, the sociological equivalent of a magnetic field."

18. For discussion of how such gestalt switches arise in even the best contextualist history, see Pickering (1992); the mention of discontinuities here connects back to the idea of writing a history of agency, mentioned in note 8 above.

19. Hence Latour's (1987) simple methodological injunction to "follow the actors around." "Cultural history" of science and technology, and cultural studies more broadly, can be seen as obeying this injunction, but their synchronic snapshots conjure up a sense of historicity without telling us much about processes of change in time.

20. Dupré (1993), Galison and Stump (1996); see also Hacking (1983) and Cartwright (1983).

21. I am reminded here of Stengers's (1997) discussion of physicists' treatments of reversibility and irreversibility in relation to the absence or presence of human control.

22. Pickering 1995b. One thinks as well of the steam engine–thermodynamics–statistical mechanics–Maxwell's demon–information theory line, which also fed into what I call the WWII regime.

23. Machine evolution has been a theme in post–World War II scientific thought at least since von Neumann's work on automata, beginning in the late 1940s; see von Neumann (1966).

24. On (b) see De Landa (1997b). With some justification, De Landa glosses Deleuze and Guattari (1987) in terms of the working of just two "abstract machines" or "diagrams" that structure emergent phenomena, though he also mentions an "evolutionary probe head" (which fits better with a metaphysics of becoming), and he insists that his list is not exhaustive. Partly at issue here is the very notion of an emergent phenomenon. I use the term to denote the brute emergence in time of novel behaviors, capacities, powers, etc. But there is also a technical scientific sense of the term: an emergent phenomenon is one that defies reductive scientific analysis. It is generally conceded, I think, that one often cannot, for example, derive collective phenomena from scientific theories of their individual constituents (see note 5 above). One response to this is that one needs somehow radically to extend scientific theory to bridge the gap, and such bridging moves are what De Landa invokes with his abstract diagrams. De Landa is realist about scientific theory at the "atomic" and the collective level, and especially about the diagrams that connect them. As stated, my emphasis on imagination rather than realism follows from the discussion of section 6. Given that De Landa follows Deleuze in being realist about the "virtual real" as well as the "actual real" (1998, 12), it is not clear that there is much to choose between his realism and my emphasis on imagination, though I still think that the former leads into a rather attenuated and half-hearted sense of the open-ended becoming of the world. Stengers (1997) is also realist about physics, brilliantly pursuing the physicists onto their home theoretical ground and arguing that the issue is whether we should identify physics with reversible laws of matter. Her essay contains many insights about nature, theory, and control, but for me displays some of the perils of such realism. Technical arguments about reversible and irreversible systems seem to start in the wrong place if becoming is the issue.

BIBLIOGRAPHY

Ashby, W. Ross. 1960. *Design for a Brain: The Origin of Adaptive Behavior.* New York: Wiley.

Bohr, Niels. 1960. "Quantum Physics and Biology." *Symposia of the Society of Experimental Biology* 14: 1–5.

Bowker, Geoffrey. 1993. "How to Be Universal: Some Cybernetic Strategies, 1943–70." *Social Studies of Science* 23: 107–127.

Cartwright, Nancy. 1983. *How the Laws of Physics Lie.* Oxford: Oxford University Press.

Collins, Harry, and Steve Yearley. 1992. "Epistemological Chicken." In *Science as Practice and Culture,* edited by Andrew Pickering. Chicago: University of Chicago Press.

De Landa, Manuel. 1991. *War in the Age of Intelligent Machines.* New York: Swerve Editions.

———.1997a. *A Thousand Years of Nonlinear History.* New York: Swerve Editions.

———.1997b. "Immanence and Transcendence in the Genesis of Form." *South Atlantic Quarterly* 96, no. 3: 499–514.

———. 1998. "Deleuze and the Open-Ended Becoming of the World." To appear in E. Grosz (ed.), *Becomings.*

———. Forthcoming. *Deleuze and the Question of Science.* New York: Zone.

Deleuze, Gilles, and Felix Guattari. 1987. *A Thousand Plateaus: Capitalism and Schizophrenia.* Minneapolis: University of Minnesota Press.

Depew, David, and Bruce Weber. 1997. "The Second Law of Thermodynamics and Natural Selection." Paper presented at a conference on "Time, Heat and Order," University of Aarhus, Denmark.

Dupré, John. 1993. *The Disorder of Things: Metaphysical Foundations of the Disunity of Science* Cambridge, Mass.: Harvard University Press.

Emirbayer, Mustafa. 1997. "Manifesto for a Relational Sociology." *American Journal of Sociology* 103: 281–317.

Engels, Frederick. 1918. *Socialism, Utopian and Scientific.* Chicago: Charles H. Kerr & Company.

Galison, Peter, and David Stump, eds. 1996. *The Disunity of Science: Boundaries, Contexts, and Power.* Stanford, Calif.: Stanford University Press.

Hacking, Ian. 1983. *Representing and Intervening.* Cambridge: Cambridge University Press.

Hansen, Niels V. "Interpretations of the Historicity of Objects—An Interference of Latour and Whitehead in a Cloud of Relativistic Electron." University of Aarhus, draft.

———. 1997. "Process Thought, Teleology and Thermodynamics: A Reinterpretation of the Second Law of Thermodynamics." Paper presented at a conference on "Time, Heat and Order," University of Aarhus, Denmark.

———. 1998. "Spacetime and Becoming: How to Overcome the Contradiction between Special Relativity and the Passage of Time." Department of Philosophy, Aarhus University, *Skriftserie 2.*

Latour, Bruno. 1987. *Science in Action: How to Follow Scientists and Engineers through Society.* Cambridge, Mass.: Harvard University Press.

———. 1988. *The Pasteurization of France.* Cambridge, Mass.: Harvard University Press.

———. 1995. "Do Scientific Objects Have a History? Pasteur and Whitehead in a Bath of Lactic Acid Yeast." *Common Knowledge* 5: 76–91.

Naughton, James. 1998. "With the Rusty Sword of Truth." *Times Literary Supplement,* July 24, 1998, 16–17.

Nietzsche, Friedrich. 1960. *The Will to Power in Science, Nature, Society and Art.* Translated by A. M. Ludivici. New York: Frederick Publications.

Pickering, Andrew. 1992. "The Rad Lab and the World." *British Journal for History of Science* 25: 247–251.

———. 1993. "The Mangle of Practice: Agency and Emergence in the Sociology of Science." *American Journal of Sociology* 99: 559–589.

———. 1995a. *The Mangle of Practice: Time, Agency, and Science.* Chicago: University of Chicago Press.

———. 1995b. "Cyborg History and the World War II Regime." *Perspectives on Science* 3: 1–48.

———. 1997. "History of Economics and the History of Agency." In *The State of the History of Economics: Proceedings of the History of Economics Society,* edited by James Henderson. London: Routledge.

———. 2001a. "Practice and Posthumanism: Social Theory and a History of Agency." In *The Practice Turn in Contemporary Theory,* edited by Theodore Schatzki, Karin Knorr-Cetina, and Eike von Savigny. New York: Routledge.

———. 2001b. "In the Thick of Things." Keynote address presented at a conference on "Taking Nature Seriously: Citizens, Science, and Environment," University of Oregon, Eugene.

————. Forthcoming a. "Synthetic Dyes and Social Theory."

————. Forthcoming b. "Science as Alchemy." In *Schools of Thought: Twenty-five Years of Interpretive Social Science.* Edited by Joan W. Scott and Debra Keates. Princeton, N.J.: Princeton University Press.

Stengers, Isabelle. 1997. "How to Understand the Obliteration of the Irreversibility Issue?" Paper presented at the conference on "Time, Heat and Order." University of Aarhus, Denmark.

von Neumann, John. 1966. *Theory of Self-Reproducing Automata.* Urbana: University of Illinois Press.

Whitehead, Alfred North. 1929. *Process and Reality: An Essay in Cosmology.* Cambridge: Cambridge University Press.

7. Interview with Don Ihde

*Participants: Robb Eason, Jeremy Hubbell, Jari Friis Jørgenssen,
Srikanth Mallavarapu, Nikos Plevris, and Evan Selinger*

ES: Don, you have a background in Continental philosophy; but if one does a quick survey of works being published in Continental philosophy today, one finds very little on either the topics of science or technology. Even if one finds treatments of these issues, they are often very dystopian, presupposing science, technology, and their advancements are somehow encroaching on the lifeworld, damaging more productive forms of living and styles of existence. Why do you think that this is the case and how is it that you, coming out of a Continental background, seem to be taking a different path?

DI: I think that you are right about it largely or dominantly being the case. There are some people of course who do philosophy of technology out of Continental backgrounds. I suppose the two most prominent would be Andy Feenberg and Albert Borgmann. Andy comes out of critical theory. Albert comes out of a Heideggerian background. I think part of it has to do with a very bad habit. In my estimation this bad habit of Continental philosophy tends to first of all narrowly select some standard set of godfathers, or people who are widely known, and vertically cite them. For example, when it comes to technology, Heidegger and Marcuse are probably still the people who are most talked about in the field. It used to be a wider set, but other people have sort of dropped off. Both of these people tend to be highly dystopian. On the other hand, as you know, the Dutch have been reading American philosophers of technology. They read us as being at least less dystopian than the European forebears. My own take is that the more I study particular kinds of technologies, the more dissatisfied I am with traditions that would make vast generalizations about technology, particularly on a dystopian basis. I think technologies can do very bad things, but they can also do very good things.

SM: In an interview, Kuhn clearly expresses dissatisfaction with the fact that philosophy departments did not treat him fairly. This points to the problem of disciplinarity within science studies. We have history and philosophy of science departments, sociology of science, and people from cultural studies contributing as well. Where do you see science studies going now and where do you place yourself?

DI: That is really an interesting question because not only was Kuhn badly treated by the philosophers, but Latour was as well. Many of the people in contemporary science studies have been treated badly by the philosophers. Sometimes I've been treated badly by the philosophers. There is a long tradition of dismissal. Of course part of it has to do with what philosophers we are talking about. The English-speaking situation is one in which there have been two very large phases in philosophy of science, one being the early positivist phase in the early part of the century in which, ironically, most of the participants came from Europe, the second being its transformation into a more analytic, linguistic analysis version of science dominated by English and American philosophers. Both of those traditions ended up in a kind of a battle that Peter Galison characterizes as the positivist/anti-positivist controversy. Both of them together had arguments about what really was central to the philosophy of science. What was not central had to do with things like laboratory life, instrumentation and technology in science, and the sort of sociology of science and scientific knowledge production. That gap—which I think still exists, with a few exceptions, in the dominant philosophy of science—was taken up by what I call the post-Mertonian sociologists of science: the people out in the Strong Program, the Bath school, Actor-Network Theory, and Bruno Latour. If my own travels are indicative, one of the interesting things is that precisely because of the empirical studies and the emphasis upon practice that has come out of science studies, it is my estimate that old-fashioned philosophy of science has lost ground. Even somebody like Hacking, who is a kind of exception to standard philosophy of science, reluctantly admits that all of the action now seems to be in science studies. These are people who do cultural, sociological, and anthropological studies of science. It is here that I have to admit being moderately happy because one of the good things coming out of the phenomenological, hermeneutic tradition is an emphasis on praxis. It looks at human actions, particularly embodiment and perception. In my own case, it incorporates the role of technologies, such as instruments. It turns out that there is a lot more in common between the way in which I think of the philosophies of science and technology with the currents trends in science studies then there is in the dominant English-speaking or American philosophy of science traditions.

ES: You just pointed to a positive appreciation for science studies. But what if we consider a contrary question concerning disappointment? You are widely regarded as one of the first, if not the first, American philosopher of technology. It seems to me that despite the ubiquity of technology in the American landscape, philosophy of technology, as a specialized subdivision of philosophy, never quite achieved a large following. Why do you think that is?

DI: I think that observation is correct. It is not one that lacks support. In fact, in Joe Pitt's 1995 edition of *New Directions in Philosophy of Technology*, a fair number of the founders of the American Society for Philosophy of Technology admitted the same thing. It seemed to hit a level, a plateau, and hasn't grown. I have made the same point, comparing the movements in feminist philosophy of science with Continental philosophy, as it exists in the Society for Phenomenology and Existential Philosophy, both of which have, in the same period of time, multiplied their memberships by very, very large numbers. SPEP is now the second largest single-interest or special-interest philosophical society in the country. Feminist philosophy has a wide adherence. Yet the membership list of SPT stayed relatively constant. Why? That one is harder to address. My own theory is that it failed to attach itself to progressive movements. We just talked about a little earlier the general dystopian character of Continentally derived philosophy of technology in America. While SPT isn't necessarily totally dystopian, it tended to arrange itself according to what I would call non-progressivist movements. Its earlier associations, for example, were with movements like alternative technologies vis-à-vis post-colonial situations. I think that was a bad move. Similarly, it has been concerned with a number of environmental issues. In many cases the environmental issues have tended to side with, in my estimation, more conservative takes upon environmentalism. However, the spirit of the times has changed. For example, one of things that characterized early European technological dystopianism was the dominance of technologies that could be called war technologies and large industrial technologies—what we in America term rustbelt technologies. Now if that is the only thing that technology is, then of course may of the points we made about things like global pollution and the escalation of Cold War policies hit home. But on the other hand, the Cold War is—if not gone—at least highly dissipated and distributed. Secondly, the technologies that are coming on line now are largely electronic information technologies. Those movements that originated with the previous technologies have either not kept with or adapted themselves to the new type of technology. For example, in my fourteen-year-old child Mark's generation, there can hardly be a better word than technology. Technology means electronic music, computers, e-mail, laptops etc. They think it's great stuff. If you suddenly bring back somebody like Marcuse, who argues that we don't have any genuine choices, or Heidegger, who wants to say we're all standing reserve, it doesn't ring a bell anymore. I think that is partly where SPT has not been flexible enough or quick enough to see what is happening in terms of the world of technological change.

JFJ: Now that you are talking about time to some extent, Latour claims we have never been modern. How would you say this claim fits into your philosophy?

DI: That is a nice but hard question to answer. About seven or eight years ago, a young woman at McMaster University in Canada did a thesis on the oeuvre of my works on the philosophy of technology. Part of her thesis was that I was the first "post-modern philosopher of technology." While I like her characterization, I also have deep misgivings about certain aspects of post-modernism. But if by modernism you mean the attachment to modernist epistemologies such as those that came out of Galileo, Descartes, and that particular period, which hold that knowledge is the true representation of an external world, then I am clearly not modernist. I have no sympathy with that. I am clearly post-modernist in the sense that techniques mostly from phenomenology, but also from deconstruction and variants on multi-perspectivalism, are where I would stand epistemologically. Epistemologically, I suppose I am closer to a post-modern position. If by modernism you mean the movement toward a secular world, a world in which you try to evolve principles of relations between religions and ethnic groups that allow them to function within a spirit of toleration and mutual respect—what could be called Enlightenment modernism—I'm thoroughly modernist. It seems to me that the problem with the contemporary world is a kind of throwback to a pre-modernist situation with ethnic terrorism and conflicts.

ES: Remaining with the topic of history, I want to ask you a question about one of the protocols for the technoscience research seminar you lead. You stipulate that only living authors should be read in these seminars. Why did you make that choice and what does it suggest to you about the use and value of the history of philosophy? To extend the question a little bit, one of the more dominant analytic departments in our country—the philosophy department at New York University—doesn't have a history requirement for its graduate students, such as a comprehensive history examination. Some traditionalists have found that to be somewhat problematic, while others have clearly ranked the program as one of this country's best. Can you comment on why you select only living authors? How does that decision reflect your underlying convictions about history of philosophy and its value? Finally, how do you see your approach in relation to approaches taken by programs like the one at NYU?

DI: I think I would start on that question by going back to my discovery about the myth of Stony Brook. When I first came to Stony Brook in 1969, there were two standard stories. The first was that the Long Island railroad was going to be electrified and that it would take us only forty-five minutes to get from Stony Brook to Manhattan. The second myth was that Stony Brook was the Berkeley of the East and that it would only be a matter of time before we would be recognized as such. Well, as you know, it still takes an hour and forty-five minutes in the somewhat updated diesel locomotives to get from Stony Brook to Manhattan. Furthermore, whereas there are thirteen or fourteen extant Nobel Laureates currently existing at Berkeley, our only one has retired. During a visit to Berkeley a number of years ago, I decided to take a look at the bulletin board in the philosophy department to see what they were offering. As you know, they had a very large graduate program with some very eminent people. I looked at what was offered and found there were two courses that could have been termed historical. There was a course on Kant and one on Descartes. All of the other courses followed the rubric of living authors only. This anecdote is a partial response to your question. It is not only NYU. I think the dominantly analytic schools have been largely ahistorical or non-historical. In fact, if you go to English universities, many of them assign all of the historical figures like Plato or Kant to the classics, not to the philosophy department. In some sense, I suppose I'm slightly reflecting part of my own early analytic training that was in this mood. But that is not really the purpose. The purpose here at least is to promote balance by creating a perspective that I think is highly needed in our department. Our department tends to either be historically oriented, with standard courses on the major figures and texts of the history of philosophy, or is Continental in the sense that I described before of studying the godfathers. You've got to do your Husserl and you've got to do your Heidegger. I don't think that is bad. I think it's good. On the other hand, it misses the sense of what is going on here and now in a cutting-edge discipline. Science studies itself is only a few decades old. Most of the best-known principals are in fact still alive, Kuhn exempted I suppose; but he belongs to the pre-science studies era in one sense. I do it in part as a kind of sense of balance as over against the heavy weight of history and Continental thought. It is interesting because the thrust has been even more toward the progressive elements and, as you know, we end up reading a lot of people's recently published books; but we also read a lot of things that aren't even published. It is almost like we are participating in a living Internet because we are in fact on the Net with our various interlocutors. We have been on the Net with the three that occur in this volume, Pickering, Haraway, and Latour, on a quite frequent basis. It is a semi-deliberate design to live in a very contemporary setting.

JH: A related question to that. How does history work within your writings and what is your relationship to the history discipline as it is made up here at Stony Brook?

DI: This is coming from a historian so I have to be careful. First of all, I have to say that I affirm history, particularly in the areas that I read: the history of science and the history of technology. I happen to think that most of the recent and contemporary history of science and technology is considerably superior to its older forms. In that sense I am not against history in any respect. I admire and appreciate the more sensitive and precise kinds of studies that are coming out of the contemporary world. In science studies, for example, I am quite sure that if I made the claim that Shapin and Schaffer's *Leviathan and the Air-Pump* might well be the most important piece of socio-historical work in that field in the twentieth century, I probably would not find too many people that would divert from my assessment. Now that is a kind of history that seems to be more or less unique to contemporary approaches where you are dealing with the social-cultural aspects of science and technology as they develop as well. You can see I am reading history again through living authors, Shapin and Schaffer, who are very, very smart guys. This is an aside. I have from time to time thought about doing a book entitled *Against the History of Philosophy* that would maybe raise a few eyebrows. It has to do with the fact that I don't think that philosophers should really do the history of philosophy. I think what philosophers do is read historical texts and pretend in some respects that they are contemporary. I don't think that they are contemporary and I don't like the pretense.

JH: How specifically do historical actors figure in your work? This is something that is absent from the Matrix as I have read it so far. There is no discussion about how history plays within these different institutions. Could you comment on that and your own take on Shapin's and Haraway's books.

DI: That's pretty interesting, of course, because Haraway and Latour, in particular, have made extensive comments and responses to Shapin and Schaffer. Pickering has also made some responses, but not as extensive as the other two.

All of us would be different. Bruno Latour, being his usual contrary self, both says that he has no disagreements and yet goes about disagreeing with a whole series of particulars. My take upon it would be probably slightly more a take upon what he calls the instrumental technology or the machinic technology. I would look at the air pump itself and look at the way in which it becomes a kind of interpretive device which then provides the structuring of the experimental life as they are calling it through its technological selectivities. I would probably emphasize that more than either Donna or Bruno, although I can see Andy might well do the same kind of thing with the devices. I tend to focus in upon those. In fact, one of the terminological inventions that I have used in the last few years is what I call epistemology engines. An epistemology engine is a technology or a set of technologies that through use frequently become explicit models for describing how knowledge is produced. The example I have used over and over again is the camera obscura. Both Descartes and Locke deliberately use it as a model of the mind. The analogy is that the camera obscura is to the eye as the eye is to the mind. If you look at the way it is constructed and used, you can basically say the whole structure of subjectivity is inside a body trying to discern what is outside in the external world. That is not the only epistemology engine—although it is perhaps the most dramatic—which can be historically derived. That is the kind of special take I would have upon those histories.

ES: Another question about history since we are on the subject. In the Dutch interpretation of what they call American philosophy of technology, they claim that what separates American philosophy of technology from its European ancestry is a turn to historically situated, particular empirical technologies. I want to ask you a question about that. On the one hand, your works have been, from start to finish, filled with particular historical vignettes of concrete empirical technologies that you use as way to overcome metaphysical determinist positions of technologies and reified discussions of technologies that refer to different empirical technologies, as Technology, capital "T." But on the other hand, compared to other philosophers of technology, it seems that one might say you've been less empirical. For example, the early Dreyfus drew himself into a particular empirical research trajectory, artificial intelligence, in order to delineate what computers can and cannot do. More recently Feenberg seems to have gotten directly involved with distance learning and is working on the intricacies of it in relation to his own social theory. Do you see yourself as making as much of an empirical turn as these other two?

DI: That is a good observation. I think that of the people that you mentioned, Dreyfus is the most extreme. He has made an entire career out of looking at artificial intelligence, expert programs, and computerization. As a result, with the keen analysis that he has been able to employ, he is probably the single most influential philosopher upon one strand of technological development. There are so many Heideggerian, Dreyfussian computer designers these days that it is almost amusing; but that came out of a very, very long time of work. You probably are not aware that my use of perception and instrumentation had actually been built into a set of airport approaches to keep pilots from having perceptual illusions upon approaching airports. That was not something I deliberately did; rather it is an interesting kind of illustration and adaptation of some of my early work on perception and instruments. The fact of the matter is that maybe I am just coming to it late because, as you know, the last few years I have been focusing quite narrowly upon imaging technologies: mostly visual imaging technologies across a wide stretch of sciences, such as astronomy, medicine, spectroscopy, chemistry, etc. I have been focusing a lot of research on the history and use of imaging technologies. In recent times this interest has accidentally reverberated onto an earlier interest of mine: auditory experience. I am now adumbrating the visual stuff with a re-interest in auditory technologies, including electronic music, computerization, etc. There is a particular thing that I am after. I am quite convinced that if one looks at the practices of science vis-à-vis the production of knowledge, that the use of these kinds of instruments no longer fits the modern epistemological model as we are not really talking about true representations of an external world. I don't think that scientific images are either texts or pictures. I am trying to create a phenomenological, hermeneutic framework for understanding how these images and their production work in their production of scientific knowledge. One of things that keeps cropping up is the way in which these instruments are in fact not representational. They are much more constructed kinds of imaging processes. The interesting thing is that this is exactly the same, whether you are talking about producing visual images or whether you are talking about producing computer music. What computer music does now in terms of its digital and synthesized aspect is move away from "reproducing" sounds or imitating natural sounds—instead producing machinic sounds per se. I find that to be a quite distinct parallel with a lot of the topographic or computer design images that try to make composite images of projections for greenhouse gases and earth warming. None of those things are just simple pictures. They are composite, compound, complex images that allow you to see trends and tendencies at a glance.

JFJ: You talked a little bit about the importance of examples you choose. Feenberg discusses Minitel. Winner discusses nuclear power. Your examples are basically about imaging technologies. How do the examples you choose reflect your philosophy? Could you have focused on something else and would you have still come to the same philosophy you have now?

DI: Well, I guess I would get caught in that question because if you choose a different technology you obviously come out in a different place—to some degree. On the other hand, what I do find—and this is perhaps a little higher altitude observation—is that the style of phenomenology I developed reflects and revolves largely around variational method. I think that one has to go through, as early Husserl even claimed, a series of variations to find out what is variant and what is invariant—if there is any such thing as the invariant. If you remain interested in epistemology then each set of technologies provides a perspective. You need to have a series of multiple perspectives to recognize the shape, structure, and complexity of the phenomenon you are investigating. In that sense, I guess my variational theory is one that reads instruments in that particular way. That in turn leads me to such things as imaging technologies. On the other hand, I have recently become impressed with two convergent tendencies. One tendency is within science itself. Old-fashioned science wanted to say that the way in which you could be more reliant—not certain—upon scientific conclusions was by replicating the same experiment over and over again in the laboratory. If you can't get your gene to express correctly in lab one, or lab two, or lab three, it is probably unlikely that the claim that it did express itself in that way was true. That is the standard approach of science. But when you get to super-macro-scale things, like Galison's *How Experiments End*, and you need to run experiments to find out whether or not there is a neutral current, the cost and complexity of these experiments is so incredibly expensive that no single country can afford to repeat on an ad infinitum basis these kinds of experiments. Consequently, a lot more resides upon the single complex experiment. But what has developed, it seems to me, in contemporary science, which I find very impressive, is what could be called convergent instrumentation. If you want to find out the date of this anthropological remains, you don't just use one method of measurement, carbon-14 or something like that. What you do is use as many methods of measurement as possible, usually three to five, and if they all converge upon pretty close parameters, then you know you have really got something solid. We use this multiple perspective, multi-variant kind of instrumentation increasingly in things that are not repeatable. A recent author that I have been reading, who has a book on genes, people, and languages, makes the point that if you can get genetic patterns, linguistic patterns, and archeological patterns to converge upon, say, the movement of Middle Eastern farmers into Europe at a certain time period, then those multiple disciplines with their multiple methods are doing the same kind of thing—producing a convergence phenomenon, which gives you greater assurance that you have gotten something solid in the process. One of the things that I am interested in is where can you find these kinds of variant convergences which give you better results than, say, earlier kinds of either standards replication experiments or single linear kinds of approaches.

NP: My question has to do with the answer that you gave to Evan before. In *Representing and Intervening,* Ian Hacking distinguishes different kinds of realists. Do you consider yourself a realist?

DI: I have often been accused of being a realist and plead partially guilty to that. I don't have a problem with being a realist in one sense. But that doesn't answer much. You have to ask: What kind of realist are you? I think I am a Hacking kind of realist. If you can interact with the thing you are investigating in such a way that you can determine, to use Merleau-Pontyian language, that it is questioning you back, then you have something real. Hacking's famous point is that if you can spray it with electrons then it is real. I think one other thing needs to be said. This goes back to imaging technologies. The trajectory of visualism in science is to equate seeing with believing—even though it may be a complex, instrumental seeing. It seems to me that what Hacking does is to use a kinesthetic, tactical indicator. I like this because it is in line with John Dewey's kind of realism. I am not a mono-sensory person. I am a whole-bodied perception person. If you can get something to react as mediated through instrumentation or immediately through touch, then it is real.

JFJ: In your *Technology and the Lifeworld,* you write about the cultural transformation of technologies. Your current work focuses on epistemology engines and electronic music. Yet in neither of these periods do you do what science studies do: follow the actors around in the laboratory. What do you think you gain and lose by not entering the laboratory?

DI: What I've lost is clearly not doing that type of research. This is why I am appreciative of laboratory studies, especially the pioneering works of Latour, Woolgar, and Knorr-Cetina. It is an obvious place to see what the scientists are doing. But it is not true to say that I have not entirely done laboratory studies. Again, as concerns imaging technology, I've taught a seminar on this topic three times, with one more coming up this spring. In these cases I bring the image makers and image users to the seminar, or else we go to them. We do therefore go to their native lairs. We also do something else that I don't think Latour does as much. After analyzing them in their lair, we analyze ourselves and ask: What do we think they have done? This is an interdisciplinary, critical approach. At the same time, I want to be able to see what the inter-technological situations are. Hence my interests in computer-generated music and computer topography processes which converge on similar effects.

ES: Let me follow up on Jari's question concerning following the actors around. It is a variation of a question you are usually asked. You are frequently asked to clarify whether phenomenology is a subjective philosophy. Most people think that what phenomenology does is provide descriptive, first-person, experiential accounts. But rather then having you answer this question, let me ask something else. The criticism of phenomenology as subjective entails the belief that phenomenologists begin and end with the givens of experience. Even though this may not be the case with phenomenology, as you argue, it seems to hold for attempts to follow the actors around. The people at Pasteur's lab found nothing disagreeable with Latour's account. Their attitude seemed to be: That's just the way things are. What do you think is going on with that type of description—the kind provided by the early Latour? It seems to begin with the givens of what scientists are doing and ends with them having no objections to the observations made. Nevertheless, while phenomenology has been criticized for its treatment of the given, Latour's accounts have been highly praised. Why?

DI: I like this question because I don't think phenomenology returns to the given. This is one of the things that differentiate a critical phenomenological approach from a more social science–oriented approach. Once you have been able to discover the possible multi-stability of a phenomenon, you can never return to it as given. This is an intransitive or asymmetrical direction that arises out of variational method. Right now I am reading a book called *The Sun and the Cathedral*. It is a history of the use of meridian lines in European cathedrals. The purpose of this was to fix the very difficult-to-set calendar date for Easter, which is supposed to be after a certain moon in the cycle, and on the first Sunday after that moon. This is in fact what stimulated the first dissatisfaction with the first Julian calendar, the recognition that Ptolemy's tables were in fact in error, and believe it or not, they also discovered that Copernicus was in error. Technologies began to raise questions about how observations of the heavens were being made. They led to all sorts of discoveries in what we now call early modern science. One thing that the book reiterates is that it was very hard for people to shift from a geocentric to a heliocentric universe. This is where phenomenology comes in. The given is that you see the sun rising and setting and intuitively take as given the solidity of the earth, which any fool can plainly see that the sun is rotating around the earth. Suddenly, it occurred to me that this is not a given at all. The question is: How is the context situated such that seeing the sun rise and set is taken as an intuitive thing? What I have to do is dream up a thought experiment to show that you can perceive this differently. I have some clues to this end. This is a myth about experience that has been holding steady for centuries, which I think is simply wrong.

ES: Do you see a connection between our early insistence on multi-perspectivalism and the fact that the technoscience Research Group often involves visiting scholars from different parts of the world. This is a fairly unique approach to any academic discipline. Is there a connection between the two?

DI: I think that in my own history the first movement in this direction began almost twenty years ago. As you have pointed out, *Technics and Praxis* was identified as one of the first philosophy of technology books per se. The result of that book is that I went to Colombia, South America in 1982. I was supposed to be conducting a faculty seminar on the philosophy of technology. In America one of the big questions had to do with differentiating the relationship between science and technology. As a result, you come prepared to address this question. This was designed to be my second lecture. I went down and announced this and was attacked. The faculty in the seminar claimed this position was nonsense since science is not different from the technology used. Moreover, technology is an instrument of destruction of our indigenous culture. After this attack, I realized I needed to redo my presentation, in the direction of technoscience as cultural. The point of the story is that different cultural contexts, in this case, North American views on technology moving into South America, have different perceptions. Having participants in this seminar from different parts of the world is a necessary corrective feature to our limited biases.

SM: Post-humanism is a frequently endorsed position these days. We find it in theorists like Katherine Hayles. Yet your focus on human embodiment seems to run in a different direction. While you are a post-subjectivist, you probably are not post-human.

DI: I am very happy to be described as a post-subjectivist. Phenomenology is a kind of albatross. When I used this metaphor in Denmark last year, everyone wanted to know why I was discussing an albatross. I grew up in America where all elementary school children had to read the *Rime of the Ancient Mariner*. This is a story by Coleridge in which an unlucky guy presumably dooms a boat by killing an albatross. The crew makes him wear this dead albatross around his neck for the rest of the voyage. Phenomenology is my albatross because I cannot get rid of it. It has been tagged on me. It is always marked as something it isn't, such as subjectivism. So I'll bear my albatross for the moment until I invent a better term to describe what I am doing. I have a lot of problems with the terminology of post-human. Does post-human mean post-humanist? If by that you mean we are using an implicit modernist description of humans as highly autonomous, subjective individuals, atomistically linked to society, then I am obviously a post-humanist. If on the other hand you mean that there is any kind of flexibility to retaining some sense of what it means to be experiencers, to be in a world, to perceptually take into account that world, then I am clearly not post-human. You are perfectly right. The key is embodiment. The move into science studies brought with it a new list of interlocutors. As with any change of conversationalists, a new emphasis is brought to bear. The notion of embodiment and being a body has for a long time been present in my work. With this new set of interlocutors, it has been amplified. This is what I see missing, a lacunae, in some other work, especially in those who want to use a strictly semiotic, symmetrical model. For me embodiment does not mean going to the limits of your skin, but also incorporating instruments and technologies.

JFJ: You call yourself a critical phenomenologist. How normative is this? Haraway is very normative. Pickering is much less so. Where to you fit in?

DI: And Latour wants to claim not being critical at all, wanting to eliminate the notion of the critical. The first thing I want to say is that in the early days I constantly experienced the critique of being a descriptive phenomenologist. I was continually asked why I was not normative and failed to develop axiological notions. What I mean by critical is epistemologically critical. What phenomenology does, when you practice it along the lines of multi-perspectival theory, is eliminate the ability to make certain kinds of claims. I also call myself a nonfoundational phenomenologist because I do not believe I can make absolute claims about a lot of things that early phenomenology wanted to claim. This because rigorous phenomenology shows that ambiguity exists around things like technologies. In the discussion earlier where I spoke of transplanting plants, I mentioned how plants can change location while their ecology is left behind. The plant can become something quite different, even a menace, or die, depending on the relationship between environment and organism. This is what critical phenomenology must take into account. The other question is more difficult. I do think there are normative dimensions in phenomenology, but they have to be normative dimensions that arise out of phenomenology. For example, many times I have used the metaphor of multiple cuisines. There is no way that one could phenomenologically establish that there is a best cuisine. On the other hand, I am equally clear that one can tell the difference between good and bad Cantonese cooking, and good and bad nouvelle French cuisine. Within genres you can easily tell what is better and worse.

ES: How can you then defend your assertion that pluriculture is better than monoculture to traditionalists who emphasize the value of custom?

DI: I run into this all the time, especially when I visit European countries. What I call pluriculture Europeans call a surface phenomenon. The ability to pick and choose, the bricolage of cultures, they claim is not too deep. To return to my plant metaphor, they insist that a plant is what it is only in its indigenous environment. Now in certain circumstances this makes some sense. In other circumstances this makes no sense at all. I argue, for better or for worse, that in our highly connected contemporary environment you cannot avoid contact with plural cultures. To take the whole thing and transplant it is impossible because there are indigenous plants coming into that environment at the same time as that environment goes elsewhere. The metaphor then is always between surface and depth. But don't forget that depth can also mean digging your own grave.

RE: One difference between your work and Haraway's is pragmatic. She finds herself situated, economically and politically, in a specific way. I think that while you would agree that you are situated, your phenomenological descriptions do not take these pragmatic aspects into account. Haraway sees all of her descriptions as working toward the projects she is engaged in. Do you see your descriptions as pragmatic as moving toward projects you are situated and engaged in?

DI: I would like to affirm yes, but will have to answer with a firm maybe. I am not entirely sure. I don't have a program that I am trying to follow in which I want this, that, or the other thing. Haraway and Feenberg do have programs. They think that greater democratization of science is a desirable thing. In theory and in general I thoroughly agree with them. But to agree with them is to then ask: How is that possible?

NOTE

This interview with Don Ihde took place on November 14, 2000 in the Technoscience Research Seminar at Stony Brook University.

8. If Phenomenology Is an Albatross, Is *Post-phenomenology* Possible?

Don Ihde

What is today more and more frequently called *technoscience studies* has emerged from a fairly short history entailing what could either be called "paradigm shifts" (Kuhn) or changed "epistemes" (Foucault), depending on whether one is more or less in the Anglophone or the Francophone world.[1] First there was the emergence in the 1960s of "anti-positivism" in the philosophy of science.[2] And although there was not yet, at least in North America, any very visible philosophy of technology, the historians of technology were at work. The 1970s saw the beginnings of what might be called a "post-Mertonian" sociology of science, and toward the end of the decade glimmers of philosophy of technology. The 1980s were fairly explosive with the sociologies of the Strong Program, youthful Actor-Network Theory, and so-called "social constructionist" approaches to science, drawing fire simultaneously from scientists and philosophers. The 1990s were times of diversification and the beginnings of more complex interdisciplinary programs which welded various social sciences to earlier sixties HPS programs (History and Philosophy of Science), now SSK (Sociology of Scientific Knowledge), STS (Science and Technology Studies), etc. The 1990s also saw the emergence of the "science wars" which were sparked by growing reactions to the newer philosophical, social science, and cultural studies of the hybrid phenomenon *technoscience*. Even so short an overview shows how rapidly the studies of science and technology have changed in the last third of the twentieth century. In part, this proliferation of approaches was also a contestation about who and how science, or technoscience, can be interpreted.

If one then switches to an equally brief look at the major practitioners of today's technoscience studies, one finds a similar pattern of individual career changes. For example, Bruno Latour, who is perhaps the single most cited figure in the social studies of science fields and who occupies a forefront role presently similar to that of Thomas Kuhn, has called himself an anthropologist, a sociologist, and a philosopher (see our interview in this volume). Similarly, Donna Haraway began as a biologist, turned to the history of biology, to literary theory and philosophy, and today is identified as a leading feminist technoscience studies figure. Andrew Pickering began as a physicist, became a sociologist of science, and has ambitions toward philosophy through his "theory of everything" with what he calls metaphysics. In each case multidisciplinary approaches prevail, both individually and for the field as a whole.

My role in this volume partially fits this pattern as well, although it remains more closely within philosophical concerns. I was first a phenomenological philosopher, then a philosopher of technology, and today am engaged in technoscience studies. I rehearse this highly abbreviated personal history in order to place my own position within this set of shifting battlefields and war zones. I completed my doctorate just two years (1964) after the publication of Kuhn's *The Structure of Scientific Revolutions* (1962). In the 1960s, the larger engagement within philosophy was between a well-ensconced Anglo-American establishment of *analytic philosophy* only beginning to be challenged then by a very small movement inspired by European philosophers, particularly existential and phenomenological thinkers. And while I had been trained—as all of us were—in the mainstream analytic philosophies (We were reading Wittgenstein, both early and late, Quine's "Two Dogmas of Empiricism" and *Word and Object*, Goodman's *The Structure of Appearance*, etc.), the newly available insights of phenomenology and hermeneutics were highly appealing—at least to some of us rebels.

Given the lack of any infrastructure for Euro-American philosophy in the 1960s and 1970s, at first it did not seem onerous to have to "introduce" phenomenological (and hermeneutic) styles of analysis to the larger scene. My early program began with some analytic-phenomenological comparative studies, mostly on issues of language and perception, but soon these became boring and so I decided to "do phenomenology." *Listening and Voice: A Phenomenology of Sound* and *Experimental Phenomenology* (1976 and 1977 respectively) were the results. These studies synchronized with European-oriented foci upon perception and embodiment, themes that remained through much later work. These early works were not yet explicitly related to science or technology questions. This early career research emphasized a phenomenologically oriented philosophy of perception—it was *descriptive phenomenology*. From its beginning in the North American context, there were problems with any label of "phenomenologist." The popular belief, exaggerated if anything by analytic philosophers, held that (a) phenomenology was "subjectivist" in contrast to "objectivist"; (b) "introspective" in contrast to analytical; (c) with respect to evidence, took the "immediately or intuitively *given*" as its base; and (d) this makes it wrongly appear to be foundational. From my perspective, all four of these widely held notions about phenomenology were *false*. But in that early period, I naively believed that this could be corrected by exemplifying careful phenomenological work. And, in case one is unfamiliar with my answers to the beliefs: (a) Phenomenology, in my understanding, is neither subjectivist nor objectivist, but *relational*. Its core ontology is an analysis of interrelations between humans and environments (intentionality). Its form of analysis is closer to an "organism/environment" model than is often appreciated. (b) It is not introspective, but *reflexive* in that whatever one "experiences" is derived not from introspection but from the "what" and "how" of the "external" or environmental context in relation to embodied experience. In this sense it is "relativistic" in an approximation to an Einsteinian relativity where all observations must take into account the situatedness and positionality of the observer plus the observed. And (c) all "givens" are merely indices for the genuine work of showing how any particular "given" can become intuited or experienced. Thus there is both a deconstructive and reconstructive moment to the analysis, a questioning back and a genetic forward projection. Phenomenology investigates the conditions of what makes things appear as such. (d) And this is done through the application of variational theory. Multiple perspectives must be taken into account and if there are invariants, these must emerge concretely through the interplay of variations. (Thus I appreciate Jari Friis Jørgenssen's claim in this volume that I am "post-subjectivist.") Already in the early 1970s, however, I began to be interested in *technologies*. This interest was not absent from the two books mentioned, but it was there only in the background and developed in the foreground later. However, 1979 saw the publication of *Technics and Praxis*, which is often identified as the first North American work on philosophy of technology (Mitcham 1994, 76). At its core was my first attempt to develop a phenomenology of *human–technology relations*. These took precisely the form outlined above in that the analysis was interrelational between humans *and* the materiality of technologies. From then through the entirety of the 1980s, I was re-identified as a "philosopher of technology."

The transition to philosophy of technology was not abrupt, but actually an extension of the earlier work on perception. The four-chapter sequence in *Technics and Praxis* on the phenomenology of science instrumentation (plus other technologies) showed how science is necessarily "embodied" in technologies or instruments, but simultaneously it implicates human embodiment as that to which the "data" are reflected. It was out of this context that I began to run into trouble, not this time so much with analytic philosophy of science, but with

European takes on phenomenology in a *lifeworld*. In the early 1980s, not yet familiar with either "social constructionism" or "Actor-Network Theory," I had independently worked upon ways to take into account "non-humans." Part of the schematism of "human-technology relations" was to regard the simplest possible unity for dealing with technologies as a partial symbiosis of human-plus-artifact. This meant that "my" Galileo could not be a Galileo without a telescope, whereas the "Husserlian" Galileo was a mathematizer *without a telescope*. Even to this day, many Europeans have trouble recognizing this incorporation of technologies *into* phenomenological ontology. Many regard me as unorthodox. So now I had a double problem with being a "phenomenologist." Could there be a *phenomenological* philosophy of technology? I tried to show that both Merleau-Ponty and Heidegger had partial ways of doing this, but most Europeans retained phenomenology under an earlier Ditheyan model. What I mean by this is that the difference and distinction between the social and the natural sciences remains more intact within orthodox European circles than with those of us who have experienced revisionist pragmatism in our philosophical experiences. So while I thought one could incorporate technologies into phenomenology, others thought this to be oxymoronic.

The third move was then to *technoscience studies*. Here I thought that part of the problem had been pre-solved. The term "technoscience" implies in part that science and technology are not totally, perhaps not even discernibly, different domains. Had technology been incarnate in science, or science embodied in technology? Good, this would leave me some real breathing space. Moreover, by the mid-1980s I had discovered most of the strands which led to technoscience studies: the "social constructionists," the feminist critics of both science and technology, Actor-Network theoreticians, and even the small school of "instrumental realists" (Hacking, Galison, Dreyfus, Ackermann, and one kind of Latour) with whom I dealt in *Instrumental Realism* (1991). By mixing both Anglo- and Euro-American strands on both the philosophy of science and the philosophy of technology, I began to open some doors. And, indeed, one strand within technoscience studies, that which dealt with non-humans (Latour), mangles and machinic agency (Pickering), and cyborgs (Haraway) seemed to hold the right possibilities. And that became part of the reason why these principals are included here as well. Moreover, this latest career deflection opened the way to a new set of conversations and conversants.

This third move, however, exacerbated the identification as "phenomenologist" even more than the previous incarnations. Andy Pickering accuses me of still being a "representationalist," in spite of the thrust of work trying to develop a non-representationalist epistemology; Bruno Latour accuses me of doing "philosophy of consciousness" precisely because that is what phenomenologists do.

And while Donna Haraway has not made any accusations other than that I misunderstand her variety of semiotic method, I have found once again that the label "phenomenologist" has become burdensome. The now famous "Cyborg Conference" in Aarhus, Denmark (1999) found me saying phenomenology was my "albatross." But no one knew what that meant, so I had to explain that all of us in American schools once had to read the "Rime of the Ancient Mariner" wherein the sailor who killed an albatross had to wear the dead bird around his neck as punishment for bringing bad luck to the ship. The metaphor is appropriate because phenomenology has been pronounced "dead" several times, first after structuralism, then post-structuralism, then deconstruction, and now in the contexts of revivals of old forms of semiotics.

I thought the pronouncements of death were premature, and I was willing to affirm my belonging to a philosophical tradition from which I had learned. But its other side, heard almost with equal frequency, is that what I do is "nothing like traditional phenomenology." The relationality analysis, the central emphasis upon variational theory and its resultant multi-perspectival and multi-stable effects, the emphasis upon extended embodiment, while drawing upon classical phenomenological thinking, are not strictly modeled upon older phenomenology. I tried to re-characterize myself as a non-foundational phenomenologist (Sweden, 1984) and later a "post-phenomenologist" (1993).[3] I even toyed with creating a neologistic escape: Why not "pragmatological phenomenology"? or "phenomenological pragmatism"? Or borrow Ference Marton's "phenomenography" from Goteborg? But all such attempts seemed too clumsy, although I have found some signs that my European friends like "post-phenomenology" the best and have sometimes used this characterization in recent program announcements. The albatross still retains some of its feathers and all of its bones and I can't seem to remove it from my neck. It might seem that my meditation upon re-inventions runs in a direction opposite of those claimed by Bruno Latour. He *dissociates* himself, or at least tries to dissociate himself, from the labels that have been attached to him. He vehemently claims he has never been a "social constructionist"; that he has never used the term "Actor-Network Theory," etc., whereas I have been willing to accept the label "phenomenologist" (Latour 1999a). But, in the end, these labels are just as albatrossic whether self-stickered or stickered by others (Latour 1999b, 293–300).

In the self-explanations made by the others in this collection, one finds both Donna Haraway and Bruno Latour reviving the work of Alfred North Whitehead. Whitehead's "process"-oriented philosophy clearly resonates with all of the contemporary praxis versions of technoscience studies. I, too, read and liked Whitehead the many years ago that I read him—but his special vocabulary of neologisms put me off. "Prehensions," "concresence," and the like did not seem to connect. Rather, lying in my own background almost unavoidably was American pragmatism. Everyone knows that William James was a major influence upon Husserl (Husserl's personal library shows which books he read carefully, as is evident by the underlining and comments in the margins. William James, not often mentioned in Husserl's written texts, was well marked up and commented upon, whereas Descartes, highly mentioned, remained untouched). I, too, read James and his emphasis upon experience (and its ambiguities) remains an important aspect of whatever it is that I do. But it is John Dewey who rises to more importance in this hybridization of phenomenology and pragmatism which I like. Dewey, very early on, and at least earlier than Heidegger, developed a concrete and practice-oriented direction; clearly opposed "foundationalism"; saw "instrumentalism"—which he later would have preferred to call "technology"—as the process of philosophizing; was a fallibilist; and emphasized concrete studies and experiments; all strands of thinking which, while not "phenomenological" in either style or origin, reverberate well with the way I understand what I shall now call more explicitly *post-phenomenology.*[4]

So, why *"post"*? Because, while a pragmatically bonded phenomenology retains the emphasis upon experience, there is neither anything like a "transcendental ego" nor a restriction to "consciousness." A pragmatically bonded phenomenology evokes something like an "organism/environment" notion of interactionism, a notion I have repeatedly used as well. And the *relativity* of pragmatist and phenomenological analyses (not relativism) is a dynamic style of analysis which does not and cannot claim "absolutes," full "universality," and which remains experimental and contingent. All this takes what was once phenomenology (the bones and feathers) in a "post-phenomenological" direction. But can the albatross become a phoenix? At least this gives some sense of where and how I locate myself at the borders of technoscience.

Enough already. The above shows that there is always labeling, whether self-afflicted or attached by others. The test, however, should lie in outcomes—what produces the relatively better analysis, interpretation, or critique? Here, however, another more subtle and doubled problem arises. The first part of the problem is the level of the field. One could compare analyses, interpretations, and critiques only if the problems are genuinely comparable. Second, as the matrix project so clearly realizes, each principal thinker chooses examples which implicitly best fit the style of analysis being practiced. Cyborgs (Haraway) are collection hybrids and bring together vast and complex entities, functions, relations. OncoMouse is artificial, constructed, human-assisted, genetic, social, etc. etc. etc. But OncoMouse is not neutral in that OncoMouse-like phenomena select away from anything which looks either "simple" or "pure." Haraway's selection opens a trajectory away from the simple or pure (if such phenomena exist) and toward the complex and complicated phenomena of her version of techno-science. Pikering's mangle, dance of agency, and machinic agencies are likewise selection devices. He wants his analysis to be post-human in the sense that only the processes, emergences, and results occur when they are all "mangled." This, too, selects away from stabilities, real-time persistences, and long-lasting firm consensuses. If there is an ancient and latent Kuhnianism here, it is a Kuhnianism which elevates revolutionary over normal science. Latour's Strong Program of symmetries also serves as a selection device. The schematism of humans–non-humans, with each being declared actants (a term he repeatedly uses whether or not joined by A-N-T!) in an equivalent sense, also selects away from anything isolated, individualized, or autonomous. Even the seemingly passive non-humans such as speed bumps (sleeping policemen), door stoppers, etc. are turned into actors/actants within the symmetry. This taste for the compound-complex and symmetrical is shared by these three technoscience interpreters.

Of course, reading the others in this conversation this way means that I must read my own examples as selection devices as well. What does this show? I now realize, perhaps only because of this retrospective and comparative situation, that what I *thought* I was doing turns out to have some unexpected side effects! I have frequently deliberately chosen examples which, not unlike the thought experiments I learned doing analytic philosophy, are simple and direct and therefore enhance what I hoped would be clarity. Using a telescope, listening to a telephone, and using a dental pick are all examples from *Technics and Praxis*. More of the same accumulate through the years. All these were selected to demonstrate different kinds of *embodiment relations*, whereby the instrument is experientially taken into one's sense of body and through the instrument something is (mediatedly) perceived "out there." My aim was simplicity and thus clarity. What I did not realize was that this device could be, and was, taken as a selection device showing *individual* (rather than social), *subjective* (rather than relational or reflexive), and sometimes *simple* (rather than complex or a system of technologies) choices. So it could look like I was selecting away from the social, political, cultural; selecting away from the quantitative and analytic; and selecting away from the complex and systems technologies. Caught by my own device?

Fortunately, I do not need to leave the unhappy situation just where it is, seemingly caught by the critique of the semiotic symmetrists of this conversation. As it turns out in at least one case, the most symmetrical of all the symmetrists—Bruno Latour—has twice used exactly the same examples I have used! One revolves around handguns plus humans and the NRA slogan "guns don't kill people, people kill people." (See Aaron Smith's amusing variant on this example in Chapter 11.) The other is the use of a bodily extension device, a stick, used to knock down a piece of fruit, although in Latour's case he uses a chimpanzee instead of a human. I have recently addressed the single strictly identical example, the human-gun example. I claimed, in *Technology and the Lifeworld*—in 1990—that the phrase "guns don't kill people, people kill people" needed to undergo the kind of relativistic, phenomenological analysis which I practice:

> The . . . advantage of a relativistic account is to overcome the framework which debates about the presumed neutrality of technologies. Neutralist interpretations are invariably non-relativistic. They hold, in effect, that technologies are things-in-themselves, isolated objects. Such an interpretation stands at the extreme opposite end of the reification position [of technologies—see Latour below]. Technologies-in-themselves are thought of as simply objects, like so many pieces of junk lying about. The gun of the bumper sticker clearly, by itself, does nothing; but in a relativistic account where the primitive unit is the human-technology relation, it becomes immediately obvious that the relations of human-gun (a human with a gun) to another object or another human is very different from the human without a gun. The human-gun relation transforms the situation from any similar situation of a human without a gun. At the levels of mega-technologies, it can be seen that the transformational effects will be similarly magnified. (Ihde 1990, 26–27)

Thus I could not help but be struck when a colleague gave me a copy of Latour's 1993 article "On Technological Mediation" (later revised as Chapter Six in *Pandora's Hope*); his context is precisely the same attack upon neutrality and reification noted in my example above:

> The myth of the Neutral Tool under complete human control and the myth of the Autonomous Destiny that no human can master are symmetrical. [Then, by granting actant status to both, Latour produces a complex analysis of how both "gun" and "human" are transformed:] . . . A third possibility is more commonly realized; the creation of a new goal that corresponds to neither the agent's program of action. . . . I called this uncertainty, drift, invention, mediation, the creation of a link that did not exist before and that to some degree modifies the original two. Which of them, then, the gun or the citizen, is the *actor* in this situation? *Someone else* (a citizen-gun, a gun-citizen). . . . You are a different person with the gun in your hand. [What Latour goes on to claim, beyond the obvious parallelism with my relativity context above, is full *symmetry*] This translation is wholly symmetrical. You are different with a gun in your hand; the gun is different with you holding it. You are another subject because you hold the gun; the gun is another object because it has entered into a relationship with you. (Latour 1999b, 178–179)

And although from a framework of phenomenological interactivity, I would agree to the same conclusions about how "subjects" and "objects" are both transformed in relativistic situations, the disagreement would be secondary over whether or not "subjects" and "objects" are simply eliminated as meanings by virtue of symmetries.

While this example shows a clear convergence and agreement over some of the major factors concerning the human-gun translation (Latour) or transformation (Ihde), there are also divergences which could be noted. I would admit that the non-human actant in the complex or collective transforms the situation. Human plus gun have amplified destructive power and much else. Were we to vary this example into one about scientific instrumentation, I would likewise hold that the human-telescope has the same selective and magnificational transformation or translation effects, thus one can say more strongly than metaphorically that the telescope embodies and in use has a certain interpretive direction as a technology. This is what Latour means by its becoming a different "object" (in use rather than just lying around). But, switching examples again, I would find it hard to say—at least without claiming a highly metaphorical attribution—that the speed bump (sleeping policeman) is filled with designers, administrators, and policemen! I can't quite bring myself to the level of "socializing" the artifacts. They may be *inter*actants, but they are not quite *actants*.

In the simple examples just discussed, one could say the playing field was quite level, and thus the critics, analysts, and interpreters could meet on that field. Is the same true if we turn to more complex examples?

Donna Haraway and Andy Pickering have, most recently, selected their "non-human" examples from the animal kingdom. In her piece in this volume, Donna discusses her movement from the cyborg figure to the companion species (dogs) she now studies. And whereas Donna has "gone to the dogs" with her studies, Andy Pickering has "gone to the eels" with his mangling of Asian eels. So, following this lead, my next example set will take a quick look at animal non-humans.

The important questions of situatedness and symmetry can, indeed, take different shape with this twist. If phenomenology has the fatal flaw of necessarily being a "philosophy of consciousness," as Latour holds, and if situatedness entails both embodiment and some kind of socio-cultural situatedness, as I am quite sure Haraway and I would hold, and if animal experience can in some sense be taken as "intentional," as I suspect Pickering would affirm, then does the selection device posed by animals help us converge? I now rephrase this in my own way: animals—all of them I suspect, but especially the higher organisms such as dogs and eels—are embodied beings which interrelate with environments and thus are "situated." Nor do I have any trouble with allowing some kind of "intentionality" to animal being since, for me, intentionality is the ontological structure of this interrelationality between an experiencing being and an environment. And, again with at least higher and complex animal life, I don't even have a problem with attributing these animals with "cultures." Latour's chimp with a stick can also be the chimp who fashions a number of termite probes from vegetable matter, apparently according to some patterned plan, and thus is ready to continue the feast even after the first, then the second, wears out. The chimp is "aware" of technological fallibility and the phenomenon of breakdown and has introduced redundancy into the situation! The point of all this is, in the case of animal non-humans, one problem of symmetry is considerably eased. And it is eased in precisely one direction taken by actant theory—we can "socialize" the animals, I think, much more easily than we can the speed bump or door stopper. And because that is so, I have virtually no problem at all with either Haraway's analysis which claims, symmetrically, that dogs and humans have "mutually invented" each other. Her story, shared by others, is that wolves, probably at about the same time the first modern humans evolved, were only too glad to hang around the cave and accept easily gained tidbits and, cutting the story short, the wolves domesticated the humans at the same time the humans domesticated the now wolf-dog. Eventually, particularly with purebreds, even breeding itself could occur only with human help or, better, with human-dog cooperation. Here we have a symmetrical "collective" which can be spoken of without much hesitation or linguistic contortion.

Although not in quite as a "domesticated" context, Pickering's Asian eels are also creatures we can recognize. There are funny stories about persons who had two tanks of aquatic creatures, fish in one and eels in the other. After a night's sleep, they awoke to find the fish gone and a fat, grinning eel in its own tank, and so they discovered an unexpected side effect that eels can crawl out of their tanks and back with bellies full of fish, comfortable in their saltwater environment after having invaded a freshwater environment. My own "phenomenological" addendum to this story is that one reason why transplanted animals can either fail miserably or succeed dramatically is that they are transferred without their indigenous, complex context into a different context. If, as in the case of Asian eels now invading our southlands, they no longer have the same parasites, predators, or even the same food supply, they can nevertheless quickly adapt and even begin to displace indigenous competitors. This is a version of figure/ground change which constitutes one important and powerful phenomenological tool for analysis, now applied to animal transfer. The same observation applies to technology transfers as per my examples in *Technology and the Lifeworld* which discuss the entirely new cultural context for sardine cans (as centerpieces for elaborate New Guinean headgear, i.e., a fashion object) which were in their imported Australian context merely preservation devices for keeping food (the ovaloid can becomes a "different" artifact or technological object by context change) (Ihde 1990,125–126). And not to slight Bruno Latour, this is consonant with the process he calls "translation" whereby the object plus the human is changed as it is processed along.

While each of these analyses clearly reverberates well to some degree, there also remain degrees of differences. I would hold that it is easier to see how both dogs and humans change through interaction, particularly behaviorally but also in deeper ways, than to see how the sardine cans change by being placed in their new fashion context. This is not to say that the sardine can either remains a "sardine can" throughout, when it changes from food container to fashion object (since, phenomenologically, any object is what it is only in relation to its context or set of involvements, one can say it "changes" from container to fashion object) and it is not to say that the human-artifact interrelation lacks significant behavioral and cultural change, since technological artifacts are parts of material culture and thus are implicated in such changes. But it remains, I hold, harder to maintain that the artifact changes with the same degree of symmetry as the human, or better, the human within the technologically changed context. This is something like the old joke: "How does a psychiatrist change a light bulb? Very slowly and through many sessions—and the light bulb really has to want to be changed."

Beneath all this, I am holding out for something like a sliding scale of symmetry. This affirmation of a sliding scale can recognize some ambiguities as my last example will show. What if, in this case, our non-human is one of those "quasi-others" which I have previously described which enters into an *alterity relation* with the human of the equation? Here the human-technology or human-non-human relation is one in which the non-human gives off a selected "appearance" of being some kind of virtual "other"—I call this a "quasi-other." That is, the relation to the technology finds its focal fulfillment in the interaction with an artifact, not through an artifact by embodiment or by the hermeneutics of interpretive activity. I will pose this as a sort of challenge: *Could AIBO be a companion species?*[5]

AIBO is a "quasi-animal" entertainment robot produced by SONY, Inc. Its first version looked like a plastic—silver or black—artificial dog; its second version is more ambiguous, comes in three colors, and is sort of an artificial dog/cat. For a mass-produced robot, it claims high sophistication; the ad claims, "ignore AIBO and it will become lethargic; AIBO has four senses . . . touch, hearing, sight and a sense of balance; . . . . it will show when it is happy or sad . . . and can express six emotions: happiness, sadness, anger, surprise, fear and dislike . . . and has instincts—it wants to play with people, look for its favorite toy, move about [and in a gesture to its machinic nature] satisfy its hunger (i.e., get recharged)."[6] Like the Gamiguchis before it, AIBO demands attention and becomes lethargic if ignored. And in Japan, the AIBO rage has even led to AIBO soccer games, with quasi-animals playing with each other; to magazines which include diaries about human-AIBO interactions; and testimonials concerned with the possible superiority of AIBO over living animals (it does not die, excrete, or make a mess). Here are some testimonials printed in a slick, multicolored magazine, *Aibo Town Magazine:* "Keeping dogs is not allowed in our apartment, so actually a robot is much better." Then, in a feature piece, an interview with a television actress, Tetsuko-Kuroyangi, she describes her response to her own AIBO, "Gray":

> When my cute one first arrived in my house, the first impression that I had was, "Its color is robotic." That is where the name *Gray* comes from. "Rat-like color (this is Japanese name for gray)" does not sound cute though. *Gray* [in English] sounds a bit cuter, I guess. Since my cutie has done the classic "lift the leg and mark the territory" behaviour, I believe it is a boy. (Sony 2000)

Then the interview continues, with on the one side an anthropomorphization of the robotand on the other a recognition of its machinic being:

> Both the mother and the child do not follow the manual. For example, when I give the command, "4-1" with the performance mode, Gray follows the command once. But on the second time, Gray *does whatever he wants.* I think this is funny. . . . Usually Gray barks once then does a pee on the first try. On the second try, Gray again does *whatever he feels like.* . . . When I show him the sound commander and say, "go to sleep," Gray was shaking his head as if saying, "No, No." Again it was quite cute. Because Gray *hated it so much, I hid the sound commander under a cushion.* [italics mine.] . . . One of the good things about having AIBO. It will not get sick and die. Especially, it will not die. . . . I really feel this is great. . . . It will never feel pain since he is a robot. Beside that, he is similar with living creatures. . . . However, just as the internet has been used in a different way from the one that the developers wished, there will be people who will misuse robots. I don't want it to happen since a robot is such a cute creature. (Sony 2000)

This admixture of machine-like/animal-like responses is, in one sense, appropriate. SONY did not attempt to make a "Cartesian" robot that could be confusing for an observer—no fur, no eyes, no actual liquids, etc. No one would be deceived by a Cartesian evil genius here. AIBO is shiny, plastic; its "eyes" are red lights, its "voice" a series of tones. One has to "read through" to get it as life-like. Could this AIBO be a companion species?

The above description was secondhand, and I now turn to my own experience. Although for a base price of $1,500, with programming options more than doubling the base price, I was not tempted to go out and buy one, but I was curious enough to go to the first demonstrations of the new AIBO in New York City. As with many toy technologies, the hype proved stronger than the performance. Yes, it could perform a karate chop on (repeated) command; it (sometimes) returned a ball; it moved much more slowly than any puppy; and was highly "confused" by commands from different people. It would have been hard for me to move from the robot recognition to the other side of Tetsuko's cute recognition, although its "cuteness" is quasi-recognizable.

The question about this cyborgian robot as a companion species is clearly a question which could be put to Donna Haraway. But, as she put it to me when I asked by e-mail, "Ms. Cayenne Pepper and Roland Dog (dogs in Haraway's house) were not impressed. Smelled wrong and was awfully literal" (e-mail, 3/10/01). And, maybe the dogs are in this case the best judges.

The philosophical point is a little harder to make: Could I be reverting to a modernist position in which I am taking AIBO aka Gray as simply a machine and then seeing Tetsuko's response as a piece of romantic anthropomorphization of this machine? Or, worse, am I making a metaphysical judgment about the intrinsic nature of AIBO as simply a being of this sort? In the various discussions the four of us have had, this sometimes is what comes up. Tetsuko is making something of a hybrid description of her Gray: cute, with feelings, decisions, etc., but equally non-feeling, non-dying, and robotic. The metaphysician simply wants to wipe out half the hybrid. But the hybrid description is in a limited sense, correct, if also misleading.

But that has never been my point. It can't be, since I am opting for a perspectival, situated knowledge which lacks the god's eye view either from overhead or into the interior. Yet I also do not want to make the symmetrist's equivalent error: simply granting some kind of equality of status to the human and the non-human. One the one hand, we have seen this leads *either* to the temptation to "mechanize" the totality or to "socialize" it. There is simultaneously in the modernist and the symmetrist's positions the temptation to a kind of reduction in one or the other direction. Rather, and this has been my point, an asymmetrical but post-phenomenological *relativity* gets its "ontology" from the *interrelationship of human and non-human.* Here is where Haraway's dogs actually have it right: they can tell by smelling and playing that AIBO's responsiveness is literal and not right. They cannot interact with AIBO *as a dog*, although I doubt they are making a metaphysical judgment; rather they are finding that the *quasi* of the quasi-"dog" is forefronted in the interrelation itself.

The tendency to anthropomorphize, of course, is ancient and not restricted to quasi-human or quasi-animal technologies. Even automobiles can have attributed "personalities." And the situation is further complicated by the role of fantasy and desire. As I have claimed elsewhere (TL), we sometimes have the desire to have the magnified powers which technologies are fantasized to possess—in the case of AIBO a lack of pain and an absence of death—but without recognizing the technological materiality entailed; AIBO will wear out and can break. This technofantasy can be detected in the Tetsuko interview as well:

> Oh, I forgot about Gray's birthday. He arrived in summer and since my birthday is August 9th—which is the memorial day of the Atomic Bomb in Nagasaki—and I have some friends who passed away in August and September, it might be a good idea to think that Gray is a reincarnation. (Sony 2000)

This last quotation casts a deeper shadow on the AIBO phenomenon. It is one thing to read AIBO through technofantasy, both desiring the powers of technology yet wanting these to be so transparent that the technology disappears.

Rather, in this case, the technology must become something else. And here, too, is an ancient echo: technology as *Idol*. To see *in* the artifact certain powers which it should not seem to possess is to push the human-technology relation to its ultimate extreme. Rather than companion species, this AIBO becomes a quasi-deity, a move which I would tend to resist with an iconoclast's skepticism.

I will end on this highly ambiguous note, recognizing that if our social situatedness is "non-innocent" as Haraway claims, and that technologies are "non-neutral" as I claim, then perhaps precisely what AIBO does not have, pain and death, gets transformed into a sort of machinic vision of the immortality which technofantasies can stimulate.

NOTES

1. I show how both Thomas Kuhn and Michel Foucault, virtually simultaneously, develop disjunctive theories of the development of scientific knowledge (see Ihde 1991).

2. Peter Galison provides an excellent summary of the positivist/anti-positivist controversy of the 1960s (see Galison 1997, 787–797).

3. I originally declared myself a "non-foundationalist" in a monograph in response to Richard Rorty, but later I preferred the term "post-phenomenologist" (see Ihde 1993).

4. See the extended discussion by Carl Mitcham on phenomenology and pragmatism, Dewey and Ihde (1994, 71–78).

5. Jari Friis Jørgenssen has used AIBO as a subject in his MA thesis and he first pointed out this technology to me while a visiting scholar in the Technoscience Research Group.

6. See the *New York Times*, Thursday, January 25, 2001, G.3, for a description of AIBO. Also, SONY, Inc. advertisement, "2nd Generation Entertainment Robot," AIBO ERS 210, Nov. 16, 2000.

BIBLIOGRAPHY

Galison, Peter. 1997. *Image and Logic*. Chicago: University of Chicago Press.
Ihde, Don. 1990. *Technology and the Lifeworld*. Bloomington: Indiana University Press.
———.1991. *Instrumental Realism: The Interface between Philosophy of Science and Philosophy of Technology*. Bloomington: Indiana University Press.
———. 1993. *Postphenomenology: Essays in the Postmodern Context*. Evanston, Ill.: Northwestern University Press.
Latour, Bruno. 1999a. "On Recalling ANT." In *Actor Network Theory and After*, edited by John Law and John Hassard. Oxford: Blackwell Publishers.
———. 1999b. *Pandora's Hope: Essays on the Reality of Science Studies*. Cambridge, Mass.: Harvard University Press.
Mitcham, Carl. 1994. *Thinking through Technology: The PATH between Engineering and Philosophy*. Chicago: University of Chicago Press.
Sony. 2000. Interview and article on Tetsuko-Kuroyangi. *AIBO Town Magazine*, January.

PART TWO

9. Interdisciplinary Provocateurs: Philosophically Assessing Haraway and Pickering

Evan Selinger

INTRODUCTION

While internal debates diversify methods and subjects of inquiry, philosophical insights become revolutionary when tempered by external outlooks that sabotage universal and idealistic claims. Greek philosophy benefited from Aristotle's use of experimental conduct to challenge Plato, and when Karl Marx stood G. W. F. Hegel economically on his head, the course of modern philosophy was positively altered. Today *interdisciplinary research* also has the potential to generate radical results because it can lead to fundamental presuppositions being revised.

Two of the most prominent contemporary theoreticians in the interdisciplinary field of science studies, Donna Haraway and Andrew Pickering, question philosophical claims about practice, technology, materiality, subjectivity, temporality, responsibility, and politics. Pickering is more ambitious than Haraway because he characterizes his project as a theory of everything; in principle, it cannot be falsified and its scope equally applies to all the sciences: "And so, in the end I allow myself to be overtaken by hubris in thinking of my analysis of scientific practice as a potential TOE, a theory of everything" (Pickering 1995, 248). This is a bold position to assert since the post-Kuhnian trend in the philosophy of science suggests that a general metaphysics of science does not exist and, despite family resemblances, a single model cannot represent the different types of sciences; their diverse methods, techniques, and background assumptions render them best represented by field-specific structures.

Less bombastic than Pickering, Haraway also presents a momentous challenge. She is renowned with promoting the cyborg metaphor in science studies and the humanities: "A cyborg is a cybernetic organism, a hybrid of machine and organism, a creature of social reality as well as a creature of fiction" (Haraway 1991, 149). This metaphor exemplifies her provocative thesis that under current conditions it is impossible to find non-technologically mediated forms of subjectivity and that traditional assumptions about identity, essence, and theory are called into question in the cybernetic age:

> Cyborg imagery can help express two crucial arguments . . . first, the production of universal, totalizing theory is a major mistake that misses most of reality, probably always, but certainly now; and second, taking responsibility for the social relations of science and technology means refusing an anti-science metaphysics, a demonology of technology, and so means embracing the skilful task of reconstructing the boundaries of daily life, in partial connection with others, in communication with all of our parts. (Haraway 1991, 181)

The challenges that Haraway and Pickering pose come from outside of philosophy even though Pickering approvingly cites Gilles Deleuze and Michel Foucault, while Haraway refers to Foucault, Alfred North Whitehead, and Marx. Pickering's dual training as a physicist and sociologist sensitized him to what he perceives to be a philosophical failure to understand materiality, while Haraway's dual training as a biologist and feminist critic sensitized her to what she perceives to be a philosophical failure to understand epistemological and political dimensions of nature and culture. Their pedigrees are noteworthy because (1) they make it difficult to dismiss the theorists as scientific outsiders or anti-scientific irrationalists, and (2) they render Pickering and Haraway susceptible to the charge of being philosophically naive, even impostors.

The issue to be pursued here concerns the extent to which philosophers need to reconsider some of their own views in light of Haraway and Pickering. This topic is difficult to address because Haraway and Pickering are not systematic thinkers, and gesturing to conceptual lacunae and noting imprecise disagreements is their means of critique. While this style appears to be a hindrance only if one requires standards of refutation to be philosophical, it remains a crucial stumbling block for fostering interdisciplinary dialogue. The aim of this chapter is thus to abstract philosophical claims and stylistic rationales from their texts, and to this end I will proceed as follows. First, the problem of style will be examined by discussing Haraway and Pickering's technical terms and rhetorical strategies. Second, the political differences that separate Haraway from Pickering will be appraised. Third, an argument will be made that philosophers should better interface with other theorists in an interdisciplinary as opposed to a multi-disciplinary manner. Ultimately, the aim of this chapter is to show that while Haraway and Pickering present provocative gestures, their mode of presentation remains unconvincing; neither theorist treats any philosopher's position in enough depth to warrant the reader's assent that such a philosopher, much less the very institution of philosophy, makes faulty claims. Nevertheless, their attempt to understand how humans and non-humans relate sheds invaluable light on topics of interest to philosophers of science and technology.

I. INTERDISCIPLINARY EXPLANATION

During the science wars, both Haraway and Pickering rejected the manner in which social constructivists approached the genesis and acceptance of scientific facts. Social constructivists followed an overly discursive trend and their articles and books invariably led to the same conclusion; all reality is socially constructed, including scientifically discernible entities. Haraway and Pickering responded to this return of what Foucault characterizes as a Medieval episteme by asserting that such a textualist position is untenable; the common world we share is not only made up of ideas and concepts, but also of unavoidable materiality. They claimed that by failing to recognize the significance of non-humans, social constructivists removed the element of unpredictability from scientific practice and generated idealistic and overly reductive analyses that ignored how material entities and forces influence how subjectivity is expressed. Pickering succinctly expresses this point when he writes, "The problem is that SSK makes it impossible to take material agency seriously" (Pickering 1995, 10).

While Haraway and Pickering justifiably reject the overly discursive tendencies of social constructivists, they potentially abuse an insufficiently critical vocabulary. Unlike the social constructivists, who relied on conventional idioms such as power and interests, Haraway and Pickering use strange terms such as "cyborg," "dance of agency," "machinic agency," "Female-Man," "tuning," and "vampire" to convey critical points. Although this language serves the pedagogical function of expanding the reader's imaginative capacity, it is easy to dismiss as unintelligible jargon, as what Alan Sokal calls a fashionable instance of style replacing substance.

The best justification for why Haraway and Pickering write in an idiosyncratic style is to treat some of their technical terms as metaphors. In classical theories of language, metaphor is understood as a matter of language and not thought. However, philosophers in the Continental tradition contend that metaphors change the way we think about problems by depicting an object or event as similar to another object or event. Metaphors enable us to see things in a new light by generating analogies that expose previously unnoticed or underappreciated relations; they touch upon the realms of imagination and feeling by functioning as powerful rhetorical devices that steer our attitudes and beliefs.

In an interdisciplinary setting, metaphors are of particular importance for communicating complex notions. They are effective in the popularization of abstract and specialized concepts since a good metaphor is capable of palpably expressing something that is otherwise only capable of being baroquely denoted. It is not surprising then that the effective use of metaphor appears in popularized texts. It recently pushed Brian Greene's *The Elegant Universe: Superstrings, Hidden Dimensions, and the Quest for the Ultimate Theory* to the bestseller list because in the book he explains developments in modern physics by utilizing analogies ranging from amusement park rides to ants on a garden hose.

Since metaphorical use is a time-tested means for linguistically transmitting the procedures and ramifications of scientific practice to laypersons, Haraway and Pickering rely heavily on it in their attempts to reach an interdisciplinary audience. Members of this audience who are not natural scientists are often patronized and deemed incapable of understanding the world of science, including its norms of social organization, rules of practice, and standards of behavior. Although reading Haraway and Pickering will not increase their scientific literacy since neither theorist is a textbook-style popularizer and neither reconstructs the basic elements of science that expert practitioners are capable of taking for granted, their publications allow non-experts to recognize how much the success of scientific practice is modeled on familiar, non-scientific horizons. Both show that the manner in which scientists engage with machines, secure funding for their operations, and convince audiences that their claims are truthful resemble common strategies and actions found in everyday aspects of life.

A textual example that highlights the four prominent metaphors Pickering uses to describe scientific practice will solidify this point:

> (1) *Material Agency:* "Much of everyday life, I would say, has this character of coping with material agency, agency that comes at us from outside the human realm and that cannot be reduced to anything within that realm" (Pickering 1995, 6).
>
> (2) *Tuning:* "Now we can turn to practice, to the extension of scientific culture, and especially to the extension of the machinic field of science. I have already described this as involving a process of tuning, and the key point about tuning in the present context is that it *works both ways*, on human as well as nonhuman agency" (Pickering 1995, 16).
>
> (3) *Dance of Agency:* "Tuning in goal oriented practice takes the form, I think, of a *dance of agency*" (Pickering 1995, 21).
>
> (4) *The Mangle of Practice:* "The practical, goal-oriented and goal-revising dialectic of resistance and accommodation is, as far as I can make out, a general feature of scientific practice. And it is, in the first instance, what I call *the mangle of practice*, or just the mangle" (Pickering 1995, 22–23).

What these four metaphors help Pickering convey is that contemporary scientific practice is primarily a performative arena in which observations and theories have a derivative place alongside the primary experience of skillful embodied coping with machines. By enabling the reader to perceive machines as actively doing things, Pickering makes scientific practice come alive in a more vivacious manner than when it is described in theory-oriented terms. In Pickering's narrative, machines play a more central role than language does in enabling, thwarting, and altering scientists' goals, which is why machines, even though they lack the conscious ability to deliberate, nevertheless express some force, which he vividly captures by the phrases "material agency" and "dance of agency." Human scientists can be understood as "dancing" with machines because their attempts to adjust machinic outputs in a desired way, which he calls "tuning," entails alternating between an active and passive experimental role in which regular and unforeseeable outcomes arise. The metaphor of the "mangle"—originally an "old-fashioned device" used to squeeze the water out of washing—draws the reader's attention to this unpredictability since it evokes the specter of aleatory events and emphasizes the fragility of human intentions in a machine-saturated environment.

Unlike Pickering, Haraway not only uses metaphor to describe technoscientific activity, but also to politically contest dominant interpretations of nature and culture. Since this is a considerable undertaking, an in-depth treatment of it will be provided later on in the chapter in Section 3.

2. PICKERING'S RHETORIC

Two primary difficulties face audiences when considering the terms that Haraway and Pickering use: common sense and history. Common sense dictates that agency is inherently a human property, whereas Pickering describes machines as possessing "machinic" agency. Common sense also dictates that if there is not a clear boundary demarcating natural from technological kinds, then some inexact criteria exist. By contrast, Haraway describes nature as always already technologically and culturally encoded; hence, she believes that it makes more sense to classify humans as "cyborgs" than as tool-making and tool-using animals. Common sense rebuttals, however, are typically philosophically weak, and as a habitual manner of thinking that is determined by modern classificatory categories, common sense is rarely an epistemologically accurate measure of things. Consequently, by turning to the topic of history a substantive criticism of Pickering emerges.

Pickering claims that his two most notable achievements are the introduction of what he calls "real time" and the epistemological shift of historical narratives away from a "representational idiom" toward a "performative" one. Pickering's claims about "real time" hinge on an accusation that previous theorists failed to understand the temporally emergent nature of practice by remaining too narrowly focused on the static aspects of being while downplaying the dynamic aspects of becoming. Due to this narrowness, Pickering contends that traditional accounts impose unwarranted teleological and retrospective explanations to account for the production of knowledge. Practicing scientists, according to Pickering, are misinformed about the temporal dimension of their activities because they use "accepted scientific knowledge . . . as an interpretative yardstick in reconstructing the history of its own production" (Pickering 1995, 3). Even science studies theorists, Pickering contends, blindly engage in a "kind of purification" by relying on "atemporal cultural mappings" (Pickering 1995, 4).

The problem is that Pickering's criticisms of the atemporal accounts of his predecessors belie his ignorance of how temporally sedimented his own theoretical language is. Philosophically speaking, it is audacious to create a concept called "real time" without discussing the history of the concept of time. To this end he should have considered Martin Heidegger's notion of "ecstatic time," which was formed through a reading of the ancient Greeks, St. Augustine, Immanuel Kant, Hegel, and Søren Kierkegaard and which calls into question the vulgarity of time as experienced in everydayness, as well as Paul Ricoeur's notion of "narrative temporality," which mediates cosmological and subjective time. Omissions of philosophers such as Heidegger and Ricoeur indicate that Pickering is unaware of how technical terms, including his own idiosyncratic phrases, are always interpreted against a historical background; this background conditions the intelligibility of words, overdetermining them with traces of historically sedimented meaning. Because Pickering lacks hermeneutical sensitivity, he fails to realize that in order to responsibly use language one needs to enter into a dialogue with the traditions that develop and refine what key words mean. This problem is not unique to Pickering, but rather seems the common reef on which sociologists who venture into philosophy flounder.

Pickering also fails to note that the intelligibility of his arguments about the representational and performative idioms depends on how *performance* and *performativity*, which belong to deeply entrenched theatrical, philosophical, and sociological traditions, are understood. Theorists from all these disciplines have argued that performance cannot simply be equated with action, even Pickering's version of "mangled" action, and some of their works suggest that his discussion of "modeling" is insufficiently robust to describe how performativity refers to the iteration of power through social practices. Unlike Pickering, philosophers who embrace a performative model of intentionality struggle hard to: (1) distinguish between performance and performativity, especially as concerns consciousness and iterations of power/knowledge; (2) mark the limits of analogizing all domains of practice with aesthetic practice; and (3) clarify the relation between performative, linguistic utterances and the construction of subjectivity by non-linguistic forces.

Pickering never clearly defines what he means by the "representational idiom" because he is content to allow it to stand in as a synonym for correspondence theories of truth: "The representational idiom casts science as, above all, an activity that seeks to represent nature, to produce knowledge that maps, mirrors, or corresponds to how the world is" (Pickering 1995, 5). In essence, Pickering claims that the representational idiom extends to every school of thought that focuses on "facts and observations" at the expense of the embodied practices that constitute facts and observations. What this overly general assertion overlooks is that there are many types of correspondence theories, as well as many ways of understanding what a focus on facts and observations entails. By remaining vague, Pickering assimilates with current philosophical refutations of representation, except that his attempt to prove that representational epistemologies are flawed entails abandoning the mediating steps of argumentation and prematurely gesturing to case study data to justify the conclusion that representationalism as such is flawed.

In the final analysis, Pickering's lack of attention to intellectual history is less a scholarly oversight than a *strategy of legitimization*. It is abundantly clear why he believes that his research is important:

> It is probably true that many authors engaged in exploring the work of science once shared my interest in time. . . . But as I have been writing this book, it has dawned on me that a kind of purification has taken place. Much of the most interesting work now being done is not concerned with practice as I have defined it, but takes the form of atemporal cultural mappings and theoretical reflection thereon. My present interest in the temporality of cultural extension leaves me, I think, in the minority as far as current initiatives in science studies is concerned. (Pickering 1995, 4)

In order to legitimize his work, Pickering denigrates caricatured versions of classical positions; reveling in this allows him to valorize his own insights as novel and accurate. This is an old trick that at its most extreme goes back to the beginning of modernity when Descartes rhetorically attempted to wipe the slate clean and rebuild philosophy from scratch. But just as most of Descartes's foundationalist remarks were insincere and motivated by practical and political concerns, Pickering intentionally presents uncharitable descriptions of rival positions in order to make his own work seem more novel than it actually is. There is even a cultish aspect to this strategy. Pickering's self-congratulatory rhetoric suggests that the reader who endorses his hyperbolic narcissism is an enlightened co-conspirator. The enamored disciple who takes a "mangled" approach to his or her own research can characterize that work as elevated above the history of incompetent and shortsighted predecessors. Like all zealous iconoclasts, Pickering refuses to acknowledge that he too is standing on shoulders. Instead, one suspects that he gleefully imagines future historians citing his work as the definitive break from unhelpful technoscientific dogma.

3. HARAWAY AND TROPES

Haraway frequently makes inquires into how interactions with material culture change how humans understand who they are and how they should relate to others. For example, she discusses plutonium and ponders how the existence of transuranic elements forces human beings to redefine their own sense of identity. Plutonium does more than amplify human capacities, it fundamentally changes the environment that humans live in and the role that humans play in that environment. Not only is the existential human relation to death altered by the presence of weapons of destruction, but the existence of nuclear weapons also alters international political and economic relations. Haraway goes so far as to claim that ". . . plutonium has done more to construct species being for hominids than all of the humanist philosophers and evolutionary anthropologists put together" (Haraway 1997, 55).

Although this quote is extreme because it suggests that material culture is more transformative than intellectual history, it is philosophically interesting, especially in light of Heidegger's famous analysis of death in Division II of *Being and Time*. Not only does Heidegger derisively relegate the ontic to mundane, anthropological discourse, but he further insists that only a philosophical interpretation of death can be rigorous enough to serve as the foundation for the existentiell interpretations of death provided by other disciplines. He contends that whereas philosophical analysis begins by inquiring into what death is, historians, anthropologists, biologists, and psychologists undertake their analyses by relying upon unquestioned assumptions about what death is, and what being dead means. Insofar as Heidegger believes that these disciplines have not adequately made their underlying prejudices explicit, he claims that philosophical analysis is exclusively capable of revealing structures of death whose veracity precedes any metaphysical or biological truth. In the final analysis, Heidegger's position amounts to this: Only philosophy can demonstrate the necessary connection between an "authentic attestation" of "being-towards-death" and the "ecstatic" structure of temporality. By contrast, Haraway contends that the manner in which humans makes sense of their world, including their own death, cannot be explained in purely existential terms; the existence of non-human entities, such as plutonium, profoundly influences how features of social life, such as thanatological issues, are interpreted. Whereas Heidegger believes that a primordial analysis of death is exhausted through first-person attestation, Haraway reminds us that the significance of death extends beyond one's personal being to the collective interests of species being.

Haraway's attention to how human identity transforms in relation to technoscience extends beyond material culture to the social and political influence of tropes. Tropes are figurative words and expressions that assume a symbolic function by expressing one thing in terms that usually denote another in order to call attention to some perceivable or imagined resemblance. Sedimented tropes function as identifying signs for what they resemble, which is why Haraway claims that metaphors affect people in engaged, inhabited, and lived ways (Haraway 1997, 135). By connecting models with tropes, she evokes the Greek sense of *tropos,* which is a turn or swerve, the distorted aspect of translation that is present in analogical arguments (Haraway 1997, 135). Analogies operate inferentially by suggesting that if two or more things agree with each other in some respects they will probably agree in others. Tropes thus tend to erase deep ontological differences between entities by overemphasizing surface similarities and allowing abstract representations to illicitly stand in for concrete entities (Haraway 1997, 146–147).

Haraway contends it is fetishistic to uncritically allow tropes to conceal important differences. To make this point she investigates tropes that signify possession, including "mapping," as in the case of genetic maps, noting that cartographic imagery is indispensable for understanding how important research, such as the Human Genome Project (HGP), constitutes and influences notions of subjectivity (Haraway 1997, 137–141). According to Haraway, the data obtained through the HGP is not epistemologically significant simply because it reveals humanity's chromosomal genetic makeup; genetic information inevitably becomes rendered socially intelligible in relation to non-genetic phenomenon: "The gene, a kind of stem cell in the technoscientific body, is enmeshed in a hypertext that ramifies and intersects richly with all the other nodes in the web" (Haraway 1997, 149). When genetic analysis is represented as mapping and it stands in for human subjectivity *tout court* then: (1) nature is constituted as a program; (2) humans are constituted as the intelligent beings who are capable of deciphering this program; and (3) scientists are constituted as a secular priesthood who are able to conquer and replace nature, therein providing technoscientific salvation (Haraway 1997, 147–150).

A problem arises, however, when Haraway ironically appropriates tropes from technoscientific culture and uses them as motifs that guide her articles and books. Specifically, she fails to address the potential for ironic terms such as "cyborg," "FemaleMan," and "OncoMouse" to reinstate the dominant ideas they are used to criticize. In order for Haraway to effectively use these tropes without promoting the mistranslations of nature and culture that she found associated with the HGP, she should philosophically discuss the relation between irony and mimesis. After all, she begins her famous "Cyborg Manifesto" by referring to her project as an "ironic myth" that has epistemological and political repercussions:

> Irony is about contradictions that do not resolve into larger wholes, even dialectically, about the tension of holding incompatible things together because both or all are necessary and true. Irony is about humour and serious play. It is also a rhetorical strategy and a political method, one I would like to see more honoured within socialist-feminism. At the centre of my ironic faith, my blasphemy, is the image of the cyborg. (Haraway 1991, 149)

Haraway presupposes that when metaphors such as the cyborg are used in an ironic manner that destabilizing political consequences follow. To this end, just as the "cyborg" is supposed to problematize humanist depictions of subjectivity, so too is the evocation of "OncoMouse" and "vampires" supposed to confound how the traditional dichotomies of subject-object, pure-impure, nature-culture, and life-death are understood:

> Above all, OncoMouse is the first patented animal in the world. . . . Created through the ordinary practices that make metaphor into material fact, her status as an invention who/which remains a living animal is what makes her a vampire, subsisting in the realms of the undead. Vampires are narrative figures with specific category-crossing work to do. The essence of vampires . . . is the pollution of natural kinds. The existence of vampires tropes the purity of lineage, certainty of kind, boundary of community, order of sex, closure of race, inertness of objects, liveliness of subjects, and clarity of gender. (Haraway 1997, 80)

The problem is that Haraway never investigates how ironic gestures can fail to function according to the subversive intentions of the people who appropriate them. This issue is central to thinkers such as Jacques Derrida and Judith Butler, who spent a large part of their careers investigating the relation between iteration and power. One of Derrida's earliest philosophical challenges was to work out the problem of neologisms, which are new uses of old words. Just as irony highlights an incongruity between what might be expected and what actually occurs, neologisms are poignant because they highlight an incongruity between expected and unexpected meanings of terms. Derrida ponders whether theorists should use neologisms or invent new words when trying to convey novel points of view, and after investigating the temporal depth of tradition and language, he argued that it is metaphysically untenable for theorists to believe that new uses of words could be used to communicate new ideas; the interpretation of new deployments of language always runs up against cognitive limits imposed by pre-existing structures of language and meaning.

Unlike Derrida, Haraway fails to consider the historical sedimentation of language and meaning. She assumes that by using the tropes "vampire" and "OncoMouse," the categories of sex and gender become complicated in a way that is politically desirable. Yet Butler's early performative style of feminism received a great deal of criticism based on her view that ironic performance, for example drag, can function as a mechanism for destabilizing cultural norms, such as expectations about gender roles. Critics countered that if certain cultural norms are powerful enough, they will not be challenged, but rather will internalize, sublate, and regulate the ironic gestures that Butler suggests should be deployed to achieve anti-hegemonic ends. It is unclear how Haraway would respond to this challenge, even though it applies as much to Butler's early work as it does to her own most recent endeavors. Specifically, there are many extant *cyborg fantasies* that do not accord with Haraway's theme that human bodies and identities are always partial: (1) the immortal body that does not suffer illness and lives forever; (2) the uncontaminated body that is cleansed of an organism's viscerally expressed finitude because it does not eat, drink, or secrete; (3) the pure cerebral self who transcends nature and exemplifies the Western priority of mind over body; and (4) the omnipotent body whose originally fragile biological parts are replaced by powerful mechanical prostheses. Although Haraway repeatedly insists that "vampire" and "cyborg" figures are hybrids that epitomize the endless transformations and partial identities that humans experience, she is not sensitive enough to the ease by which these figures can slide into hegemonic fantasies.

4. LANGUAGE AND IMAGINATION

To thematically unify the first three sections, I will retrieve the main question that has thus far guided my investigation: Since there are many different hermeneutic strategies that can be used to break down inherited prejudices, why do Haraway and Pickering use idiosyncratic terms? The answer to this question has to do with *imagination*. Imagination is often evaluated as belonging more to aesthetic enterprises than scientific ones. Yet Haraway and Pickering try to show that imaginative metaphors are needed to capture the liveliness of scientific practice. They seem to believe that without using these metaphors it is difficult to conceptualize why scientific, technological, and political practices do not operate as conventionally described. Hence, one of their central points of agreement is that imagination is an essential component of good scholarship.

They both presuppose that imagination is capable of exposing productive questions about scientific practice. Their analyses imply that without imagination, one cannot locate what is questionable about a given account of subjectivity, culture, materiality, and temporality. In short, imagination functions for both theorists as a stimulus; imaginative scholars are impelled to see aspects of practice that are not currently perceived and run contrary to established fact. Some philosophers might find this reliance on imagination frustrating. While imagination is central to their theoretical enterprises, neither Haraway nor Pickering (1) develops an ontology of imagination; (2) differentiates imagination from other mental acts; (3) addresses how the mind is free or constrained to vary its contents; (4) inquires into the differences between imaginative and perceptual variation; (5) attempts to locate the origin of the imaginative impulse in bodily praxis, historical sedimentation, or spontaneous inspiration; (6) discusses the ontological status of impossible objects; and (7) addresses the relation between imagination and images.

In short, for both Haraway and Pickering, imagination is not something to be philosophically interrogated, but rather pragmatically deployed. For Pickering, imagination is a strategy for "*rebalancing* our understanding of science away from a pure obsession with knowledge and toward a recognition of science's material powers" (Pickering 1995, 7). For Haraway, imagination is a strategy used to "make explicit the tropic quality of all material semiotic processes, especially in techno-science" (Haraway 1997, 11).

In the future, it would be nice to see Haraway and Pickering address the implications stemming from the widespread acceptance of their own technoscientific metaphors. Due to the tendencies of metaphors to sediment once popularized, metaphorical reification can achieve lasting power. In this way sedimentation leads to institutionalization, ritualization, and the objectification of research possibilities. When sedimented idioms become institutionally accepted and are experienced as taken-for-granted beliefs, their continued use can become dangerous, as in instances when a speaker or writer cannot explain why a given idiom is treated reverentially. Now that Haraway's "cyborg" language and Pickering's "mangled" language are sedimented features of science studies, it remains to be seen whether or not future research benefits from being inspired by these guiding motifs.

5. POLITICAL DIFFERENCES

Pickering notes that politically his account of technoscience differs from Haraway's. He intimates that Haraway's views on the connection between politics and knowledge might inhibit her style of analysis from being compatible with his call for a wider anti-disciplinary synthesis (Pickering 1995, 228). For Haraway, it is impossible to epistemologically inquire into the constitutive realm of technoscientific practice without simultaneously engaging in the political arena of legislating who and what counts, as well as who and what is excluded, from the domain of a given analysis. By contrast, while Pickering concedes that his analysis of the "mangle" is capable of contributing to political debates, he also declares that it is neither overtly political nor wedded to any political commitments. He explicitly suggests that the rigid connection between epistemology and politics that Haraway makes in her "Cyborg Manifesto" is unwarranted: "I do not think that analysis and politics are necessarily as closely linked as, for example, Haraway's 'Manifesto' suggests" (Pickering 1995, 228).

In order to compare and contrast Haraway's and Pickering's respective positions on politics, it will be helpful to introduce a third term, Bruno Latour's notion of the "Modern Settlement."[1] Both Haraway's explicit engagement with politics and Pickering's aversion to normativity are responses to what this settlement represents. The "Modern Settlement" is a phrase used by Latour to designate the outcome and lasting cultural repercussions stemming from Thomas Hobbes's and Robert Boyle's early modernist positions on science and politics. According to Latour, their debates thematize an overly simplistic understanding of scientific and political endeavors; they simplify how science and politics can be demarcated from one another, as well as how they should relate to one another. Their shared presuppositions, Latour insists, can be interpreted as a parable for how science and politics are understood throughout modernity.

Briefly stated, Latour contends that as a result of the Hobbes and Boyle debate, the link between epistemology and social order took on a "completely new meaning" (Latour 1993, 27). Through their confrontation, the representation of things as depicted through the intermediary of the laboratory appears to be forever dissociated from the representation of citizens, as depicted through the intermediary of the social contract (Latour 1993, 27). According to Latour, Hobbes and Boyle created distinct scientific and political realms by relying on an exclusionary logic: "Boyle is creating a political discourse from which politics is to be excluded, while Hobbes is imagining a politics from which experimental science is to be excluded" (Latour 1993, 27). The result of their segregated planning is that the domains of science and politics appear to require separation from each other as a necessary condition for maintaining authority. Latour summarizes the binary oppositions that support this logic as:

> In their common debate, Hobbes's and Boyle's descendants offer us the resources we have used up to now: on the one hand, social force and power; on the other, natural force and mechanism. On the one hand, the subject of law; on the other, the object of science. The political spokespersons come to represent the quarrelsome and calculating multitude of citizens; the scientific spokespersons come to represent the mute and material multitude of objects. The former translate their principals, who cannot all speak at once; the latter translate their principals who are mute from birth. . . . Soon the word 'representation' will take on two different meanings, according to whether elected agents or things are at stake. Epistemology and science will go their opposite ways. (Latour 1993, 29)

Haraway addresses Boyle and his fictitious separation of science and politics by inserting her own "non-innocent" figure of the witness as a contrast to Boyle's "invisible" and "transparent" modest witness; the latter, Haraway contends, is a witness that produces itself from "the culture of no culture" (Latour 1993, 32–33). Even in Haraway's early essays, she argues that knowledge is always situated, which means that it is localized and influenced by observer biases. For example, she contends that discussions of perception are always political and never merely epistemological: "Vision requires instruments of vision; an optics is a politics of positioning" (Haraway 1991, 193). Employing a method similar to Nietzsche's perspectivism, she contends that the existence of different practices of visualization gives rise to the following questions: "How to see? Where to see from? What limits vision? What to see for? Who to see with? Who gets to have more than one point of view? Who gets blinded? Who wears blinders? Who interprets the visual field?" (Haraway 1991, 194). In other words, Haraway finds that the practices of technologically mediated vision always involve elements of selection. She interprets this selectivity as inherently exclusionary and therein overtly political. She pursues the issue of selectivity as the perennially evaluative question of *cui bono*—who lives and who dies in the field of technoscience? (Haraway 1997, 113).

For example, she frames her lengthy discussion of OncoMouse by asking, "For whom does OncoMouse live and die? . . . Who lives and dies—human, nonhuman, and cyborg—and how, because OncoMouse exists?" (Haraway 1997, 113). For Haraway, the culturally evaluative questions surrounding transgenic animals should not be viewed as supplemental to ones that statistically appraise the success of medical pursuits, such as fighting cancer (Haraway 1997, 113). She thus criticizes Latour for limiting his analyses of technoscience to descriptive endeavors and being satisfied with highlighting the existence of hybrids. According to Haraway, Latour should further inquire into for whom and how these hybrids work; by ignoring this task, Haraway believes that Latour's "mobilized" epistemology generates overly stable and reductive analyses (Haraway 1997, 279–280 fn.1). This criticism of Latour appears to be one that she would direct against Pickering.

Because Haraway attempts to inextricably link politics with epistemology, she backs herself into a corner when she is forced to argue for both "situated knowledge" and democratic measures in technoscientific production. Although Haraway does not distinguish between her two types of politics, it is helpful to call the latter P2 and the former P1. P1 is the ubiquitous political application of situated knowledge to everything in technoscience. It is a broad notion of politics that does not refer to the traditional elements of political discourse such as rights and responsibilities. In short, P1 is Haraway's attempt to be politically committed without accepting the Hobbes-Boyle dictum of restricting political discussions to traditional political idioms.

Haraway never works out a systematic position on P2. She routinely suggests that more voices need to be democratically absorbed into the processes of decision making that govern how technoscientific research should be conducted. However, she never thoroughly discusses the claims made by theorists who are explicitly concerned about what policies are truly democratic.

At face value, Haraway's stand on P2 is paradoxical. Her conception of "situated knowledge" is based on the view that a contextually bound practitioner always produces politically exclusionary knowledge; whereas her prescriptive call for democratic measures in P2 involves a categorical commitment to traverse the multiplicity of perspectives and situations. Haraway thus appears to argue for (1) a perspectival account of truth-politics and (2) an objectivist account of politics that is dissociated from perspectival truth. This dilemma is reminiscent of Paul Feyerabend's unsuccessful attempt to reconcile relativist and democratic commitments.

Furthermore, while P1 highlights the inextricably bound relations between humans, non-humans, and mediating technologies, P2 solely emphasizes the process of *human decision making*. In other words, Haraway simultaneously argues for cyborg and non-cyborg approaches to engaging with political issues. On the non-cyborg side, she references Denmark's democratic science and technology policies and claims that the Danes are able to foster both objectivity (at least according to Sandra Harding's notion of "strong objectivity," which closely resembles a reflexive, democratic consensus) as well as situated knowledge by placing a multiplicity of stakeholders in dialogue with one another (e.g., scientific practitioners, technical manufacturers, and lay citizens alike) (Haraway 1997, 95–96). Haraway reports that the result of these dialogues is not only consensus, but also a greater awareness of the particular interests that mark the various intersections of nature and culture (Haraway 1997, 96). Although she recognizes that this call for democracy sounds a bit too idealistic, Haraway claims that "[t]he degree of scientific and technical literacy encouraged in ordinary people—as well as the degree of respect for citizens' considerations encouraged among technical and professional people . . . is stunning to anyone inhabiting the depleted democratic air of U.S. technoscience" (Haraway 1997, 96).

A more generous reading of Haraway than the one I gave would suggest that her call for more democratic structures in the discursive formation of technoscience is not at all contradictory. It would emphasize that her vision of democracy does not rely on the idea of participatory power as expressed by full human agency. Although the figure of the cyborg entails a radical dissolution of the human–non-human distinction, it does not preclude every instance of agency or the introduction of a new type of political formation, namely a cyborg democracy. Hence, Haraway can be taken to argue that closer attention to the immanence of praxis is compatible with genuine democracy.

Unlike Haraway, Pickering does not treat epistemological and political analysis as synonymous. He briefly discusses politically relevant issues, such as the transformations experienced by science and the military through their World War II encounter (Pickering 1995, 234–242). However, his response to the "Modern Settlement" appears to be a rejection of discussions of P2 on the grounds that democratic discourse appears to be grounded in the Hobbes dominated half of the Hobbes-Boyle split. Pickering takes questions about democracy to be idle; he envisions them as producing obvious answers, such as the military wins and democracy loses. From this perspective, standard political questions lack what Isabelle Stengers calls "risk" (Stengers 1997, xi–xiii). Yet one should keep in mind that Haraway is not asking whether democracy is a better form of government than socialism, nor is she asking whether democracy or consciousness raising are intrinsically good political platforms; she inquires into whether democracy and consciousness raising are good for situated knowledge in a contemporary technoscience climate.

Additionally, while reflecting on Haraway's overt political commitments to P1, Pickering asks what, if anything, binds epistemological revolutions in the sciences to political ones. Referencing Haraway's "Cyborg Manifesto," Pickering claims that her epistemological analysis of human–non-human couplings vis-à-vis cyborg imagery cannot be divorced from her commitment to non-essentialist socialist feminism. By contrast, he notes that while his epistemological analysis is comparable and congruent to Haraway's, it is nevertheless not wedded to any feminist principles; in fact, it is entirely bereft of a political agenda. Its driving force is a concern over temporality and "mangled" framing (Pickering 1995, 228). Observing that the mangle is fundamentally apolitical leads Pickering to ponder whether his analysis should be considered politically valuable, even though it is not politically motivated. He argues that since the post-humanist account of practice that emerges from his analysis of science undermines faith in a distinctly humanist politics, his concerns about the limits and techniques of knowledge are politically relevant. Furthermore, he contends that the temporal emergence of the "mangle" suggests that political agendas should always be formed on the basis of situated cultural formations and not on non-emergent master narratives. Thus, he acknowledges a close relation between his own "performative idiom" and Marxist historiography. His main divergence from Marxist accounts lies in his suspicion that many Marxists remain embedded within traditional humanist and non-emergent conceptual schemes (Pickering 1995, 231).

The upshot of this comparison of Haraway and Pickering is that their political differences cannot be reduced to a difference in theoretical understanding. For all of his novelty, one way of interpreting Pickering is that he is quite traditional in his tendency to deny a necessary connection between scientific practice and either P1 or P2. Although Pickering departs from traditional views of science as a neutral instrument, he can be interpreted as somewhat conservative based on his position that the mangle is not wedded to grounding democratic values. Put in traditional, deontological terms, Pickering's notion of what there is in the mangle does not yield a necessary connection to any prescriptive statements; whereas Haraway's notion of what there is in situated knowledge yields a necessary connection to P1 and P2. For Haraway, it is not enough to describe a mangled situation; one needs to take a non-innocent stand on what the mangle reveals. Additionally, the question of what the mangle reveals is in part determined by its lack of political focus. After all, as Haraway relentlessly argues, how one frames his or her analysis constrains what results are obtainable; what is foregrounded and what is backgrounded reveals the limits of one's imagination and the extent of one's commitments. Still, one need not necessarily interpret Pickering as conservatively maintaining the status quo because his analysis does not directly support a radical political agenda. One could argue that it is Haraway who lacks the nerve to realize that the present state of the mangle renders the preference for one kind of a humanist political stance against another untenable.

Despite the noted differences, in the final analysis both Haraway and Pickering seem to agree on the following four political points about P1:

(1) They both resist political accounts that ignore materiality and material agency. Moreover, both are explicitly concerned with the unpredictable connections that emerge when humans and non-humans intersect.

(2) They both are critical of historical accounts that attempt to explain away or ignore the non-metaphysical dimensions of political engagements. As Pickering's account of numerically controlled machines illustrates, while the mangle is not an explicitly political framework, it is capable of addressing issues like the relation between workers, management, and machines (Pickering 1995, 157–176).

(3) They both contend that the grounds for political criticism are not simply to be found in straightforward political analyses (examinations of class structure, power distribution, etc.), but can be found within epistemological investigations of the relation between human and non-human agency.

(4) They both contend that political interests do not belong to timeless and stable interests, but rather arise within the temporally mediated plane of practice.

The question that remains after this brief political exposition is: In what sense, if any, do the political comments provided by Haraway and Pickering suggest the need for philosophical revision on related matters? Their comments are provocative because they reinforce the importance of breaking the Diltheyan divide between the natural and social sciences. According to this divide, scientific explanation and humanistic understanding are fundamentally different. Despite well-known criticisms of Dilthey's historicist proclivities and misunderstanding of bias and tradition, theorists belonging to the post-Diltheyan hermeneutic tradition (e.g., Karl-Otto Appel, Jürgen Habermas, and even to some degree Ian Hacking) reinforce his essential views by largely identifying with the humanities and social sciences and contrasting their interpretative methods with physicalist approaches to the phenomena of nature. Haraway and Pickering are thus valuable resources for anyone concerned with re-evaluating the scope of interpretation and its application to putatively natural and cultural entities.

However, it remains disconcerting that both of them are able to evoke the problem of politics without ever substantially engaging with classical or contemporary political philosophers. In this respect, Pickering's post-humanist refusal to take part in a political discussion seems nihilistic. While the tenor of Pickering's work suggests that so-called humanist political programs are untenable, he never provides good reasons for abandoning them. Although there are many good arguments that could be made to justify this position, they are arguments to be made and not conclusions to be presumed. Likewise, Haraway's insistence on the virtue of consciousness raising needs to be placed in a more direct dialogue with other feminist criticisms of liberalism; otherwise it is unclear how politically effective consciousness raising is.

6. INTERDISCIPLINARY CONCLUSIONS

Throughout this essay the discussion of Haraway and Pickering was framed in terms of the merits and detriments of interdisciplinary research. The aim was to show that philosophers can benefit from reflectively considering many of Haraway's and Pickering's claims, and that Haraway and Pickering need to take the history of philosophy more seriously if they want to present defensible theses. These considerations suggest the need to distinguish between *multi-disciplinary* and *interdisciplinary* research.

Multi-disciplinary research occurs when researchers from different disciplines apply their specific methodologies to a common problem. For example, philosophers, biologists, and psychologists can approach the topic of vision and each type of research can structure its investigation around its own disciplinary strengths: philosophers can inquire into the metaphysical commitments presupposed by particular models of vision; biologists can investigate the anatomy of the eye in relation to particular optical trajectories; and psychologists can study the relationship between the cultural acquisition of knowledge and the propensity to see things in a certain way. Within a multi-disciplinary framework, each type of research is considered valid within its own limited sphere and therein does not require members of one type of research community to discuss or read the works of members of another research community.

By contrast, interdisciplinary research occurs when investigators from different disciplines inform their own research with the arguments and results of investigations done in other disciplines. Of course, different research communities have their own professionally rewarded norms of conducting and publishing research. National rankings of many hard science departments have a tradition of multiple-authored and interdisciplinary projects that are evaluated as strongly as single-authored pieces. By contrast, other disciplines, such as philosophy, are embedded within single-authored traditions. At best, crucial conversations that were necessary conditions for a philosophy paper being written are often relegated to thankful footnotes.

Although not fully respectful of philosophical rigor, Haraway and Pickering make the interdisciplinary attempt to engage with philosophical insights. Rather than completely ignoring philosophy, they incorporate philosophical thinking into a valued research canon that also includes works in anthropology, sociology, and the empirical and theoretical sciences. The Diltheyan divide and the philosophical desideratum of universal structures, by contrast, often inhibits philosophers from analyzing and reinterpreting empirical research generated in other disciplines, especially in the hard sciences. Consequently, science studies can hopefully continue to flourish in a more philosophical manner, philosophy should also become less multi-disciplinary and more frequently engage with provocative authors such as Haraway and Pickering.

This vision of the future, however, is not one that Pickering shares. He looks forward to the day that an "*antidisciplinary synthesis*" arises "in which the microdisciplinary fractures in and around science studies are more or less erased" (Pickering 1995, 216). In other words, Pickering yearns for a time in which different disciplines come together to construct a "common vision of science" (Pickering 1995, 216). By contrast, the value of *interdisciplinary* investigation lies in its propensity to push researchers to take a more critical stance toward their own work; as such, it impels theorists in a number of directions, and not necessarily toward a common vantage point.

NOTE

1. Latour's analysis of Hobbes and Boyle is based upon his interpretation of *Leviathan and the Air-Pump: Hobbes, Boyle and the Experimental Life.*

BIBLIOGRAPHY

Butler, Judith, and Joan Scott, eds. 1992. *Feminists Theorize the Political*. New York: Routledge.

Derrida, Jacques. 1974. *Speech and Phenomena*. Translated by David Allison. Evanston: Northwestern University Press.

———. 1989. *Edmund Husserl's The Origin of Geometry: An Introduction*. Translated by John Leavey. Lincoln: University of Nebraska Press.

Casey, Edward. 1976. *Imagining: A Phenomenological Study*. Bloomington: Indiana University Press.

Greene, Brian. 2000. *The Elegant Universe: Superstrings, Hidden Dimensions, and the Quest for the Ultimate Theory*. New York: Vintage Books.

Haraway, Donna 1991. *Simians, Cyborgs, and Women: The Reinvention of Nature*. New York: Routledge/Free Association Books.

———. 1997. *Modest_Witness@Second_Millennium. FemaleMan© _Meets_OncoMouse™*. New York: Routledge.

Heidegger, Martin. 1962. *Being and Time*. Translated by John Macquarrie and Edward Robinson. New York: Harper and Row.

Latour, Bruno. 1993. *We Have Never Been Modern*. Translated by Catherine Porter. Cambridge, Mass.: Harvard University Press.

Pickering, Andrew. 1995. *The Mangle of Practice: Time, Agency and Science*. Chicago: University of Chicago Press.

———, ed. 1992. *Science as Practice and Culture*. Chicago: University of Chicago Press.

Ricoeur, Paul. 1977. *The Rule of Metaphor*. Translated by Robert Czerny. Toronto: University of Toronto Press.

Shapin, Steven, and Simon Schaffer. 1985. *Leviathan and the Air-Pump: Hobbes, Boyle, and the Experimental Life*. Princeton, N.J.: Princeton University Press.

Stengers, Isabelle. 1997. *Power and Invention: Situating Science*. Translated by Paul Bains. Minneapolis: University of Minnesota Press.

10. Hypertext: Rortean Links between Ihde and Haraway

Robb Eason

SECTION 1.

The Internet serves as both a subject and a literary troping device for Donna Haraway in her most recent book, *Modest_Witness@Second_Millennium.FemaleMan© Meets_OncoMouse™*. Specifically, the Internet provides for Haraway the concept of "hypertext," which, on the one hand, is at the same time both a product and a symbol of technoscience, that blend or perceptible family resemblances by means of which technology, science, culture, economics, industry, etc., can be gathered up together for study, and on the other hand, is itself an ever-elusive, always deferring source, which seems to extend endlessly into the world via chains of signification and relation to other texts, sources, and even material entities. What I would like to take from this metaphor of hypertext, in order to begin this study, is its specific capability to link together multiple sources of information, that is, multiple textual sources. I would like to use this metaphor of hypertext myself as a model in guiding my cross-analysis of Haraway's and Don Ihde's positions taken toward technoscience and a phenomenology of technology. I will focus primarily on Haraway's stance as it is espoused in her *Modest Witness*, though I will also periodically draw from some of her older work from her *Simians, Cyborgs, and Women: The Reinvention of Nature*. One of Don Ihde's more recent works, *Technology and the Lifeworld: From Garden to Earth*, will serve as my primary source in fleshing out his stance taken toward technology. Although here too I will draw from some of his other more recent work including his *Expanding Hermeneutics: Visualism in Science*.

By being explicit about the choice to use the metaphor of hypertext in my analysis, I am not merely trying to lay bare to the reader a stylistic choice that I have consciously made, but rather I do so in order to elucidate my thesis. In this chapter I will show that while Haraway's and Ihde's theoretical approaches to questions concerning technology differ, it is nevertheless the case that both approaches make implicit assumptions about how it is that we come into a relationship with and come to "understand" technological artifacts, practices, and institutions, implicit assumptions which highlight, I want to claim, a kind of epistemological forced option. This forced epistemological option, I will contend, might be jettisoned by considering a third approach to our dealings with technology which, like the metaphorical hypertext, will "link" crucial aspects of Ihde's approach to similarly crucial aspects of Haraway's approach to the questions of technology and technoscience. On the one hand, I will suggest that, despite his efforts, Ihde's "phenomenological" approach to the analysis of technology, if swallowed whole, saddles us with an individualistic and problematic realist account of what it is to be a knower and a user of technology. On the other hand, I will suggest, while Haraway's "semiotic" approach to an analysis of technoscience does more carefully try to capture the ineluctable social character of our dealings with technology, Haraway's account nevertheless throws out the proverbial baby with the bathwater. For all her vast meditations on the multiple ways the many different epistemological strands—cultural, economic, political, etc.—contribute to our experience of technology and situate us, Haraway has herself implicitly saddled us with an account of what it is to be a knower and user of technology which is almost totally *disembodied, a-individualized,* and wholly culturally constructed. I will contend that both Ihde's and Haraway's implicit epistemological positions present us with interesting and valuable new ways to look at the epistemological problem with regards to how it is that we encounter and ultimately come to know technology. Their two epistemological positions differ insofar as Ihde's account implies a particular brand of individualistic, non-inferential, non-normative, phenomenological realism which, under scrutiny, leaves us unsatisfied, whereas Haraway's account, despite her best efforts, reduces to an all too thoroughgoing and irresponsible nominalism where all possible subjects and objects are reduced to similar matrices of semiotic-material strands of meaning. Thus, I will begin, in Section 2, by laying out what I take to be Ihde's and Haraway's respective positions or accounts of technology and technoscience. I will show how we might see a connection between the two thinkers' different positions via an interesting analysis made by the philosopher of technology Andrew Feenberg. In Section 3 I will, with a helpful set of distinctions drawn up by Richard Rorty, show how each thinker's implicit epistemological stance carries with it both a theoretical and a practical inadequacy when applied to the analysis of technology. And, finally, in Section 4, I will suggest (a) what kind of epistemological stance might be proposed to mediate between Ihde's and Haraway's stances, and (b) the effect such an epistemological stance would have with regards to the analysis of technology and technoscience.

SECTION 2. CROSS-ANALYSIS

Ihde's *Technology and the Lifeworld: From Garden to Earth* characterizes humanity's ascent from the mythological conception of our environment as "Garden" to the present conception we have of it now as "Earth" as an ascent colored by humanity's dealings with technology. In an effort to show the almost equiprimordial relationship between humans and technology, Ihde spends much time debunking the notion of a pre-technological humanity. Ihde asks: What kind of human is it that is not *always already* bound up in a technological comportment toward his or her world? This question becomes, for the reader of Ihde's account, more and more enigmatic, and the answer to this question becomes more and more elusive. Humanity's existence has been, from the beginning or at least the near beginning, a *technological existence.* Ihde writes,

> Virtually every area of praxis implicates a technology. From burial to birth to eating and working, the use of artifacts embedded in a patterned praxis demarcates the human within his or her world. . . . By looking at technologies in this initially broadest sense, we can note that in contrast to the non-technological Garden, *human activity from immemorial time and across the diversity of cultures has always been technologically embedded.* (Ihde 1990, 20)

The lifeworld, that environment of lived relations in which we, as humans, always already find ourselves, is shot through with technology and technological practices. Through his phenomenological analysis, Ihde reveals three variant modes by means of which we humans have a relation with technology. First, according to Ihde, humans can participate in an *"embodiment relation"* with technology. This type of relation is exemplified in those artifacts and those practices whereby our desire for the technological manifests itself as a desire to take into ourselves, to live through, and to literally *embody* our various technologies. Drawing on Heidegger's famous example of the technological apparatus of the hammer (Heidegger 1962, 95–102) in which the hammer becomes an extension of the arm, something enmeshed within our dealings and practices and never presenting itself to us as a mere object with which we are dealing until it breaks down, Ihde shows us that there are many such technologies which recede into the background of our practices and which become simply part of the body which we are. Eyeglasses, bionic joints, and hearing aids are examples of technological artifacts which become embodied, which slip into the background and which only become present to us when they fail to do or do poorly the task for which they were produced.

Second, in Ihde's view, humans can participate in a *"hermeneutic relation"* with technology. Within this relation our technological artifacts and practices work to interpret the world and make it available to us in ways which, without the technology, it would not be. Here Ihde has in mind, for instance, and perhaps in its most simple form, the technology of the gauge, a technology which makes present and available to us aspects of our world or ourselves which would be otherwise imperceptible. The gauge of the barometer, for instance, makes clear to the human reading it a fluctuation or a stability in the atmosphere which heretofore could not have been noticed or accessed, at least with the same level of ease, by user of that particular technology.

Third, and finally, Ihde suggests that humans can also participate in an *"alterity relation"* with technology whereby humans come to regard the technology as "other." In this relation the technology itself, not our practices nor our world, is the focus of the relationship we have with it. We engage with technology, in this relation, as though it were another null point of perception, as though it were an agent in the world to which we must address ourselves. The technology of the video game, for instance, presents to us in some cases an other with which we must deal, another agent which "schemes" to beat us, which "plots" our demise, and which we treat *as if* it were another rationally acting agent in the world.

What perhaps is most important for Ihde's analysis is that in each of these three types of relations in which we might participate with technology, the technology in question must always take as its reference the user's *body*. In the obvious case of the embodiment relation with technology, the technology (sometimes literally) recedes into the body, becoming, at least phenomenologically, part of it. In the case of the hermeneutic relation, the technology in question must always be perceptible (usually visually, but sometimes audibly or tactically) to the perceptual faculties of a body. And even in the case of the alterity relation, we treat the technology *as if* it too were an embodied technology. This last phenomenon occurs both when I, like Garry Kasparov, sit adjacent to a computer and play a game of chess with it, or, more radically, when I, in the midst of a video game, am assaulted and assailed by my virtual combatants (Ihde 1998b, 349–357). In either case the virtual body on the screen and even the CPU housing of the circuitry represent to me another embodied intelligence. The *body*, in Ihde's phenomenological analysis, takes primacy. My knowledge of and experience with the technology with which I am confronted is a knowledge and experience gained from my embodied perspective taken on the world. Technology is, for the phenomenologically minded Ihde, first and foremost a set of practices and artifacts which stand in a constant referential relationship with our bodies.

Donna Haraway's approach to technology and technoscience differs quite radically from Ihde's approach. However, we can now use, as a springboard into Haraway's work, some of the questions that ought to be surfacing after our preliminary survey of Ihde's approach. Insofar as Ihde's approach to an analysis of technology takes the body as primary, the question immediately arises: What *kind* of body is it to which technology so constantly refers? Is the body which Ihde has in mind, first and foremost, a male or a female body? What is the ethnicity of such a body? Does this body have a history of relations with the world and with other bodies? Is the body politically directed (or minded)? Just as Merleau-Ponty's phenomenological conception of the body has been the focus of charges claiming that it is merely an empty transcendentalized conception of the body through the works of, for instance, Iris Young and Susan Bordo (Young 1998a, 259–290, 84–98), Ihde's conception of the body too falls subject to such a critique. Such a critique maintains that while the phenomenologist is doing epistemology and philosophy as such a service by bringing the body to theory and showing how an analysis of its part in understanding the way we humans come to understand the world is crucial, nevertheless there are better and worse ways by means of which we might come to theorize about the body.

Bodies are always particular bodies with particular histories. Bodies are gendered. Bodies have a particular ethnicity. Bodies are motivated to action by different political ends, etc. Thus to suggest that there is something like *the* body or a transcendental category of *embodiment* which phenomenology informs us of is misleading. Likewise, if at least part of the essence of technology is that it is constantly in a referential relationship with the bodies of those who use and are acted upon by it, then we must ask: Do technologies more easily refer to some bodies than others? Do different bodies have different *kinds* of relationships with technology? Does, for instance, a male body handle, refer to, and work with this or that technology with more ease than a female body? In short, each of Ihde's variant structures of the technology / human relation take for granted the possibility of there being some category like *the* body which is meant to capture at the same time the essence of *all* bodies and yet *no* body in particular. To be sure, this criticism is not meant to be a halting one, but rather it is meant to be indicative of the need for a conception of the subject involved with technology which is more inclusive, which better describes the kind or kinds of relationships that varied embodied humans have with technology. I come back to address this point in Section 3.

For now, let us take an example from a recent work on the philosophy of technology by Andrew Feenberg which shows the necessity for an analysis which integrates phenomenology but also goes beyond it. In *Questioning Technology*, Feenberg writes,

> When one looks at old photos of child factory works, one is struck by the adaptation of the machines to their height (Newhall, 1964:140). The images disturb us, but were no doubt taken for granted until child labor became controversial. Design specifications simply incorporated the sociological fact of child

labor into the structure of devices. The impress of social relations can be traced in the technology. (1999)

Technology, more than in a mere *referential* relationship with *the* body, is in each and every case *intended* for *a* body. Technology never simply has *the* body, a non-gendered, non-specific body as that to which it refers. In Feenberg's example, the technology, the machines in the factories, were intended for *a* body under five feet tall, probably lighter than 110 pounds etc. . . . . Technology, as Feenberg shows, is far more than just the site at the cross-trajectories of "man and machine." Technology is also the intersection at which not only a non-human and a particular body come into contact, but it is also the site at which cultural values and *norms* are expressed, political ends are met, and economic interests are secured. In short, technology is the material and practical matrix in which all these things are bound up together. A strong account of the relation between humans and technology thus must account for the way in which this matrix is embodied in and yet refers to particular bodies.

A more thorough account in line with Feenberg's movement toward a conception of technology as this matrix of the expression of cultural values and norms, political ends, and economic interests etc. can be found in Haraway's *Modest_Witness@Second_ Millennium.FemaleMan© Meets_OncoMouse™*. The title, essentially an Internet address, gives us license to once again pick up the metaphor of hypertext. Our critique of Ihde's purely phenomenological approach to the analysis of the human / technology relation, while certainly critical toward a conception of the body which takes the body as a transcendental category, does in no way invalidate the attempt to include the body, the fact that all knowing and technology-using subjects are embodied subjects. Donna Haraway's account of "technoscience" takes as its object of study the interconnected set of relations between technology, social, cultural, political, and scientific institutions, practices, and participants. Technoscience, for Haraway, is a hybrid that "extravagantly exceeds the distinction between science and technology as well as that between nature and society, subjects and objects, and the natural and the artificial that structured that imaginary time called modernity" (Haraway 1997, 3). Thus what I want to show in this paper is how to "link" up the phenomenological embodied account of our relation with technology provided by Ihde with Haraway's more robust, more epistemologically inclusive account proffered in her *Modest Witness.*

Technoscience, the burgeoning new field at the beginning of the new millennium, is for Haraway the site at which our epistemologies broaden to form a multi-dimensional, polymorphous object of study. Haraway goes so far as to claim that within the epistemological bounds of technoscience, subjects and objects themselves no longer remain discrete and exclusive. She writes,

> Both the subjects and the objects of technoscience are forged and branded in the crucible of specific, located practices, some of which are global in their location. In the intensity of the fire, the subjects and the objects regularly melt into each other. (Haraway 1997, 3)

Unlike Ihde's phenomenological approach to the analysis of the relation between humans and technology, Haraway's analysis is not a phenomenological one, that is, not in the strict sense of following in the line of theorists which begins with Husserl and moves through Heidegger and Merleau-Ponty. Haraway, instead, takes as her model of analysis the *pragmatic semiotic* model. She sees her project as "semiotic" insofar as it is a project which traces the multiple strands of meaning which flow into any technoscientific practice, artifact, or institution, strands of meaning which include cultural, economic, social, political, and scientific aspects. Technoscientific analysis is an analysis consisting of sign interpretation. However, as Haraway sees it, the "crucible" of technoscience melds together signs with material artifacts. Thus Haraway's semiotics allow her to trace multiple chains of meaning in conjunction with the many material entities which we find ourselves confronted with. Such a tracing is "pragmatic" because through the process of the interpretation of signs and material entities, we are, as Haraway sees it, participating in describing ourselves and our world in ways which are always situated, directed, and put to *use* to fulfill particular social, political, and economic ends.

One such semiotic-material artifact that Haraway sees as ore for the crucible of technoscience is Dupont's OncoMouse™, the world's first patented mammal, guaranteed to carry an activated cancer-causing oncogene. Haraway writes, "OncoMouse™ and its academic-corporate family are like civic sacraments: signs and referents all rolled into one fleshy mystery in a secularized salvation history of civilian and military wars, scientific knowledge, progress, democracy, and economic power" (Haraway 1997, 3). OncoMouse™ and the many other artifacts, practices, and institutions of technoscience are not, for Haraway's project, to be considered, studied, observed, and analyzed as though they are simply mere discrete entities which can be circumscribed within the gaze of the carefully observing subject. Instead, the artifacts, practices, and institutions of technoscience are like signifiers, place-holders, at the matrices of multiple relations, all of which might be ferreted out and uncovered. However, Haraway wants us to recognize that in tracing the relations within the matrix of technoscience, we are also constructing accounts of practices, artifacts, and institutions, and these accounts do not simply function as *neutral* objective histories. Instead, the accounts we give are always already in the service of fostering and aiming to fulfill particular social, political, and economic ends.

SECTION 3. EPISTEMOLOGICAL ASSUMPTIONS

What I hope has become clear at this point is that both Ihde's and Haraway's methods differ radically. While Ihde's method of investigation is a fixed phenomenological approach, taking the human (body) / technology relation as its primary phenomenon of investigation, Haraway's method or approach, broader in scope, focuses upon the many relationships and social forces which contribute to the production, installation, and proliferation of the artifacts, practices, and institutions of the technological, scientific field of technoscience. To tease out these differences, though, I would like to go a step further and borrow a few distinctions made by Richard Rorty. Though Rorty himself does not specifically focus his work on the philosophy of technology or technoscience, he does take as one of his interests the cashing out of the epistemological assumptions held by various philosophers, theorists, and writers. Also, Rorty's method, much like the methodological spirit behind this paper, involves cashing out the implicit epistemological assumptions of a position, always in the light of a second position. The aim of this paper (which, as I have suggested, might itself be considered to be a piece of hypertext) is to link Ihde and Haraway in a useful way. To make good on this task, however, I think it is necessary to cash out what both Ihde and Haraway take themselves and their projects to be doing when they make claims about technology and how technology, in a larger context, in many cases works as an intermediary between a conception or understanding of ourselves and a conception or understanding of our environment or world. In his "Solidarity or Objectivity," Rorty makes a distinction between two principal ways in which "reflective human beings try, by placing their lives in a larger context, to give sense to those lives" (Rorty 1991, 21–34). He goes on,

> The first is by telling the story of their contribution to a community. This community may be the actual historical one in which they live, or another actual one, distant in time or place, or a quite imaginary one, consisting perhaps of a dozen heroes and heroines selected from history or fiction or both. The second way is to describe themselves as standing in immediate relation to a non-human reality. This relation is immediate in the sense that it does not derive from a relation between such a reality and their tribe, their nation, or their imagined band of comrades. I shall say that the stories of the former kind exemplify the desire for solidarity, and that stories of the later kind exemplify the desire for objectivity. (Rorty 1991, 21)

We are, Rorty claims, the heirs to the objectivist tradition. Developing the means to make the distinctions between appearance and reality, and knowledge and opinion, Plato, the father of this tradition, was the first, according to Rorty, to produce a picture of intellectual life which takes as its impetus the desire to step away from and ultimately outside of our human community in order to examine the non-human world which necessarily transcends that community. He writes, "Much of the rhetoric of contemporary intellectual life takes for granted that the goal of scientific inquiry into man is to understand 'underlying structures,' or 'culturally invariant factors,' or 'biologically determined patterns'" (Rorty 1991, 22). The second tradition, the tradition which in *its* intellectual life manifests the desire for solidarity, on the other hand, takes the project of communing with a transcendent non-human reality to be uninteresting and not a particularly useful way of going about scientific inquiry. For the pragmatists, those whom Rorty sees as motivated by the desire for solidarity, the expansion of referents, subjects, and objects in a theoretical project is of the greatest importance. He tells us, "For the pragmatists, the desire for objectivity is not the desire to escape the limitations of one's community, but simply the desire for as much intersubjective agreement as possible, the desire to extend the reference of 'us' as far as we can" (Rorty 1991, 22).

While neither Haraway's nor Ihde's projects or explorations into the realm of technoscience or the philosophy of technology can be perfectly grafted into the bifurcated framework that Rorty provides for us above, I do, nevertheless, think that his framework provides us with a helpful heuristic by means of which we can begin to cash out some of the epistemological assumptions at work in both Haraway's and Ihde's projects. In the remainder of this section I am going to provide an argument for how, by means of focusing on the epistemologies of each thinker, we might find it helpful to read Ihde as Rorty's proverbial "objectivist" and Haraway as Rorty's "pragmatist."[1]

As a phenomenologist investigating the realm of technology, Ihde, much like the Rortean objectivist, takes himself to be revealing, unconcealing, and describing a number of different types of relations humans have with technology. For the phenomenologist, Truth lies embedded within the structure of phenomena, and not merely, as for the Rortean objectivist, in the world of objects "out there." But, like the Rortean objectivist, the phenomenologist, Ihde, at least within the bounds of *Technology and the Lifeworld*, takes himself to be involved in revealing a reality, a reality of phenomena, otherwise hidden to the subject were it not for a particular methodological employment of the phenomenologist's theoretical machinery. The three structures of the human / technology relation and the context out of which they are revealed, namely an environment explored and manipulated by an embodied subject, are *quasi*-transcendental structures. I say "quasi-transcendental" here and not simply "transcendental" because the structures that Ihde takes himself to be revealing do not lie "out there" wholly independent of humans, their practices, and their communities. However, his project retains a "quasi-transcendental" status because the phenomena of these relations do still, nevertheless, reveal themselves as something more than merely products of a kind of description leveled by the phenomenological method. The phenomenologist, though somewhat reformed, still takes as his project the *discovery* of something, something independent from the kind of story he chooses to tell, something not readily apparent within the world as it is normally inhabited by himself and members of his community.

To be sure, the phenomenologist, Ihde, does not wholly fall under the description Rorty gives of the objectivist. Truths, the phenomena, the *Ding an sich*, are at least in part, for Ihde, *constituted by* the subject which experiences those phenomena. And these truths are not wholly free from cultural and historical contexts. In fact, much of Ihde's *Technology and the Lifeworld* is devoted to fleshing out what he calls a "cultural hermeneutics" (Ihde 1990, 125–161). Such a hermeneutics brings to light the way in which technologies get "embedded" into various cultures in various and sometimes quite surprising ways.[2] Furthermore, in his more recent *Expanding Hermeneutics: Visualism in Science*, Ihde explicitly addresses Rorty and his plea for a philosophical approach which is "edifying" (or takes as its impetus as the desire for solidarity) (Ihde 1998a, 113–126).

However, in both his program for a "cultural hermeneutics" and his discussion of phenomenology as "edifying," the quasi-transcendental aspect of Ihde's philosophy of technology remains present. In the first case, that of a cultural hermeneutics, the *invariant* structures revealed through the phenomenological method are still central to the analysis. While technology is embedded into different cultures in different ways, what must be noted is that it is not the phenomenologically revealed structures which change and vary from culture to culture. *Those* remain stabile, *necessarily*. It is only the ways in which these structures are inhabited which vary. Ihde writes, "I have contended that insofar as there are a limited number of types of human-technology relations following from human existential structures, *all cultures exemplify* the full range of *these* relations (*invariantly*), although the mixes are clearly highly variant" (Ihde 1990, 124). Thus, these structures are quasi-transcendental, though their application varies from culture to culture.

In the second case, in response to the imaginary, though possible, question posed by Rorty, "Is phenomenology edifying?" Ihde's position is less clear. He wants to argue against the possible Rortean position that would claim that phenomenology is "foundational" and thus a part of the objectivist desire to commune with the transcendental "out there." Yet, at the same time, Ihde wants to hold onto the view which takes phenomenology as a method of investigation which discovers "structures" and thus is more scientific than Rorty's own strand of philosophy.

> By removing both truth seeking and referentiality entirely from edifying philosophy, Rorty joins the ranks of the poststructuralists and deconstructionists who have, while genuinely creating a new type of historical and cultural "sci-

ence," also simply sidestepped the possibilities of what I prefer to call a *noematic* science. (The natural sciences, interestingly enough, come closer to this sense of phenomenological praxis—of the investigation of possible structures—than the previous human sciences) (Ihde 1998a, 126).

Ihde sees Rorty's position, which famously gives up on the idea that what we philosophers or theorists ought to be doing is looking for a theory which best hooks up with or corresponds to the world, as somehow irresponsibly "sidestepping" the possibility of a science or theory which hooks up with or corresponds to not the world, *but the phenomena of experience.* Ihde goes on to say, "If this is a vestigial 'foundationalism,' it is both oddly so, since the investigation and the horizontalization of the field of structure is neither selective (all are context relative) nor reductive (there is no 'best' or 'only' structure)" (Ihde 1998a, 126). Yet there are two problems with Ihde's position as he elaborates it. The first problem lies in his call for the possibility of the constitution of a *noematic* science. While it is true that such a science would not so much look toward bringing to light a non-human reality "out there," it would nevertheless look toward the possibility of "discovering" structures previously hidden. Such a science would see itself as revealing something which is, at least in part, "out there," namely the invariant structures of human existential experience. Rorty, in his effort to debunk the notion of a reality that is "out there," even if only in part, would necessarily reject the possibility of such a *noematic* science.

The second problem in Ihde's position lies in his defense to the possible charge that his phenomenological approach is akin to a foundationalist approach. He argues that his phenomenological approach cannot really be thought of as foundational because the discoverable structures yielded up by such an analysis are "context relative" and that there is no "only structure." There is seemingly, however, a contradiction here in Ihde's position, at least as it applies to the philosophy of technology. For, as we saw above, there are certain "only structures" of the human / technology relation. There were in fact just three particular human / technology relational structures. And, further, far from being contextually or culturally relative, they remained invariant across the gamut of actual and possible cultures.

Although Ihde's project does not wholly fit Rorty's description of an objectivist project, it does reasonably enough resemble it. While it is unclear what to make of the seeming contradiction in Ihde's self-description and his phenomenology of technology, we can be sure that Rorty would reject Ihde's call for the possibility of a *noematic* science or science of the structures of experience (Rorty 1998, 122–137, 138–152). Ihde's project, though, can be, with the help of Rorty's distinction, contrasted to Haraway's project in her *Modest Witness.* Haraway, as Rorty's "pragmatist," takes as the impetus for her theoretical work the desire for an ever-increasing "solidarity." Such an impetus in her work is clear. The artifacts, practices, and institutions of technoscience do not, in Haraway's account, exhibit any particular invariant or quasi-transcendental structures. What these artifacts, practices, and institutions do exhibit, however, is that they are, every one of them, matrices, signs of much larger semiotic-material chains of meaning which are, like tentacles, wrapped up with economic, industrial, cultural, and political aims, intents, and interests. Thus the phenomenologically revealed human / technology relation hardly seems an appropriate or, perhaps better, *adequate* model to employ. Instead, these long chains of semiotic-material meaning are traced by the figure of, as the title of her work suggests, the "modest witness."

The modest witness is, much like Ihde's "human" of the human / technology relation, always embodied. Yet, unlike Ihde's human, the modest witness is always already embodied in a *particular* body, one which is gendered, ethnically non-neutral, politically and economically motivated, socially conscious, and historically situated. Taking the term "modest witness" from Steven Shapin's and Simon Schaffer's (1985) *Leviathan and the Air-Pump: Hobbes, Boyle, and the Experimental Life*, where it serves to function as the marker for the model of the modern experimental scientist, "whose accounts mirror reality" (as Rorty would describe, whose desire is for a correspondence theory of Truth) and whose "self-invisibility is the specifically modern, European, masculine, scientific, form of the virtue of modesty," Haraway transforms, genders, and re-situates the witness in the world of technoscience at the end of the Second Millennium (Haraway 1997, 23). Haraway's "modest witness," a self-reflective witness who, rather than taking as a regulative ideal the "modest objectivity" sedimented from Enlightenment rational science, instead engenders a form of what Haraway calls "strong objectivity." Strong objectivity is a conception of objectivity that takes account not just of those categories which give shape to and ground scientific discourse, but that also takes account of the community out of which such scientific discourse and, perhaps most importantly, *research* can come forth. Whole social communities, not merely specialized individuals nor no one in particular, ought to be, according to Haraway, recognized as knowers of scientific claims. Like Rorty's analyses, Haraway's are aimed at working to increase solidarity by articulating that which counts as "we" (in this case, the "we" that is the aggregate members of the technoscientific community in question). At the same time, however, she is also engaged in a project which takes into account the differences of the individuals within the communities in question. Knowers of scientific knowledge and technological artifacts, practices, and institutions in this sense, then, are always located, situated as subjects in economic, political, social, cultural, and scientific contexts. Haraway depicts the conception of a "strong objectivity" as follows:

> Strong objectivity insists that both the objects and the subjects of knowledge-making practices must be located. Location is not a listing of adjectives or assigning of labels such as race, sex, and class. Location is the always partial, always finite, always fraught play of foreground and background, text and context, that constitutes critical inquiry. Above all, location is not self-evident or transparent. (Haraway 1997, 37)

The modest witness is not the bearer of a transcendental (nor even "quasi-transcendental") set of categories, but instead is a situated knower, in part a product of the same semiotic-material chains of meaning which run through the technological artifacts, practices, and institutions with which she deals (Haraway 1991, 183–202).

SECTION 4. HYPERTEXT: THE ENTANGLEMENT OF BODIES AND TECHNOLOGY

As a conclusion to this piece of hypertext, I would like to make a suggestion as to how we might come to see Ihde's epistemology, at least in part, despite the criticisms leveled at it above, as integral to a project like Haraway's. But first we need to take stock of where we now, in this bit of hypertext, stand. Using a rather infamous distinction originally drawn by Rorty, I have identified Ihde's phenomenologically oriented project as one which is in line with what Rorty calls the "objectivist" project, a project which takes as its impetus the desire to commune with at least a quasi-transcendental set of structures of experience which are not themselves a product of the way in which we choose to describe ourselves and the community we inhabit. I have also shown how Haraway's project can be seen as a project which is in line with what Rorty calls the "pragmatist" project, a theoretical undertaking which takes as its impetus the desire for increased solidarity with one's community directed toward fulfilling particular social, political, and economic ends. However, by totally eschewing the phenomenological model, which has as its motor or impetus the recognition of the ineluctable centrality of the body in any description of how it is that we come to know and understand the things, in this case, *technological* things, with which we deal, a project like Haraway's risks losing the ability to take account of the most prevalent aspect of our situatedness as knowers.

Recognizing the fact that all knowledge is always situated, itself embedded within long chains of semiotic-material meaning, does not occlude the recognition that human embodiment is *not* merely just another aspect of that situatedness akin to all its other aspects, e.g., social, ethnic, political, economic, etc. . . .

Our embodied condition is *the* central situation we find ourselves in as knowers of the world. We are situated *first and foremost* always *as* bodies. By not taking this centrality of body into account, Haraway risks losing this key aspect of what it is to be a human knower. The body is, for Haraway, lumped together with all the nodes of meaning, sites, and matrices of long semiotic-material strands which stretch out into the far reaches of the economy, the culture, the society, industry, the military, etc. . . . Haraway is at risk, as it were, of losing an understanding of the body's role in knowing. The body is that *from which* all descriptions of the multitude of artifacts, practices, and institutions of the technoscientific world are leveled. Maxine Sheets-Johnstone, in her "Corporeal Archetypes and Power: Preliminary Clarifications and Considerations of Sex" (Sheets-Johnstone 1998, 149–179), levels just this criticism at Haraway's project. She writes,

> It is not surprising, then, that the program of "embodied knowledges" (Haraway, 1988:583) actually takes the body itself for granted in its entire epistemological enterprise; functioning as an indexical, the body is simply the place one puts one's epistemology. While it is true that "we must be hostile to easy relativisms and holisms built out of summing and subsuming parts" (Haraway, 1988:585), we should also be wary of an "embodied objectivity" that, amid "ethnophilosophies," "heteroglossia," "deconstruction," "oppositional positioning," "local knowledges," and "webbed accounts" (Haraway, 1988:588), in truth thoroughly distances itself from the body except as an epistemological receptacle. *Unless we are wary, we will easily find ourselves distanced from the real, living body that is the very ground of our knowledge, for it lies buried at the bottom of the barrel.* (Sheets-Johnstone 1998, 149–179)

Human embodiment is not just one more node in the nexus of concepts and their relations, but rather it holds a certain primacy as that which is a common condition to all human knowers. If it is Haraway's intent to capture a conception of technology that takes as its aim a more thorough articulation of the role of technology in the form of technoscience which includes social, political, and economic aspects, then she must also demonstrate the possibility of grounding this articulation of the role of technology within an account of particular situated embodiment. In order to do this it will be necessary for Haraway to incorporate aspects of Ihde's account of a phenomenologically articulated conception of embodiment. However, to accomplish this task adequately, Haraway will have to steer between the *Scylla* of a phenomenologically articulated account of embodiment drawing on transcendental categories (*cum* Ihde) and the *Charybdis* of an account of the embodied subject of technoscience which holds that subject to be simply one possible node in the plastic matrix of technoscientific concepts. To chart this course successfully there needs to be careful dialogue between Haraway and Ihde, a dialogue for which I hope this bit of hypertext marks the first exchange.

NOTES

1. Here I am not attempting to "misread" both Ihde and Haraway into the relevant Rortean category. I hope, instead, to show while, at one level, we might be tempted to think of Ihde in terms of the Rortean "objectivist" and Haraway in terms of the Rortean "pragmatist," while on another level this distinction will not, at least completely, remain intact.

2. See for instance Ihde's example of Polynesian technological innovation in oceanic navigation (Ihde 1990, 146–151).

BIBLIOGRAPHY

Bordo, Susan. 1998. "Bringing the Body to Theory." In *Body and Flesh: A Philosophical Reader,* edited by Donn Welton. Oxford: Blackwell Publishers.

Feenberg, Andrew. 1999. *Questioning Technology.* New York: Routledge.

Haraway, Donna. 1991. *Simians, Cyborgs, and Women: The Reinvention of Nature.* New York: Routledge.

———.1997. *Modest_Witness@Second_Millennium. FemaleMan© _Meets_OncoMouse™.* New York: Routledge.

Heidegger, Martin. 1962. *Being and Time,* translated by John Macquarrie and Edward Robinson. New York: Harper and Row.

Ihde, Don. 1990. *Technology and the Lifeworld: From Garden to Earth.* Bloomington: Indiana Press.

———. 1998a. *Expanding Hermeneutics: Visualism in Science.* Evanston, Ill.: Northwestern University Press.

———. 1998b. "Bodies, Virtual Bodies, and Technology." In *Body and Flesh: A Philosophical Reader,* edited by Donn Welton. Oxford: Blackwell Publishers.

Rorty, Richard. 1991. "Solidarity or Objectivity." In *Objectivity, Relativism, and Truth.* Cambridge: Cambridge University Press.

———. 1998. "Robert Brandom on Social Practices and Representation" and "The Very Idea of Human Answerability to the World: John McDowell's Version of Empiricism." In *Truth and Progress: Philosophical Papers Volume 3.* Cambridge: Cambridge University Press.

Sheets-Johnstone, Maxine. 1998. "Corporeal Archetypes and Power: Preliminary Clarifications and Considerations of Sex." In *Body and Flesh: A Philosophical Reader,* edited by Donn Welton. Oxford: Blackwell Publishers.

Young, Iris. 1998a. "Throwing Like a Girl." In *Body and Flesh: A Philosophical Reader,* edited by Donn Welton. Oxford: Blackwell Publishers.

———. 1998b. "Throwing Like a Girl: 20 Years Later." In *Body and Flesh: A Philosophical Reader,* edited by Donn Welton. Oxford: Blackwell Publishers.

———. 1998c. "Pregnant Embodiment." In *Body and Flesh: A Philosophical Reader,* edited by Donn Welton. Oxford: Blackwell Publishers.

11. Do You Believe in Ethics? Latour and Ihde in the Trenches of the Science Wars (Or: Watch Out, Latour, Ihde's Got a Gun)

Aaron Smith

Two figures stand twenty paces apart staring silently at one another. The first one is an American phenomenologist. The other is a refugee from the science wars. Both are armed with knowledge of philosophy and a few other more mundane technical artifacts and actants.[1] The tension breaks as Ihde reaches for his gun. He draws and shoots with the experience of someone who has an embodied relation to his gun. His shot strikes Latour in the chest as Latour reaches for his non-human actant. Latour had attempted to form an actor-actant association with his gun, but this simply took too long when compared in this most concrete and potentially lethal manner to Ihde's embodied relation. Latour slumps to the ground and dies a seemingly quick and painless death.

The townspeople rush to the scene after the violent episode is over. A voice is heard coming from the back of the crowd. "Do we take him to jail?"

Another replies, "Of course we do."

The townspeople rush to take "him" to jail. Several corral Ihde. A few attempt to extract the bullet embedded in Latour. Others, assuming "him" is merely a generic description fitting all objects, grab the gun. And a couple of misguided souls grasp Latour's corpse. The townspeople look at each other with great confusion.

"Ihde just killed a man."

"But Ihde did not kill him. The bullet caused the wound that ended Latour's life. Let's take the bullet to jail."

"No, wait. The gun should go to jail because the gun is what gave the bullet the force to make the wound that ended Latour's life."

"Latour is culpable. After all, his philosophy books suggest that dead philosophers *are* responsible for the problems of the present."

Who or what is responsible for Latour's death would seem to be an easy question to answer—Ihde. Does this entail that the townspeople who thought otherwise are wrong? If we say they are wrong because the technological arti-facts in this scene have little or no importance, then we are in agreement with the dominant views in contemporary philosophical debates on ethics. Most eth-ical theories leave the status of technology and technical artifacts as neutral or playing a small, unimportant role. A deontologist, consequentialist, or a virtue theorist would argue that it just does not make sense to bring the objects into the discussion. This is not necessarily wrong or false. It follows from a key epis-temological, ontological, and metaphysical presupposition that undergirds these theories: that objects are passive and simply waiting for the subject to ma-nipulate them. Given that in challenging this assumption Latour's *Pandora's Hope* and Ihde's *Technology and the Lifeworld* focus on assessing our technolog-ical relations and not specifically on ethics, it is reasonable to wonder if we can extend their work to ethical questions.

Consider some of the very difficult ethical problems involving human tech-nological relations that are being currently debated: human cloning, how much environmental destruction can we or the earth stand, and when to employ eu-thanasia or even deciding if this practice is acceptable. These problems are hard to solve using traditional approaches based on consequentialism, deontology, or virtue theory in part because of the manner in which these problems involve technologies and because these theories often overlook the ways in which we are *involved* with technologies and artifacts (non-humans).[2] Looking closely at these ethical problems suggests first the need to examine our technological in-volvements and second that the problems themselves are products of our tech-nological involvements. Thus, to assume that the non-humans play no impor-tant role leaves us in the doubly impoverished position of being unable to either fully assess all the potentially relevant aspects of the questions or address what would be needed to answer them. Rectifying this neglect would require inquir-ing into our relationships with non-humans and grasping that *objects* are not necessarily neutral, passive things waiting to be acted upon by subjects.

Beginning from the premise that objects are not necessarily neutral, passive things changes our assumptions about what information we consider germane to ethics. Deontic, consequentialist, virtue theorist, or even Continental[3] views, are compatible with Ihde's and Latour's as long as the positions can accept the premise that objects *could* be more than neutral objects. All that Ihde and La-tour need is the admittance that these objects *could* be more than neutral. Once this is admitted, then it must be discovered what, if any, role the objects play.

While a seemingly small step, this shift in perspective is the most important aspect of their work for ethicists and it is what we will turn to next.

IHDE AND HIS GUN

Ihde emphasizes a hermeneutic and phenomenological interpretation of technologies and artifacts and their influence upon human lives. He begins with the three sorts of intentional relations that humans can have with technological artifacts—embodiment, hermeneutic, and alterity relations—and from these Ihde's ethical stance will emerge.

Ihde defines embodiment relations as "those technologies that I can so take into my experience that through their semi-transparency they allow the world to be made immediate [and] thus enter into the existential relation which constitutes my self" (Ihde 1990, 107). These are perceptual extensions of human senses (e.g., telescopes, microscopes, and eyeglasses) that in some way heighten or reduce in intensity what is experienced through them. Embodiment relations also include learned relations with objects that are incorporated into embodied physical activities (e.g., Heidegger's hammer, Merleau-Ponty's feather, Ihde's gun) (Ihde 1990, 72–80).

Those "objects" that fall under embodiment relations are extensions of human activity and as such it would not make sense to think of them as the originator of ethical actions or of possibly being held culpable for actions carried out through them. They should, however, still be seen as being a relevant part of an ethical discussion because they affect and alter the very ways we think, act, and perceive. Ihde's view is that when we look to human praxis even the most transparent of technologies shape and modify human activities and values. They are *non-neutral* artifacts because they play a role in the formation and change of human values. It might be hard to think of an artifact such as a hammer as shaping culture and values; it does, but admittedly to a small degree. Ihde's point is that as the technologies and artifacts become more complicated and less transparent (e.g., computers), their role in affecting values and cultures become greater.

Here it could be argued that Ihde's position ought to be dismissed because it extends values to "objects" and in doing so commits a category mistake. Objects can be helpful (a needle with a vaccine against polio) as well as being dangerous (the same needle infected with the AIDS virus), but in neither case does the object have an ethical property in and for itself. The needle is neutral. It is the human valuation of the AIDS virus as bad and the vaccine as good that gives the needle the false appearance of being non-neutral. To suggest that an object is non-neutral entails that it has some sort of value. Ihde commits a category mistake. To go further, what Ihde should have said is that an object can only have a value given by humans and that this object has no value in and of itself.

But such an objection misunderstands the nature of Ihde's claim and much of the research from phenomenology and hermeneutics in the last hundred years. This tells us that humans are always in relation to and with technologies and artifacts, and these in turn alter human praxis. To claim that they are non-neutral is to remove the seemingly passive status that technologies and artifacts are assigned by more traditional views and not to commit a category mistake.

The second type of relations are hermeneutic ones, and these are "relation[s] with technologies that both mediate and yet also fulfill my perceptual and bodily relation[s] with technologies" (Ihde 1990, 107). Ihde emphasizes that these are intentional objects of perception (e.g., a thermometer, a navigation chart, the infrared scope attached to Ihde's gun). They also refer to the world in some manner (the thermometer responds to the temperature of its surroundings and reports this information through mercury levels rising or falling). To use these technologies entails having to learn to *read* them (the mercury level in a thermometer rises is not useful information unless one has learned to translate these levels into a temperature scale). After one learns how to properly *read* these technologies, they can substantially alter perceptions of one's environment (e.g., thinking of how warm or cold an environment is in terms of a Fahrenheit scale). These objects still give us a direct relation to the surroundings (e.g., the temperature or the landscape seen in infrared), but they lack the perceptual transparency that was part of the embodiment relations. Again we would be hard-pressed to consider these technologies as the originators of ethical actions. It is easier to grasp that these objects are non-neutral. They alter our interactions with and understanding of our world to a much greater degree then embodied relations, thus affecting human praxis to a significantly greater degree (Ihde 1990, 80–97).

The third set of relations are alterity relations, "in which the technology becomes quasi-other, or technology 'as' other *to* which I relate" (Ihde 1990, 107). These technologies are technologies that one relates to as such. They are much closer to being the originator of ethical actions as they have a quasi-autonomy to which we relate (e.g., a religious idol or an anthropomorphized sports car). He emphasizes that we relate *to* and *with* these in ways that set them distinctly apart from the other types of relations. They do not reach the full sense of Levinasian *otherness*, which would give them status as moral agents, because they are not fully independent. Even though Ihde is very careful not to ascribe to technologies the same status as humans and animals, in part because these machines lack the decisional ability that humans and animals have, he implies that ethical culpability could be attributed to those which do fulfill the status of *Other*. This would mean that if there were a computer capable of true independent thought and action, then it would qualify as true *Other* in the full and rich Levinasian sense (Ihde 1990, 97–107).

Using these intentional relations as a springboard, Ihde goes on to address many of the ways in which technology has been falsely characterized. He shows that our involvements are somewhere between complete human control of technology and humans being controlled by technology. He argues that almost every human practice has its associated technologies and these affect human actions, human cultures, and human histories. While this may not seem revolutionary, it offers a way of understanding our relations to and with technology and technological artifacts that reveals how deeply intertwined our lives are with technology. This knowledge makes it possible to make much more informed ethical decisions based on our enriched understanding of the three types of intentional relations Ihde describes.

There are a variety of current debates regarding technology and technological artifacts that would benefit from Ihde's approach. For example, those living in countries with access to "state of the art" medical techniques are often confronted with the problem of deciding when someone is dead. Due to medical technology, we now have the possibility of a "brain-dead" person still giving other signs of life. How do we make the best possible decision regarding this person? This is a difficult ethical question that has emerged from our involvements with technologies that have changed how we think of death and dying. A great wealth of information is contained within this nexus of practices that is often concealed when we think of the technologies as neutral or of little importance. In the case of a "brain-dead" individual, a large number of technological relations and artifacts—ranging from monitors informing a member of the medical staff of the lack of brain activity, to respirators, to intravenous feeding tubes—are involved. It would be hard to claim that these are irrelevant to the decision-making process regarding this person. We may consider quality of life, the possibility that the patient will recover, or a host of other questions in attempting to make the most informed decision. The one thing that we should not neglect is the technologies and the technological artifacts that make this situation possible because they affect and alter our practices. If we are looking at an ethical problem being raised by a new technological trajectory, then it only makes sense to fully examine our relationships with these technologies and artifacts so that we can make the best possible decisions armed with as much information as possible (Ihde 1990, 182).

LATOUR'S CORPSE AND THE PROBLEM OF INTENTIONALITY

Latour would agree with much of Ihde's work clarifying the nature of human intentional relations and would find it to be a useful, but ultimately limited, method of analysis. For Latour, phenomenology is a mistaken enterprise from the very beginning, especially when it comes to addressing the technological relations involved in science. He tells us:

> Phenomenology deals only with the world-for-a-human-consciousness. It will teach us a lot about how we never distance ourselves from what we see, how we never gaze at a distant spectacle, how we are always immersed in the world's rich and lived texture, but alas, this knowledge will be of no use in accounting for how things really are, since we will never be able to escape from the narrow focus of human intentionality. Instead of exploring the ways we can shift from standpoint to standpoint, we will always be fastened down into the human one. . . . Phenomenology leaves us with the most dramatic split in this whole sad story: a world of science left entirely to itself, entirely cold, absolutely inhuman; and a rich lived world of intentional stances entirely limited to humans, absolutely divorced from what things are in and for themselves. (Latour 1999, 9)

It is true that phenomenologists accept the necessity of a human intentional stance as the beginning point of inquiry. But phenomenology does not abandon the sciences or technological relations as beyond the possibility of human perspective; rather it suggests that in any study of science or technology, human intentionality is implicit and must be considered. Latour makes a strong case that the removal of science to a realm of its own is undesirable, but because many phenomenologists take this into account, Latour's rejection of phenomenology purely on these grounds is not enough. Phenomenology does, however, seem guilty of never being able to remove itself from being entrenched in a human perspective, but this does not necessarily jettison science to the dark side of a "human world"/"real world for science" division. Instead, many phenomenologists would claim, much as Latour does, that what one experiences is always the "real world" and that even though one is a human experiencing the world, the world experienced is the real world. Presumably, this would be enough to provide the grounding that Latour wants to give the sciences.

To be fair to Latour, important critiques of phenomenology have asserted that it just rehashes old epistemological, ontological, and metaphysical themes without offering us anything more then a slightly different methodology. To the contrary, Latour could cite this literature critiquing Husserl and other phenomenologists for simply replacing the subject-object split on a pre-conscious level with the *noesis-noema* split. But if he were to take the approach that Husserl has not really escaped from the subject-object split, it would seem that he would open himself up to the same challenge regarding his human–non-human split. He could respond that he offers a framework the goal of which is to avoid these old dichotomies, but then again so would Husserl's supporters. Where Latour could make headway is by holding tightly to his claims against phenomenology for being handcuffed to a human perspective.

LATOUR'S ASSOCIATION WITH AN ACTANT

Turning away from the specifics of Latour's critique of phenomenology, we find him engaged in a project that critiques epistemology, politics, ontology, and metaphysics. It is much more ambitious in scope than Ihde's clarification of technological relations with artifacts. To pose a question similar to the one that launched *Pandora's Hope* of whether or not he "believes in ethics," we can suppose that Latour would respond in a similar fashion because the question forces him to choose a side in a battle that he is not interested in fighting. He argues that to reject the either/or of what he calls "realism" and "relativism" is possible, though a difficult task because it requires questioning almost all of modern philosophy. He wants to take up a position somewhere between the realists on one side and the post-modern relativists on the other. He begins this project by detailing that human and non-human relations do not entail many of the positions in modern philosophy. Latour's critique of modernist epistemology, ontology, and metaphysics opens the door to the development of an ethical stance. His attempt to avoid the either/or of relativism/realism through providing a positive alternative to many of the concepts from modern philosophy can be applied to a similar either/or in ethics. Specifically, Latour's analysis of human–non-human relations allows us to generate an ethical position that addresses actions that are the products of large-scale systems.

First, to clarify a bit of terminology: "Non-human" is the term that Latour uses to replace "object" as well as to widen its scope. It is a "concept that has meaning only in the difference between the pair 'human-nonhuman' and the subject-object dichotomy [and] is not a way to 'overcome' the subject-object distinction but a way to bypass it entirely" (Latour 1999, 308). It has a very wide reference, referring, literally, to that which is non-human.

Latour employs the terms "actor" and "actant" to designate an active participant in an association. Humans are the actors, but not all non-humans are actants. Latour's view is that non-humans often have active roles (he even suggests that "actant" is an appropriate substitution for agent!) and using "actant" gives voice to these entities that have been denied having an important role in philosophy and science (Latour 1999, 181). He employs these terms in part to avoid the restricted roles for subjects and objects that suggest that objects are passive things for human subjects to use (Latour 1999, 303).

An "association" is literally a connection between actors and actants that brings the relationships between these to the fore (Latour 1999, 303–304). Mediate "means an event or an actor that cannot be exactly defined by its input and output" (Latour 1999, 307). Finally, a "collective":

unlike society, which is an artifact imposed by the modernist settlement, this terms refers to the associations of humans and nonhumans. While a division between nature and society renders invisible the political process by which the cosmos is collected in one livable whole, the word 'collective' makes this process central. (Latour 1999, 304)

Latour uses this technical vocabulary to help reveal that the ways we normally characterize our relationships to non-humans are inadequate to our real experiences and relations with them. He argues that thinking in terms of subjects as agents and objects as things that are manipulated by agents does not allow us to understand how human and non-human interactions actually work. He calls these actor-actant to avoid the limiting terminology of subject-object. This brings to light many unforeseen and important mediations that have been overlooked because modernist philosophical frameworks have blinded us to them.

There are many similarities between Latour's and Ihde's views regarding the need to rethink "subject-object" relations. Latour's view, however, does not develop in nearly the same depth the direct personal relations with artifacts that Ihde's does. Instead, Latour's project could be seen as picking up where Ihde's ends because it emphasizes systems of relations. By distributing potential responsibility across the actor-actant spectrum, Latour's work becomes an effective way of dealing with questions that do not fit within an intentional analysis.

Going back to the opening example when we place Ihde, Latour, and the guns in Latourian terms, we have two actors in associations with many different actants. One actor-actant association acts and the other actor-actant association falls to the ground.[4] How can any member of the actor-actant association of Ihde, bullet, and gun be held culpable in a way that would allow us to avoid putting all of them on trial? How could we suggest that Ihde was more culpable than the bullet or the gun itself (it does seem unavoidable to ask this question)?

Referring to an example similar to the one with which I began, Latour states:

"actor-actant" symmetry force[s] us to abandon the subject-object dichotomy, a distinction that prevents the understanding of the actual operation of human-technological associations. It is neither people nor guns that kill. Responsibility for actions must be shared among the various actants. (Latour 1999, 180)

While tempting to interpret Latour as implying that neither Ihde nor the bullet is responsible, this would be an obvious misreading of his work, especially when "the prime mover of an action becomes a new, distributed, and nested series of practices whose sum may be possible to add up but only if we respect the mediating role of all the actants mobilized in the series" (Latour 1999, 181). Arguing that responsibility must be shared entails that first we must look across the entire actor-actant spectrum. On the basis of this move we can assign culpability through locating the prime mover, thus bringing non-humans into ethical discussions. Instead of assigning culpability directly to Ihde as the subject and ignoring the role of the gun and the bullet as objects, Latour places culpability on the Ihde-gun-bullet association. This may appear to have the same result as stating that Ihde is guilty. Instead, it is a subtle shift in characterizing relations with non-humans because it approaches these questions with a different methodology. This will pay dividends for us when the associations become much more complex and the technologies more opaque.

The idea that there is a prime mover behind the actions expands our understanding of ethical responsibility further to "things" that are not normally viewed as potential bearers of ethical responsibility. Latour argues that we have to distribute potential responsibility to the actants in the association so that we can see their respective roles and mediations clearly. Accepting this point still leaves us wondering what actor or actant could be assigned the role of prime mover? In our example, finding the prime mover would mean considering the Ihde-gun-bullet association and from this group finding the culpable party. Why can we say that Ihde is the prime mover? We can make a distinction by using one of most basic foundations of ethics, between actions that are willfully chosen and ones that are not. Ethically we want to hold Ihde responsible for his actions because he *chose* that action. He had the choice of whether or not to pull the trigger. We can easily exclude the gun, the bullet, and the other actants because they were not able to make choices about their actions in this association. They responded as we would have expected in following causal laws.

The objection could be raised that according to "willful choice" Ihde was no more responsible than the actors and actants that have not been mentioned (e.g., the human that designed the gun). To continue the objection, even if we are only potentially distributing culpability to actors and actants as a way of seeing their involvement, it is difficult to determine which actor among the multitude from Ihde to the gun designer is culpable. Presumably the gun designer *chose* to make money selling weapons to philosophy professors, but does that mean that the designer is also culpable for Latour's death? Latour could respond that just as the bullet is not responsible to the same degree as Ihde, the gun designer can also be absolved. We have to give *potential* responsibility to the actors and actants in the associations in order to respect their mediating roles, but we do not have to go to the extreme of laying culpability upon every willfully chosen action that could be brought into the discussion. In a situation where we want or need to lay culpability on some actant's shoulders one of the most important aspects is the scope of the question being asked. In our example, the question of who is culpable is obviously of small scope and we can readily find the prime mover without consulting whoever designed the gun. It is when the questions become of much larger scope (e.g., responsibility for environmental degradation) that a much larger number of actors and actants need to be considered.

Given Latour's strong position regarding "human centered" analyses in his critique of phenomenology, it is not clear that his limiting the prime mover status to human choices can be sustained. If he completely rejects the centrality of the human-centered viewpoint, then it becomes difficult to see how to interpret his work. The consequences of rejecting the limitation of prime mover status to humans would be to take the implausible position of attributing prime mover status to non-humans such as automatic doors, guns, automobiles, and atomic reactors. But if Latour were to make a slightly weaker claim and if he were willing to cede the "prime mover" to human actions or decisions, then this extension of his work would have something to offer us. The weaker claim still brings the non-human actants into the discussion as being held responsible as part of an association, but leaves ethical culpability as "prime movers" to humans. If he does hold to a claim that non-humans such as doors, cars, and the like should be thought of as prime movers *and* ethically accountable, which is what his critique of phenomenology would entail, then this is a place where most of us would step off of the Latourian bus and join the physicists in the picket lines. Given that Latour's goal is to give "voice" to the actants in the situation in order to change our understanding of them and our relations to them, it would seem that he would be willing to make the weaker claim.

LATOUR, IHDE, AND THE SMOKING ACTANT

The Latour, Ihde, and gun example was relatively simplistic because it portrayed one person committing an obviously criminal act. Furthermore, the example displays definitive culpability. The example allowed us to see in greater clarity the roles of the technologies and actants present. It also seemed to privilege Ihde's approach because it focused upon intentional relations. There are other cases in which culpability is much harder to locate, but can potentially be accounted for in terms of actor-actant associations.

Take for example the atomic bomb dropped on Hiroshima. Who or what is (are) responsible for the deaths of the Japanese, the poisoning of the landscape with radiation, and the destruction of a city? Harry Truman? The pilot? The bomb? The scientists who created the theory that allowed the atomic bomb to be built? The engineers who designed it? The mechanic who loaded the bomb? The person who mined the uranium? The Japanese generals for invading China? It is not so obvious where we could find those culpable. To look for culpability solely in terms of human choices in the dropping of the bomb leaves very few sources (e.g., Harry Truman or the pilot) and neglects the large number of actors and actants (e.g., the scientists, the bomb builders, etc.) that were also involved. In this context, Latour's approach is a starting point for addressing culpability. It gives the different actants in the situation an interconnected life and does not isolate the politics, the physics, or the engineering aspects from one another. This diffusing of potential responsibility across the human–non-human spectrum allows many humans and non-humans to be considered. This is a case where there is no prime mover to be found and where it would be impossible to assign culpability, but to arrive at such a decision requires an analysis that brings both humans and non-humans into the discussion.

Another more recent example is liability claims for the health problems of smokers. In the United States, the way that culpability was assigned to the tobacco companies operated according to Latour's model and suggests how we might begin to apply his work to issues involving ethical culpability. First, health problems from smoking were not considered (to be in existence) before our medical technologies and science changed our understanding of the relationship between smoking and health. A standard claim of assigning culpability failed for many years because there was not a single individual responsible for the health problems of the smokers. Assigning culpability purely in terms of the personal choices made by the smokers allowed the tobacco companies to be found not culpable because the individuals claiming ill effects from smoking chose to smoke even after warning labels were attached to cigarette packages. This is a case where thinking in deontological, consequentialist, or even intentional terms did not get very far because the problem was hidden among a very complex group of entities. It was only after the American legal system began to think of the corporations, the farmers, the tobacco plants, the chemicals added to the tobacco, the smokers, and the state health care systems in what can be described as a rudimentary Latourian framework with actors-actants playing different roles that progress was made in assigning culpability.

The Latourian analysis is useful because it helps us sift through the multiple layers of non-human activity to discover the actors. It is when we consider cases where there is not a human prime mover to be found culpable that the Latourian analysis reaches its explanatory apex. For example, take the environmental degradation of air quality. This is a question with an enormous number of actors and actants. Whether it is humans herding cattle earning subsistence wages, a diligent student using public transportation commuting to a university library, a scientist flying in a plane to the Antarctic to research the degradation of the ozone layer—seemingly everyone acts in ways that negatively affect air quality. But it is not just individuals. Companies, firms, and even nations act in ways that hurt air quality. But then we can step a bit further and suggest that volcanoes, forest fires, and cosmic radiation also affect air quality. So where do we begin to isolate the guilty actants and lay prime mover status on their shoulders? Is this not a case where spreading the culpability far and wide is a good idea? Approaching this problem only in terms of subjects and objects makes it difficult to bring the political, scientific, and philosophical aspects together and recognize that they are part of a larger whole. Worse, it denies the possibility of placing some of the responsibility on actants in the association that do not have any humans lurking behind them (e.g., a volcano).

Latour offers a new way of taking up such large complex questions that clarifies the organic relations between many disparate parts as well as opens the question of culpability to many potential sources. In many situations it is impossible to pin culpability on a single actant or actor and the only way to make sense of the situation is be to distribute potential responsibility throughout a group of actors and actants and give up our preconceived notions of humans being solely culpable. Perhaps in most situations we could conclude that the non-humans are not culpable. However, to begin with that assumption neglects any potential role that non-humans could play, discounts our relationships with the non-humans, and blinds us from seeing the deeply intertwined nature of human and non-human interactions.

There is an objection to what I have described as Latour's position. He mistakes a difference of degree for a difference in kind. There is only a difference in degree between Ihde and Philip Morris. At the root of both cases we find a human prime mover that bears culpability. It is true that when we look to very complicated situations the human prime mover is concealed and difficult to find, but it is always there. Thus, in any question regarding ethics and morality it is superfluous to consider the non-humans involved when we know that we will ultimately arrive at a human being.

This is not a devastating objection because Latour would concede that the prime mover will probably always be human in questions of ethical culpability. What is not always obvious is the status of the non-humans involved. It is only through opening up the debate to include non-humans that many of the important aspects of human and non-human relations become clear and distinct. It is especially the case when we deal with very large, complex questions regarding humans and non-humans that we need to have a much more fluid and dynamic approach than is attained via more mainstream approaches. It is when the questions of responsibility and ethics involve many more actors and actants, and the situations are not so transparent as to readily disclose the prime mover behind them, that Latour's approach reaches its full stature.

In the end it would seem that we have a whole with two distinct parts in our ethical views with regard to technology. There are personal interactions with technologies and artifacts. There are also interactions involving large numbers of actors and actants. In every situation there is an existential involvement with technologies as they implicate an individual in her life. There is also a large web of interconnected actors and actants that extends far beyond intentional relations. When we address questions of personal relations with technology, then Ihde's approach needs to be emphasized. When we look to questions of much wider scope, then we should focus upon Latour's approach. Both positions are always available to be used because both types of relations are always present. In every Latourian association there are also found intentional relations. In every Ihdean intentional analysis there are associations that extend beyond the immediate intentional.

Ihde's and Latour's respective writings definitively show that *objects* are more than passive things manipulated by subjects. They place in stark relief the multiplicity of roles that non-humans play in our lives. They reject the inherent subject-object dichotomy of modernist philosophy that forces everything to be cast into the limiting boxes of active subjects and passive objects. Whether we are Continental ethicists, analytic ethicists, or something else entirely, Latour and Ihde have given us a new perspective to understand our relations with *objects* that reveals the wealth of previously overlooked information that affects simply every aspect of our lives, especially our ethical decisions and decision-making processes.

NOTES

1. "Non-human," "actant," and "association" are technical terms used by Latour that will be defined when we turn to Latour's position.

2. When I am referring to both Ihde's and Latour's work I will use Latour's term "non-human" as shorthand to refer to Latour's "non-humans" and Ihde's "artifacts" and "technologies." These are not entirely interchangeable because they are technical terms used by Latour and Ihde; however, they are similar enough so that what is lost in precision is made up for by the substantial gains in clarity.

3. Latour and Ihde are obviously writing within the Continental tradition, and their work would generally fit with the ethical viewpoints from this tradition. For a discussion of Continental ethics, see Schroeder (2000).

4. I omitted many levels that might be of interest (e.g., gun manufacturers, engineers, etc.).

Bibliography

Ihde, Don. 1990. *Technology and the Lifeworld: From Garden to Earth*. Bloomington: Indiana University Press.
Latour, Bruno. 1999. *Pandora's Hope: Essays on the Reality of Science Studies*. Cambridge, Mass.: Harvard University Press.
Schroeder, William. 2000. "Continental Ethics." In *Blackwell Guide to Ethical Theory*, edited by Hugh LaFollette. Oxford: Blackwell Publishers.

12. Distance and Alignment: Haraway's and Latour's Nietzschean Legacies

Casper Bruun Jensen and Evan Selinger

INTRODUCTION

In this chapter we compare Donna Haraway with Bruno Latour by addressing the presence of Nietzschean themes in their works.[1] We take this to be an instance of Haraway's notion of "diffraction" in which patterns of meaning engage and interfere with each other in order for new worlds to be imagined.

In the first part of this chapter, Haraway's interpretation of the Human Genome Project (henceforth HGP) is depicted as a Nietzschean effort that deals with the social significance of metaphorical and religious imagery as it appears in scientific discourse and scientific popularizations. Her analysis suggests that religious values bolster a sensationalized understanding of scientific practice and a deified view of scientific power that leads to more authority being granted to experts than they deserve. The second part of this chapter directly compares Latour with Friedrich Nietzsche. Here we establish a connection between the two by addressing their common preoccupation with the concept of force. While both theorists maintain positions based on an ontological understanding of force, different political views are proffered due to their respective evaluations of what force is and what it can do. Nietzsche defines the philosopher's primary task as evaluating the activity and reactivity of forces, and he insists that stronger forces should be protected against weaker ones. This analysis of force leads Nietzsche to become skeptical of scientific values, and he even characterizes scientists as secular priests who ensure that society remains enslaved to nihilism. By contrast, Latour denies that forces have any inherent properties; this is why he portrays reactive ones as capable of becoming active and active ones as capable of becoming reactive. Since he depicts forces as multi-stable, Latour positively appraises scientific practice and claims that it allows human identity to be creatively reinvented.

Our chapter thus clarifies the ways in which Haraway and Latour display a certain Nietzscheanism, while also translating it to fit their particular goals. In noting this simultaneous alignment and distancing we bring Nietzschean insights into dialogue with issues facing contemporary science studies.

1. HARAWAY, NIETZSCHE, AND THE HUMAN GENOME PROJECT

The proximity of science to religion is one of the most recurring themes that Haraway explores. Other theorists typically investigate this relation by: (1) inquiring into whether scientific findings, such as evolutionary theory, agree or disagree with religious cosmology; (2) inquiring into whether religious scripture is dependent upon a particular scientific paradigm, such as a geocentric model of the universe; (3) inquiring into whether a scientist's religious or secular beliefs predisposed him or her to selectively evaluate evidence; and (4) inquiring into whether science and religion can be formally demarcated (Ruse 1988). What sets Haraway apart from her peers is that she is interested in how *religious ideals* are appropriated in putatively secular representations of technoscience (in both scholarly and popular instances). In particular, she focuses on how *salvational* and *apocalyptic* rhetoric is used to justify or thwart the pursuit of knowledge. Considering Haraway's interpretation of the HGP can concretize this point.

2. HUMAN GENOME PROJECT

Sequencing the 3.2 billion base pairs of the human genome is a considerable undertaking. It has involved numerous international collaborations, publicly and privately funded research institutes, and various debates on critical policy. This is why planners of the HGP have, since its inception, acknowledged that information acquired from mapping and sequencing the human genome would have momentous cultural as well as scientific implications. On the one hand, this information has the potential to dramatically improve human health by increasing the genetic component of scientific and medical expertise. On the other hand, the HGP raises a number of intricate ethical, legal, and social issues.[2]

Haraway contends that as a result of the complex interactions between science, technology, and culture, the social significance of the HGP cannot easily be determined. For example, historical ties link the HGP and the military-industrial complex:

> In part because of the tremendous physical computing power and human expertise that resulted from nuclear weapons research, informatics development in the U.S. Human Genome Project began under the auspices of GenBank© at the U.S. National Laboratories at Los Alamos, New Mexico. (Haraway 1997, 244)

Furthermore, scientific and lay opinions, business agendas, political ideologies, and religious outlooks all contribute to the determination of what the project is and what it is capable of doing. Due to this confluence of perspectives, public perception of the HGP is not solely derived from scientific experts; rather, it is an interpretation that is influenced by a number of non-scientific forces. Lay perception of DNA is rarely just a more down-to-earth and less technical version of scientific knowledge, but rather, extra-scientific factors powerfully buffet and even coerce lay understanding.

For example, in an effort to assure continued public funding, enhance the image of genetic research, and strengthen public confidence, genome researchers sometimes write for the popular media and give public talks. They often refer to the predictive powers of genomic research with exuberant terms such as the "Delphic oracle," "a time machine," a "trip into the future," and a "medical crystal ball" (Nelkin and Lindee 1995, 7). Haraway notes that the theme of *genetic essentialism* needs to be present in order for the predictive theme to seem plausible. Genetic essentialism is a form of determinist metaphysics that reduces human selves to molecular entities and the entire social, historical, and moral complexity of these entities to epiphenomena of genetic activity. By reinforcing the view that human behavior is directly caused by genes to the exclusion of non-genetic factors, DNA becomes highlighted as the primary explanation for how identity is constituted: "DNA in this view is a master molecule, the code of codes, the foundation of unity and diversity" (Haraway 1997, 245). This propensity is found whenever discussions of genes are used to completely explain obesity, criminality, passive and aggressive aspects of personality, intelligence, and even political leanings. Linguistically, this tendency is exemplified in the popularized "blueprint of destiny" metaphor, which, in conjunction with computer analogies that posit genes as "instructions" that follow a "program" from one generation to the next, are distributed onto selfish genes, gay genes, depression genes, genes for genius, alcoholic genes, and athletic genes. These metaphors suggest that mapping genetic sequences is equivalent to mapping geographical areas; both seemingly present objective and context-free information that can be surveyed and delineated without distortion (Haraway 1997, 131–172). Due to the prevalence of these metaphors, Haraway claims that cartographic tropes are "perhaps the chief tool-metaphor of technoscience," and that they are often used in a manner that obscures their metaphorical character (Haraway 1997, 163).

Common use gives the illusion that genetic truth is solely arrived at through objective scientific techniques and conveyed by terms that precisely express scientific information. When the metaphorical dimension of genetic discourse remains obscured, Haraway observes, a category mistake is made, an error that Alfred North Whitehead calls the fallacy of misplaced concreteness: "I ally myself with Whitehead's analysis to highlight the ways that the gene fetishist mistakes the abstraction of the gene for the concrete entities and nexuses" (Haraway 1997, 146–147).

When a popular understanding of genetics becomes inextricably connected with essentialism, then not only do *apocalyptic* narratives become commonplace, but *salvational* ones proliferate as well. Apocalyptic images are proffered by *dystopians* who believe that advances in science and technology lead to dehumanizing results. They claim that the HGP revives the question of eugenics, which is the fear that once a free-floating knowledge of the "human blueprint" is generated, it will be applied for the wrong ends. They speculate that once genetic science is perfected to the point of allowing for low risk modification, elitist ideals will prejudicially select which human characteristics are acceptable to possess. A common rhetorical locus for this apocalyptic pessimism is perceived antecedents, such as Nazi history and Aldous Huxley's novel *Brave New World,* in which government engineers eliminate individual reproductive choices in order to promote social efficiency. In the popular media, the Nash family—who recently used in vitro fertilization to give birth to a son capable of donating marrow to an ailing, older sibling—came to be depicted as engaging in laissez-faire eugenics, designing a baby for the sake of efficient and selective parts.

Salvational images are presented by *utopians* who believe that advances in science and technology will inevitably lead to the perfectibility of human society. To counter dystopian dismay, utopians insist that knowledge of the HGP is necessary for the right ends. As many critics assert, eugenics is done all the time in a weak sense and has been occurring for thousands of years. The utopian promise of the HGP is that it has the potential to dramatically improve human health. This promise is exemplified in the following maxim expressed in a recent editorial written by James Watson (who co-discovered the structure of DNA and was the first director of the HGP): "Never postpone experiments that have clearly defined future benefits for fears of dangers that cannot be quantified" (Watson 1999, 91). Watson claims that since humans know better than nature what is desirable in life, we owe it to ourselves, and future generations, to seek genetic improvement as a fundamental component of social progress.

Both salvational and apocalyptic pronouncements are *sensationalist* rhetorical styles. Sensationalist writers attempt to arouse the reader's curiosity by focusing on the novel and life-altering aspects of the HGP. Sensational reporting is found whenever epochal pronouncements are made: "Ring farewell to the century of physics, the one in which we split the atom and turned silicon into computing power. It is time to ring in the century of biotechnology" (Isaacson 1999, 42). They are also present whenever claims of unsurpassed novelty are made such that high-tech equipment is deemed obsolete in light of HGP research. For example, it is outdated to discuss the HGP as a project that can be accomplished with ordinary computers. Due to the length of time it takes to analyze even a single protein, "supercomputers" have become necessary research tools. A recent popular article begins by claiming this technology is so new that in a sense it does not even exist: "The fastest supercomputer in the world doesn't really exist. Or rather, it exists, but only in a virtual sense" (Gorman 1999, 78).

The *financial arena* is a prominent domain in which all three—essentialist, salvational, and sensationalist—representations prevail. Haraway claims that "[a]lthough biotechnology has not yet produced many successful products . . . molecular biology, including the Human Genome Project, has germinated its share of millionaire scientists" (Haraway 1997, 93). It is not only the scientists who benefited economically, but also the stakeholders who are connected with what Haraway calls "*systems of research*" (Haraway 1997, 93). It is tempting to think that monetary gain from genetic inquiry is limited to people directly involved in genetic research. Hence we expect companies who make automated genetic sequencers, such as Applera Corporation, to profit, and even anticipate moral philosophers who devote their professional time to normative issues that affect science and society to indirectly receive dividends.[3] Arthur Caplan, director of the University of Pennsylvania's Center for Bioethics, went so far as to celebrate the HGP as the "full employment act for bioethicists" (Shenk 2000, 84–90). Yet even a cursory look at investment reports from the last decade shows that lay investors, even ones who are uninformed about the technical dimensions of genetic research, made money. This is because the belief that scientific research will lead to the development of technologies that can cure previously untreatable diseases generates enough interest to create high-yield returns on genetically based stocks. The following quote from the "Money and Business" section of the *New York Times* illustrates this point.

> . . . the *joke* circulating around Wall Street not that long ago [was]: If you want to cause a buying stampede among investors, just insert the prefix "gen" into a company's name. . . . Investors saw a bright future in genomics, believing that science, which identifies the genetic roots of illness, would lead to the development of lucrative life prolonging drug. (Siwolop 2000, 8)

It is noteworthy that this narrative is framed as the circulation of a joke. Haraway emphasizes that jokes are an important dimension of popularized science: "My focus is on advertising, *joking*, and gaming dimensions of scientific portraiture and mapping" (Haraway 1997, 131). For Haraway, jokes are informative not because they are Freudian slips of the tongue that render unconscious and inappropriate thoughts explicit, but because they are "sign[s] of successful interpellation." The *Times* quote suggests that genetic research is lucrative not only for scientists and technicians whose research programs thrive, but also for lay investors who do not need to understand genetics or pharmacology. In order to become enthusiastic investors they simply need to believe that a strong causal connection exists between genetic research and the development of life-enhancing drugs such that the conviction arises that illnesses have a discernible genetic foundation that can be cured with marketable products:

> But for investors, picking apart the genomics industry can seem as complicated as picking apart the genes themselves. "A fundamental problem is that people do not understand exactly what these companies do. . . ." Dr. Martinez [an internist who is a co-manager of the Dresdner RCM Biotechnology fund]. Meirav Chovav, an analyst at Smith Barney, agreed: "what we're hearing from both institutional and individual investors is that everything is confusing in terms of what fits where." (Siwolop 2000, 8)

In short, genetic determinism is marketed as a reason for investing in biotechnology stocks since investors whose only knowledge of genetic projects comes from the popular press often uncritically accept deterministic accounts and as a result are financially rewarded. Haraway thus questions whether the tendency to make utopian claims about the HGP is simply the outcome of skewed popular reporting, because if it is then a simple solution exists: journalists need to become more scientifically literate. She contends, however, that experts whose viewpoints successfully influence public opinion also make comparable sensational claims.

Daniel Koshland, the editor of the 1990 edition of *Science* devoted to the HGP, made some comments about the HGP that left a lasting impact on the popular imagination (Koshland 1989). In his editorial, Koshland argues that money spent researching single diseases, specifically cystic fibrosis, is misallocated because the HGP will lead to multigenic diseases, such as heart disease, manic depression, Alzheimer's, and schizophrenia, being cured. Koshland further speculates that "the root of many social problems," such as homelessness, will be helped by the HGP. He even suggests the eventual screening capabilities of the HGP—to facilitate identification of those predisposed to "alcoholism, colon cancer, and depression"—will be used in the service of aiding "the poor, the infirm, the underprivileged."[4] Haraway thus claims that Koshland believes ". . . that hope for the mentally ill—and for society—lies in the high cultures of neuroscience and genetics" (Haraway 1997, 162).

Koshland's salvational and utopian interpretation of the HGP is supported by Thomas Bouchard's essay on the relation between genetics and behavior that appears in the same issue. Bouchard, a former student of Arthur Jensen, promotes the idea that a direct link exists between genetic inheritance, IQ, and race. Commenting on the social significance of this issue, Haraway claims that Bouchard influentially manipulates public debate even though he was rejected in professional circles and panned in the peer review process:

> The special gene-map issue of *Science* was the first major professional journal to publish Bouchard's controversial work, which ascribes most aspects of personality and behavior to genes. Many of Bouchard's papers had been rejected through peer review, but he brought his message successfully to the popular media anyway. Following *Science*'s publication of his study, Bouchard's ideas gained authority and prominence in public debates about genetic and behavior. (Haraway 1997, 162)

By indicating that the normative distinction between normal and pathological can be demarcated in exclusively natural terms, Koshland's editorial and Bouchard's ideas suggest that social problems, such as homelessness and poverty, are less the result of economic and social factors and more centrally behavior produced by, and deducible from, genetics. Haraway is troubled by these claims not only because consensus in the scientific literature fails to back them, but also because pharmaceutical companies who manufacture products to biologically combat mental illness and an industry of mental health experts profit when genetic discourse supplants discussion of social influences.

We began by claiming that Haraway engages in a Nietzschean project by focusing on how religious ideals are appropriated to justify or thwart the pursuit of scientific knowledge. As is well-known, Nietzsche's main genealogical claim is that complex phenomena are always overdetermined and capable of adhering to as many interpretations as there are perspectives that contribute to these. Haraway contends that the HGP is an overdetermined and complex phenomena that is constituted by multiple perspectives; scientific, lay, advertising, economic, and political perspectives all contribute to determining what the project is and what it is capable of doing. Furthermore, Nietzsche argues that styles of existence give rise to the inclination to perceive complex phenomena in particular and simplified ways. Existence is stylized through contextually sensitive processes of habituation that shape the apprenticeship of affect and intellect. According to Nietzsche, social norms and the cognitively mediating power of language retain traces of cultural-historical depth that precede and influence the singularization of any individual existence. Haraway similarly argues that genetic research and genetic narratives are framed by multiple contexts—economic, political, and recreational—that are historically rooted; these contexts and their correlate language games precede and influence empirical investigation into genetic activity. Finally, Nietzsche argues that in order to understand the prestige given to modern science, one needs to do philosophical psychology and attend to the transfer of salvational beliefs that arise in the transition from the loss of faith in a redeeming theological God to the deification of scientists, whom he refers to as the "secular priesthood." Likewise, Haraway's analysis of the HGP connects the scientific rhetoric of biological determinism to the deification of genetic research endeavors; better life through genetic manipulation is a dominant message and it overly empowers those associated with the HGP.

3. ONTOLOGY, POLITICS, AND SCIENCE IN NIETZSCHE AND LATOUR

In what follows, we aim to discern what affinities can be found when Nietzsche's philosophy and Latour's theoretical and empirical investigations are compared. To this end, we discuss the importance of ontological considerations for both thinkers, and the different perspectives on politics and science they hold. The combination of ontology, politics, and science may at first seem peculiar. However, it is important to investigate because both Nietzsche and Latour attempt to historicize ontological questions, and this common project influences how they understand the nature of technoscientific practices. We thus continue by investigating Nietzsche's and Latour's ontologies, both of which are tied to an understanding of the concept of "force."

4. FORCES

Nietzsche views force as the most basic ontological element. Subjects and objects, for example, are constituted as the result of interactions and combinations of forces. This position is remarkably similar to Latour's understanding of force according to which actors associate with each other in order to partake in network building (Lee and Brown 1994). Despite this similar conception of what force is and how it organizes the world, an important difference separates the two thinkers; Nietzsche's explicit philosophical aim is to evaluate forces, whereas Latour is often characterized as eschewing normative judgment. Nietzsche develops a test called eternal return that is designed to separate active forces from reactive ones, whereas Latour not only refrains from defining forces as solely active or reactive but further insists that they are always capable of changing their mode of expression.

In the preface to the English edition of *Nietzsche and Philosophy*, Gilles Deleuze suggests that Nietzsche's philosophy is organized along two axes, one dealing with forces and the other with ethics. Deleuze writes:

> Phenomena, things, organisms, societies, consciousness and spirits are signs, or rather symptoms, and themselves reflect states of forces. This is the origin of the conception of the philosopher as "physiologist and physician." We can

ask, for any given thing, what state of exterior and interior forces it presupposes. (Deleuze 1983, x)

Nietzsche defines the world, and the entities that populate it, as struggling forces that only temporarily balance against each other in the guise of stable forms. From this perspective, entities are composed of constellations of forces, while force itself remains irreducibly singular. On this basis Nietzsche opposes ontological interpretations found in the history of philosophy that give primacy to identity or equivalence rather than difference: "To dream of two equal forces, even if they are said to be of opposite senses is a coarse and approximate dream, a statistical dream" (Deleuze 1983, 43).

Nietzsche's most general view of the meaning of life is that it is struggle, and he arrives at this view because he understands forces as being in a state of constant tension, striving to take hold of each other. In this tension between forces, bodies—chemical, biological, social, or political—are constituted: "Being composed of a plurality of irreducible forces, the body is a multiple phenomenon, its unity is that of a multiple phenomenon, a unity of domination" (Deleuze 1983, 40). A body is best conceived as a "fruit of chance," because its capabilities are dependent on random encounters between forces; hence, we cannot know what a body is capable of doing without understanding the balance of forces of which it consists. The most important philosophical task, according to Nietzsche, is thus to evaluate the bodies that are formed in these encounters, assessing them according to their ability to affirm or negate each other.

Latour does not speak of interacting forces, but rather, he uses terms such as "actor" and "actant."[5] These resemble Nietzschean forces because they become stronger or weaker through their interactions and associations with other actors; they change their composition through what Latour calls trials of strength: "There are only trials of strength, of weakness. Or more simply, there are only trials" (Callon 1986, 200). A trial of strength takes place whenever actors encounter each other; like Nietzschean forces, actors try to accomplish specific goals and in order to pursue these ends, they have to subsume others, or at least convince them that allying is mutually beneficial. According to Latour, the ability of actors to endure strengthening and debilitating encounters with other actors is the only measure of reality.

As previously noted, Nietzsche finds the idea of equivalence to be a coarse dream; forces are characterized by their radical singularity and heterogeneity. According to Latour, however, equivalencies can be established through trials of strength since the issue of determining whether an actor can be rendered equivalent to another is not *a priori* decidable but something that needs to be tested in practice. Expressing this point, Latour writes, "Entelechies [actors] agree about nothing and can agree about everything, for nothing is, in and of itself, either commensurable or incommensurable" (Latour 1988a, 163). Whether it is possible to achieve commensurability, which is to say, to construct identities, can only be determined in concrete trials among actors, and should thus not be judged in the abstract. This is an important point for Latour to consider because the work required to redefine other actors so that they become commensurable with oneself is always undermined in practice. When actors test each other in trials of strength, they are inevitably slightly taken over by the process, which is why encounters between actors always yield many uncontrollable side effects: "Since nothing is, in and of itself, either equivalent, or not equivalent (1.2.1), two forces cannot associate without misunderstanding" (Latour 1988a, 168).

5. EVALUATION

According to Deleuze, the second axis of Nietzsche's philosophy "is concerned with power and forms an ethics and an ontology" (Deleuze 1983, x–xi). The point of this ethics is to become capable of evaluating forces by deciphering the sense and value of the perspectives expressed in them. This is not simply a matter of developing an especially acute critical ability, for in Nietzsche's view criticism is itself a reactive endeavor and part of a problem that needs to be solved. As Deleuze writes, Nietzsche "denounces our deplorable mania for accusing, for seeking out those responsible outside, or even inside, ourselves" (Deleuze 1983, 22).

Nietzsche proposes that each force has different vectors of attraction, or "wills," that draw them toward some forces and make others repulsive.[6] In spite of the irreducible singularity that is implied in this view, he nevertheless hypothesizes that there are two basic ways in which forces can associate, an active and a reactive mode. Deleuze sums up these opposing tendencies with two slightly different formulae that specify how active and reactive forces engage with each other: "I am good therefore you are evil"—"You are evil therefore I am good" (Deleuze 1983, 119). In the first formulation, an active force expresses itself through self-affirmation, which is to say by first constituting its own identity and then subsequently downgrading other non-resembling forces. By contrast, in the second formulation, the expressiveness of a force is enabled by its negative judgment of other forces; without an opposing and hostile force to compare itself with, this reactive judgment would not be possible. Thus, forces are affirmative insofar as they will their own expression and singularization, whereas they are reactive if they strive to subsume other forces and limit their capabilities.

Nietzsche depicts reactive forces as always prevailing, but he notes that in doing so they remain reactive.[7] They prevail because they prevent active forces from expressing their strength, and through this inhibition, active forces are co-opted and rendered reactive. This is the reason why Nietzsche wants to always defend stronger against weaker forces:

> We have said that active forces are the superior, dominant and strongest forces. But inferior forces can prevail without ceasing to be inferior in quantity and reactive in quality, without ceasing to be slaves in this sense. . . . The strong always have to be defended against the weak. (Deleuze 1983, 58)

In this paradoxical formulation, strength is not a matter of brute physical power. Such a conception of power refers to situations in which forces relate in an inexpressive way, since one merely oppresses the other. This mode of engagement is clearly reactive as it seeks to diminish the capabilities of other forces without becoming more expressive as a consequence. Contrarily, active forces work to attain new levels of expression by entering into compositions with different entities in order to experiment with new forms of existence and new ways of life. The philosopher's job is thus to ensure that this experimentation is not hindered by reactive forces. Nietzsche's philosophical weapon in this battle against reactivity is the test of eternal return. Eternal return is a mechanism of selection that enables one to determine whether a given force or a composition of forces is suitable to reproduce itself. Deleuze writes:

> The eternal return gives the will a rule as rigorous as the Kantian one. We have noted that the eternal return, as a physical doctrine, was the new formulation of the speculative synthesis. As an ethical thought the eternal return, as a physical doctrine is the new formulation of the practical synthesis: *whatever you will, will it in such a way that you also will its eternal return.* (Deleuze 1983, 68)

Eternal return is, therefore, "an answer to the problem of passage" (Deleuze 1983, 48). But the paradox of the eternal return is that in spite of its name, nothing can repeat itself in exactly the same way due to the continual chance encounters between forces. As Deleuze puts it, the idea of the test presupposes "a critique of the terminal or equilibrium state" (Deleuze 1983, 47). Hence, the test ensures not the identity but the differential capability of the forces that pass it; it sorts out the reactive forces that are unable to bear continual transformation. Active forces, on the other hand, willingly transform by entering into new compositions with other forces, as they attempt to become more expressive. For this reason, they are able to eternally return in new guises. In this sense, eternal return accomplishes a trans-valuation of the ontological primacy of identity.[8]

However, according to Latour, the philosopher's primary goal is not the evaluation of forces. He proposes instead that we redescribe worldly and technoscientific processes in less reductionist ways (Latour 1988b). From a Latourian perspective, only the concrete relations between actors determine how activity and reactivity is distributed, and he is therefore interested in accounting for the interactions between actors on their own terms. Only by first redescribing the relationships between forces in their own language is it possible to truly become able to evaluate their propensities and capabilities. Hence, we are urged to "follow the actors" whether they are human or non-human (Latour 1987).

6. MIGHT AND RIGHT

In the last two sections we discussed Nietzsche and Latour's theories of force. Both attempt to reverse classical approaches to ontology by viewing becoming as primary and being merely as a temporary balance between forces. While this discussion may appear esoteric, it is important for understanding how politics and science relate. In order to clarify this point, we turn to Plato's *Gorgias* dialogue. In *Nietzsche and Philosophy*, Deleuze compares Nietzsche with one of Socrates' interlocutors, the Sophist Callicles, and in *Pandora's Hope*, Latour devotes two chapters to analyzing the political implications of this dialogue for "the invention of the science wars" (Latour 1999, 216–236).

The dialogue is about how to properly organize political life in Athens. Socrates debates this issue with three famous Sophists, Gorgias, Polus, and Callicles, and Plato leaves the reader with the impression that he defeats all of them. Deleuze, however, does not interpret the dialogue as indicating Socrates' triumph:

> Callicles strives to distinguish nature and law. Everything that separates a force from that it can do he calls law. Law, in this sense, expresses the triumph of the weak over the strong. Nietzsche adds: the triumph of reaction over action. Indeed, everything which separates a force is reactive as the state of the force is separated from what it can do. Every force which goes to the limit of its power is, on the contrary, active. It is not a law that every force goes to the limit, it is even the opposite of law. Socrates replies to Callicles that there is no way of distinguishing nature and law; for the weak can only prevail if, by banding together, they can form a stronger force than the strong. Law triumphs from the point of view of nature itself. (Deleuze 1983, 58–59)

In Deleuze's interpretation, rather than complain that he is being willfully misunderstood, Callicles continues the argument by pursuing an another angle:

> The slave does not stop being a slave by being triumphant; when the weak triumph it is not by forming a greater force but by separating force from what it can do. Force must not be compared abstractly; from the point of view of nature concrete force is that which goes to its ultimate consequences, to the limit of power or desire. Socrates objects a second time: "what matters for you Callicles is pleasure. . . . you define all good in terms of pleasure." (Deleuze 1983, 59)

Since the pattern of refutation repeats itself, Callicles eventually decides to discontinue the conversation; this is not because he is defeated but because of the realization that Socrates cannot or will not understand him. When Callicles stops talking, in other words, it is to protect himself against Socrates' reactive force.[9] Deleuze thus depicts Callicles as an exemplary Nietzschean figure: "The resemblance is so striking that it seems to us that Nietzsche is close to Callicles and that Callicles is immediately completed by Nietzsche" (Deleuze 1983, 58). Latour also notes this similarity, but in his hands, it is interpreted as unfortunate:

> Others, like Nietzsche, have shamelessly accepted Callicles' position and claimed, against the degenerate and moralistic Socrates, that only violence could bend both the mob and its retinue of priests and other men of *ressentiment*. . . . None of these critiques, however, has disputed *simultaneously* the definition of science *and* the definition of the body politic that it implies. Inhumanity is accepted in both or at least in one of them. Only the connection between the two, or its expediency, has been disputed. (Latour 1999, 217–218)

According to Latour, the most striking feature of the dialogue is that despite surface quibbles, Socrates and Callicles agree on almost everything. In particular he suggests that they agree on the aim of their conversation, which is to silence the mob of the *agora* as effectively as possible. From this perspective, the dialogue functions as a contest of finding the best political weapon to use against the Athenian population. Callicles' weapon is rhetorical prowess and his powerful use of language makes him so strong that he can induce sick people to take medicine when doctors have failed to convince them. This ability makes him naturally superior to the ten thousand fools of the agora. Socrates' ability is quite different; it is based in the knowledge of geometrical equality (*geometrias gar ameleis*) and he uses it for the same purpose as the Sophists:

> The trouble, Polus, is that you're trying to use on me the kind of rhetorical refutation, which *people in lawcourts* think is successful. There too, you see, people think they're proving the other side wrong if they produce a *large number of eminent witnesses* in support of the points they're making, but their opponent comes up with only a *single witness* or none at all. This kind of refutation, however, is completely *worthless* in the *context of truth*, since it's perfectly possible for someone to be defeated in court by a *horde of witnesses* with no more than apparent respectability who all testify falsely against him. (Latour 1999, 224)

Latour characterizes the result of the dialogue as Socrates and Callicles' settlement. In his analysis, neither combatant is able to deal with the felicitous conditions of political decision making: one must take everything and everyone into account in real time, living with all the insecurity this entails. Latour thus views the dialogue as a settlement designed to exclude the majority of the population from due political process. He proposes that in order to re-invent politics it is necessary to suspend belief in this settlement and its distribution: truth cannot be equated with science (geometrical equality) and power cannot be equated with politics. In our time, this way of conceptualizing the relationship between truth and power has become almost universal; prior to Socrates and Callicles' settlement, many other possibilities existed.

In short, Nietzsche would prefer Callicles to be protected against the mob, whereas Latour would prefer to let the mob in as active participants in the debates on what sorts of politics and sciences are desirable. According to Nietzsche, the mob is inherently reactive, whereas for Latour, the mob is inherently unpredictable and we cannot even determine its composition in advance of investigations of real-time practices. But in order to pinpoint the differences between Nietzsche and Latour, the question concerning the nature of science needs to be raised.

From a Nietzschean perspective, an active science has three aspects: (1) it is a *symptomatology* because it interprets phenomena through the sense given in the forces that compose them; (2) it is a *typology* because it filters forces according to their activity and reactivity; and (3) it is a *genealogy* that determines the nobility or baseness, positivity or negativity of the internal element of force, which he calls the will (Deleuze 1983, 75). According to Nietzsche, we are "not yet thinking" as long as we are unable to carry out this threefold analysis, which is why he views the science pursued by his contemporaries as nihilistic. He thought that the science of his day was utilitarian and egalitarian because it tried to equalize forces rather than aid them to express themselves in a more powerful manner:

> This is why his whole critique operates on three levels; against logical identity, against mathematical equality and against physical equilibrium. *Against the three forms of the undifferentiated.* According to Nietzsche science will inevitably fall short of and endanger the true theory of force. (Deleuze 1983, 45)

This perspective contrasts with the Latourian view that nothing is *a priori* equal or unequal to anything else, but rather is constructed through practice. Latour's refusal to hold a normative position affects his view of science. First, it leads him to suggest that it is impossible for us to evaluate scientific programs or projects on a general level. Instead, we should make specific empirical studies in order to discern the concrete reasons why a specific composition of forces is active or reactive. To this end, we have to closely monitor the actors and describe their local means of associating and negotiating, agreeing and disagreeing. From this perspective, the Nietzschean idea that scientists are primarily trying to achieve logical identity, mathematical equality, or physical equilibrium is problematic. The problem stems from the human-centered assumption that scientists can achieve these goals unhindered by resistances stemming from the non-human actors that would disagree with these aims. Latour thus contends that science is a collective experiment composed of human and non-human forces and not the unilateral imposition of one upon the other. The analysis of Louis Pasteur's invention of pasteurization, for instance, leads Latour to propose reciprocity between the participants: "Who is the active force in this experiment? Both Pasteur *and* his yeast. More precisely, Pasteur acts *so that* the yeast acts alone" (Latour 1999, 129). In this formulation, science is a drama where increasing amounts and kinds of forces are made to bear upon each other and redefine each other in the process. Good science is about constructing highly specific settings, where heterogeneous actors encounter each other in such a way that all become more expressive and, consequently, act more interestingly. It is hard not to think of this as an entirely active understanding.

The way science is articulated, according to Latour, can only be determined through immersion in the empirical details of the laboratory, and through closely describing the many ways in which scientists relate forces that were previously unconnected. This vision of an articulated science bears a profound resemblance to the affirmation of active forces that Nietzsche was after. Well-articulated science allows human and non-human actors to engage in novel compositions and to reach new levels of expressiveness and creativity. Latour views the continual inclusion of actors into scientific networks as an important way of constructing novelty. Novelty emerges from the tension of innumerable, heterogeneous actors who negotiate their differences, expand their alliances, and continually redefine who they are and what they can do. The sciences do not need philosophers to abstractly judge their activity or reactivity since this is always a local, empirical problem to be solved. The Latourian perspective, however, does not necessarily undermine the Nietzschean view; rather, Latour develops Nietzsche's philosophical program in a subtle and differentiated way. According to Latour, science is an articulation-oriented enterprise; it constructs situations where interactions between humans and non-humans enable a creative expansion of the multiple ways in which they express themselves. This view explicates processes of becoming active in technoscience and seems to us to meet the test of the eternal return.

7. CONCLUSION

In this chapter, we highlighted affinities and differences between Haraway and Nietzsche and Latour and Nietzsche. Haraway's Nietzscheanism manifests itself through her appraisal of religious imagery in science and its popular versions. But unlike Nietzsche, her understanding of the irreducible metaphoricity of science does not lead her to criticize science as predominantly ascetic; rather, it offers new tools for understanding science as a part of a wider cultural arena. Latour's Nietzscheanism displays itself in his development of an ontology of forces. Unlike Nietzsche, Latour does not judge the forces of science to be inherently reactive; rather, he finds them to be vital components of technoscientific society. What attract Haraway and Latour to Nietzsche is his sensitivity to relationships, genealogies, and the blurred boundary between metaphor and lived reality. What worries both thinkers is Nietzsche's designation of science as reactive. According to both Haraway and Latour, science is inherently plural, both active and reactive, which is why, contra Nietzsche, we should not evaluate it as if it were a single force with a single will.

Nietzsche's project of evaluation is relevant because symptomatology, typology, and genealogy need to be further extended to the philosophy of science. Traditional philosophy of science is narrowly prescriptive; its goal is to contribute to a better understanding of how scientists should go about improving the ways they think about and do science. The result of this aim is the production of a series of dichotomies: prescription versus description, normative versus empirical, and necessary versus contingent. These are some of the dichotomies Nietzsche attempted to overcome by introducing the genealogical method to the prescriptive domain of ethics. The contemporary relevance of this project is made visible in the way Haraway and Latour constructively develop many of these themes. Our hope is that an appreciation of these projects can mediate a constructive encounter between science studies and philosophy of science.

NOTES

1. Our perspective on Nietzsche is based on the interpretation advanced by Gilles Deleuze (1983).

2. Five percent of the project's funds ($100 million over fifteen years) is dedicated to ethical and social research.

3. One might also be tempted to think that financial gain does not influence scientific research. This is false, because profit has been a motive in the cease-fire between Francis Collins, director of the HGP, and Craig Venter. After a joint declaration by President Bill Clinton and Prime Minister Tony Blair in March that all genomic information should be free, the value of Celera stock plummeted from $189 a share to $149.25.

4. See also Lewontin (1993),

5. For Bruno Latour and Michel Callon, it is uncertain who or what will turn out to be active entities. This complicates the question of what terms could or should be used in analyses. As Callon writes, "We know that the ingredients of controversies are a mixture of considerations concerning both Society and Nature. For this reason we require the observer to use a single repertoire when they are described. The vocabulary chosen for these descriptions and explanations can be left to the discretion of the observer. He can not simply repeat the analysis suggested by the actors he is studying. However, an infinite number of repertoires is possible" (Callon 1986, 200). In practice it has proved problematic to find a word which points at the equal level of activity granted *a priori* to humans and non-humans. The term actor has often been misconstrued as implying an anthropomorphization of things, whereas the term actant enables a misconception of humans and non-humans as merely texts or narrative relations, as in semiotics.

6. Although this term is anthropomorphic and psychologistic, Nietzsche's discourse

is in fact post-human. The "will" has nothing to do with intentionality in a humanist sense, but is a vector of force that determines what composites it will be capable of entering into and whether they will strengthen or delimit its capabilities. Deleuze characterizes the relationship between a force and its will in the following way: "the victorious concept of force needs a *complement* and this complement is *internal,* an internal will. It would not be victorious without such an addition. This is because relations of forces remain indeterminate unless an element, which is capable of determining them from a double point of view, is added to force itself. Forces in relation reflect a simultaneous double genesis: the reciprocal genesis of their difference in quantity and the absolute genesis of their respective qualities. The will to power is thus added to force, but as the differential and genetic element, as the internal element of its production" (Deleuze 1983, 51).

7. Nietzsche's argument is in fact historical rather than categorical. According to Nietzsche, up to this point we have witnessed a progressive degradation of force, and a continual increase in reactivity: "Each time that Nietzsche speaks of active men, he does so with the sadness of seeing the destiny to which they are predetermined as their essential becoming: the Greek world overthrown by the theoretical man, Rome overthrown by Judea, the renaissance of the reformation" (Deleuze 1983, 167). Since Nietzsche's ontology is a historical ontology, the historical argument is, in a sense, categorical. Thus, Deleuze is able to write (without contradiction): "Nietzsche's critique is not directed against an accidental property of man, but against his very essence; it is in his essence that man is called the skin-disease of the earth" (Deleuze 1983, 167). For the very same reason, this reactivity is capable of becoming-active, and the very point of Nietzsche's development of the test of the eternal return is to enable a different movement, a reactivation of forces, which would be a change in history *and* ontology, and an overthrow of the prevalent reactive forces.

8. As Deleuze writes, "The eternal return is the being of becoming. But becoming is double: becoming-active and becoming-reactive, becoming-active of reactive forces and becoming-reactive of active forces. But only becoming-active has being; it would be contradictory for the being of becoming to be affirmed of a becoming-reactive, of a becoming that is itself nihilistic. The eternal return would become contradictory if it were the return of reactive forces. The eternal return teaches us that becoming-reactive has no being. Indeed, it also teaches us of the existence of a becoming-active. It necessarily produces a becoming-active by reproducing becoming" (Deleuze 1983, 71–72).

9. As Deleuze writes, "We can see here what happens between the sophist and the dialectician, on which side the good faith and the rigorous reasoning is. Callicles is aggressive but has no ressentiment. He prefers to give up talking because it is clear that Socrates does not understand the first time and the second time speaks of something else" (Deleuze 1983, 59).

Bibliography

Callon, Michael. 1986. "Some Elements of a Sociology of Translation: Domestication of the Scallops and the Fishermen of St. Brieuc Bay." In *Power, Action, and Belief: A New Sociology of Knowledge,* edited by John Law. London: Routledge.

Callon, Michael, and Bruno Latour. 1981. "Unscrewing the Big Leviathan—How Actors Macro- Structure Reality and How Sociologists Help Them Do It." In *Ad-*

vances in Social Theory and Methodology: Toward an Integration of Micro and Macro Sociologies, edited by Karin Knorr-Cetina and Aron Cicourel. London: Routledge.

Deleuze, Gilles. 1983. Nietzsche and Philosophy. London: The Athlone Press.

Goodeve, Thyrza. 2000. How Like a Leaf: An Interview with Donna Haraway. New York: Routledge.

Gorman, Christine. 1999. "Drugs by Design: Thanks to Genetics, the Pharmaceutical Industry Is Exploding with New Ideas." Time, 153: 78.

Haraway, Donna. 1997. Modest_Witness@Second_Millennium. FemaleMan© _Meets_ OncoMouse™. New York: Routledge.

Huxley, Aldous. 1998. Brave New World. New York: Harper Collins Perennial Classics.

Isaacson, Walter. 1999. "The Biotech Century." Time, 153: 42.

Koshland, Daniel. 1989. "Sequences and Consequences of the Human Genome." Science 246: 189.

Latour, Bruno. 1987. Science in Action: How to Follow Scientists and Engineers through Society. Cambridge, Mass.: Harvard University Press.

———. 1988a. The Pasteurization of France. Cambridge, Mass.: Harvard University Press.

———. 1988b. "The Politics of Explanation." In Knowledge and Reflexivity, edited by Steve Woolgar. London: Sage.

———. 1999. Pandora's Hope: Essays on the Reality of Science Studies. Cambridge, Mass.: Harvard University Press.

Lee, Nick, and Steve Brown. 1994. "Otherness and the Actor-Network: The Undiscovered Continent." American Behavioural Scientist 37, no. 6: 772–790.

Lewontin, Richard C. 1993. The Doctrine of DNA: Biology as Ideology. New York: Penguin Books.

Nelkin, Dorothy, and Susan Lindee. 1995. The DNA Mystique: The Gene as a Cultural Icon. New York: W. H. Freeman.

Ridley, Mathew. 2000. Genome: The Autobiography of a Species in 23 Chapters. New York: Harper Collins.

Ruse, Michael, ed. 1988. But Is It Science: The Philosophical Question in the Creation/Evolution Controversy. New York: Prometheus.

Shenk, David. 2000. "Biocapitalism: What Price the Genetic Revolution." In Contemporary Moral Issues: Diversity and Consensus, edited by Lawrence Hinman. Upper Saddle River, N.J.: Prentice Hall.

Siwolop, Sana. 2000. "A Hunt for the Gems in Genomics." The New York Times, Money and Business Section, October 29, p. 8.

Smith, Barbara H. 1997. Belief and Resistance: Dynamics of Contemporary Intellectual Controversy. Cambridge, Mass.: Harvard University Press.

Watson, James. 1999. "All for the Good: Why Genetic Engineering Must Soldier On." Time 153: 42.

13. A Garden Meeting: Ihde and Pickering

Jari Friis Jørgenssen

In this chapter we will encounter a philosopher, Don Ihde, and a sociologist, Andrew Pickering, meeting in a non-technological place, the Garden of Eden, to discuss their theories concerning culture, practice, and human and non-human agency. Both of the thinkers agree that technologies have become an integrated part of our daily life; it is an undisputable fact that most of our activities are so thoroughly intertwined with technologies that we no longer feel comfortable or at home in a place without them. However, today Ihde and Pickering are going to meet in such a place in order to discuss how their different backgrounds—Ihde representing the philosophical tradition and Pickering representing the sociological one—affect their interpretation of materiality. I will carry out most of the discussion by myself, although at times Ihde and Pickering will speak for themselves and try to clarify their views.

INTRODUCING ANDREW PICKERING

Pickering views science through what he calls the *performative* idiom, and he characterizes this motif as being in opposition to representational theories. He claims that the latter distorts science by idealizing practice: "The representational idiom casts science as, above all, an activity that seeks to represent nature, to produce knowledge that maps, mirrors, or corresponds to how the world really is" (Pickering 1995a, 5). Unlike representational thinkers, Pickering depicts the world as permeated by action, and not just full of facts and observations. He claims that in order to get a better understanding of the world we have to abandon the representational idiom and look at performance, focusing our attention on how humans and machines interact:

> The performative idiom that I [Pickering] seek to develop thus subverts the black-and-white distinctions of humanism/antihumanism and moves into a posthumanist space, a space in which the human actors are still there but now inextricably entangled with the non-human, no longer at the center of the action and calling the shots. (Pickering 1995a, 26)

When scientists work, they always have some intended goals or ideas of what they are looking for and how they are going to get a result, in short, a model. This model is the starting point for Pickering, and everything else is subject to a process of tinkering, including conceptual ideas and material instruments. In this process of tinkering, Pickering contends, non-humans and material agency come into play: "Scientists are human agents in a field of material agency which they struggle to capture in machines" (Pickering 1995a, 21). This temporal struggle between human and material agency constitutes one of Pickering's most important notions, *the dance of agency*. This dance of agency takes the form of a real-time dialectic of accommodation and resistance, where resistance is understood as a problem or obstacle that blocks further progress. To overcome this emerged obstacle, the scientists have to accommodate it, adjusting to the new situation by revising their goals, theories, approaches, or experimental settings. Together this real-time dialectic of accommodation and resistance constitutes Pickering's notion of *the mangle of practice*.

INTRODUCING DON IHDE

Now that Pickering has been formally introduced, let us take a look at the philosopher in the Garden. Unlike Pickering, Ihde comes out of a strong phenomenological and hermeneutic tradition inspired by Edmund Husserl, Martin Heidegger, and Maurice Merleau-Ponty. This background shines through in his approach to technologies and scientific practice, which is focused on the human body and its relations to technology and the world. The aim of Ihde's philosophy is to "provide a perspective from which to view the terrain—in this case, the phenomenon of technology, or better, the phenomenon of human-technology relations" (Ihde 1990, 21). Inspired by Kierkegaard's *Fear and Trembling*, Ihde suggests that to establish such a perspective we have to see ourselves as navigators on an open sea: "The navigator, in the very midst of the sea where both boat and sea is in motion, must take bearings, find a direction, and locate both himself and his destination" (Ihde 1990, 10). This view implies the need to use phenomenology and hermeneutics to present a radically demythologized story of the structures and limits of human-technology relations, as well as a critical reflection on technologies and their uses (Ihde 1997).

Concerning human-technology relations, Ihde focuses on human perception and distinguishes between what he calls micro- and macroperception. These perceptual structures are modifications of Husserl's "lifeworld":

> What is usually taken as a sensory perception (what is immediate and focused bodily in actual seeing, hearing, etc.) I [Ihde] shall call microperception. But there is also what might be called a cultural, or hermeneutic, perception, which I [Ihde] shall call macroperception. Both belong equally to the 'lifeworld'. And both dimensions of perceptions are closely linked and intertwined. There is no microperception (sensory-bodily) without its location within a field of macroperception and no macroperception without its microperceptual foci. (Ihde 1990, 29)

Looking at the flexible and ambiguous ways that micro- and macroperceptions are linked and are mutually dependent on each other provides the best account of how lifeworlds change. At this point it should be clear that the invariant ground in Ihde's account is bodily praxis and that variations only can occur within these parameters. Ihde acknowledges three variants of human-technology relations:

a) *Embodiment relations:* (I-technology) → world.
Relations where technologies become almost transparent and are seen as quasi-me. Eyeglasses are a technology that fits this description. After a short adaptation period you do not feel the eyeglasses; they have become an embodied part of you.
b) *Hermeneutic relations:* I → (technology—world).
Relations that do "not extend or mimic the sensory-bodily capacities, but rather linguistic and interpretative capacities" (Ihde 1991, 85). Technologies are seen as "text-like" and are "read" in this relation. An example would be when you read a thermometer to find out how hot or cold it is. You read the thermometer and make an interpretation.
c) *Alterity relations:* Human → technology—(-world).
Relations *to* or *with* a technology. Technologies are not seen as embodied but as other or quasi-other to which I as a human being relate. An example of this relation would be Virtual Reality, where human beings relate *to* a simulated world.

The task of a phenomenology of human-technology relations is thus to discover the various structural features of these ambiguous relations.

CULTURE AND TECHNOLOGICAL TRANSFORMATIONS

Now that our two participants have been formally introduced—let us welcome them and start our session. The first topic and point of discussion is culture and technological transformations.

First up is Pickering, who wants to expand our concepts of scientific culture to indicate more than a field of knowledge. Culture, Pickering argues, has to be taken in a broader sense "to denote the 'made things' of science, in which I [Pickering] include skills and social relations, machines and instruments, as well as scientific facts and theories" (Pickering 1995a, 3). For Pickering, scientific practice has to be understood as an extension of culture. This understanding implies that one must not just look at how knowledge is produced in science, but must go beyond this traditional view and look at the real-time transformations of the social and material dimensions of science as they happen. This view contrasts with the classical retrospective "reading" of scientific practice where the newly acquired knowledge is transferred back in time in order to understand the practice of the past. Pickering's mangle has to be seen as opposed to this view and as a form of cultural relativism. [Pickering, after listening to the account given of his views, stands up and clarifies]: "The relativism of the mangle is not social relativism nor is it technical relativism. It is relativism to culture that can not be specified in terms of enduring—non-emergent, non-mangled—properties of either the social or the technical in science" (Pickering 1995a, 204).

Culture is something that gets established through the mangle of the social *and* the technical, through the mangle of humans *and* non-humans. There is no pre-established culture that scientists can confront and "look up" what to do. They have to mangle it, and then see what might pop up. If we connect this to Pickering's argument against retrospective readings, we see how important real-time practice is; it is not what did happen and what we can conclude that matters, but what happens when it happens.

The idea of real-time practice can be exemplified by the physicist Donald Glaser's development of the bubble chamber, which started out as modeled upon existing cloud chambers. During Glaser's initial research, the cloud chamber was an established instrument of the scientific community; it could be taken for granted and had its place in scientific culture. Still, Glaser managed, through the mangle of practice, to find new ways of looking and extending the cloud chamber, and they in turn led to the development of the bubble chamber (Pickering 1995a).

This incident illustrates that culture gets transformed through the mangle of practice. Culture, then, is seen as a temporal end product of the mangle that is always subject to further mangling. If we consider the invention of the bubble chamber illustrated in the example above, the cloud chamber would be understood as such an "end product" still open for further developments and mangling. Any specific instance of time is the result of what has been mangled and thus is a temporal closure that yields culture. Instead of trying to explain closure in non-emergent terms, which Pickering sees as characteristic of the traditional relativist and objectivist approaches, "the mangle points to temporally extended processes—to machinic, conceptual and social maneuverings in fields of material and disciplinary agency, and to stabilization and destabilization of cultural elements and strata" (Pickering 1995a, 194). The knowledge we have about culture is thus temporally mediated, open to further mangling, and revisable. [Pickering clears his throat and in a clear voice gives the following statement:] "The culture to which knowledge production is relative is itself indefinitely re-configurable" (Pickering 1995a, 205).

Consequently, Ihde and Pickering share some of the same ideas about culture and its role in science and life. Ihde argues that "the technological form of life is part and parcel of culture, just as culture in the human sense inevitably implies technologies" (Ihde 1990, 20). Ihde's view on culture, or rather interest in culture, revolves around the ways in which cultures embed technologies. In all cultures the three encountered variants of human-technology relations are represented. As previously mentioned, Ihde's main goal is to give an embodied perspective from which to view technology, including the macroperceptual field in which we act.

When we adopt a new technology we also adopt a new set of cultural relations. Ihde illustrates this point with a story about Guineans receiving steel knives, thereby becoming part of Western culture, and establishing dependence on the Western world. Technology transfers, in this case from the Western world to New Guinea, are accompanied by cultural-perceptual changes. The Guineans old knives may lose their value and completely disappear, and with them part of their culture. For a technology to be adopted, Ihde argues, it has to fit into some known use, a practice. [Ihde stands up and clarifies this point:] "The artifact becomes technologically what it 'is' in relation to the degree and type of transferability to which the respective cultures overlap in practice" (Ihde 1990, 128). If there is no cultural overlap between the different cultures, an artifact, technology or non-human, becomes or gets its "identity" in relation to the new cultural field it is transferred to. In other words, technologies are always culturally relative. An example of this is the Indian prayer wheel, which became Lowland water pumps through a hermeneutic process (Ihde 1999, 48).

For Ihde, a culture can undergo two levels of technology transfer. One level is the level of "instrumental involvement," a level where people use the new technology as something they know how to use. At this level, Ihde argues, there will be overlaps between different cultures. However, there is also the broader cultural view where the prayer wheel becomes or rather transforms into a water pump, a technology transfer that may influence and change society.

If we stop here and think about how this relates to Pickering, we will see that there is a certain extent of agreement. They both agree that culture is influential for determining the role of technologies. Ihde argues that culture is part of the human lifeworld, whereas Pickering is post-human in his approach.

Pickering is interested in post-human phenomena that are not centered in the human lifeworld. This means that Pickering does not focus on invariant bodily activities, but rather is concerned with the becoming of human and non-human phenomena. An example of this is his study of the intersection of science and the military during World War II (Pickering 1995b). Before we go further into detail with Pickering's approach, I find it important to clarify Ihde's use of the term "lifeworld." The term was originally coined by Edmund Husserl to designate what happens in the perceptual-bodily world, and Ihde expounds on this notion to include material and non-human dimensions. Consequently, Ihde has a post-subjective, but not a post-human, position. In this case post-subjective means that Ihde breaks free from classical phenomenology where the subject is privileged to include the non-human dimension. The human, though, is ever-present in Ihde's analysis. By contrast, Pickering's notion of culture does not focus on the world as it appears to individual humans. As previously mentioned, his analysis of the intersection of science and the military focuses on institutions and machines and not on the human subject. Another illustration of Pickering's post-humanness is his recent interest in cybernetics.

To sum up, Ihde looks at the structures of technology transfers in culture, and reflects retrospectively over the impact of the different technologies. Pickering on the other hand argues that there are no such structures; since everything is subject to further mangling there are not even any informative patterns that describe what does and does not change—*it just happens*. The relativism of the mangle is what Pickering calls a "*hyperrelativism*" [Pickering is getting comfortable in the Garden and again takes over] that "offer[s] us nothing substantive at all to hang onto in understanding cultural extension—not interests or social structures or gestalts or constraints of varying temporality or epistemic rules or metaphysics" (Pickering 1995a, 208). Scientific culture for Pickering has to be seen as a big blurry "entity" which is deeply connected with empirical practices. [Pickering, still standing, continues making gestures as he explains:] "Conceptual and machinic elements evolve together in empirical practice. Scientific culture, then, appears as itself a wild kind of machine built from radically heterogeneous parts, a supercyborg, harnessing material and disciplinary agency in material and human performances, some of which lead out into the world of representation, of facts and theories" (Pickering 1995a, 145).

By insisting that technology-culture structures are multi-stable, Ihde allows a certain degree of relativism in his cultural hermeneutics. Unlike Pickering, who views cultural influence on technology as a result of the mangle, Ihde looks for structures in multiple cultures. This is indicated in the manner which he categorizes cultural responses to technologies. [After listening to Pickering, Ihde also gets up and starts to point out the following modes of technology transfer between cultures:]

a) There are what I [Ihde] call "monocultures," cultures that will be overwhelmed by a new technology and adapt it.

b) Compromise adaptations, where some selected technologies will be adapted as part of a new context or as part of the old practice.

c) Total resistance to incoming technologies.

d) Cultures that adapt the new technology and in the adaptation process modify themselves in approximation to the new group. (Ihde 1990, 151)

The main difference between Pickering and Ihde concerning culture is that Ihde looks for structures and believes that there are structures in technology transformations embedded in culture. One of the structures that a phenomenological analysis shows is "that all technologies are non-neutral. Technologies change and transform situations, however minimally. There is no such thing as a 'mere use' of technologies" (Ihde 1999, 47). The non-neutrality of technologies is a universal feature, but technologies are able to display different amplification/reduction patterns. Pickering, as opposed to Ihde, does not want to present us with structures or multiple perspectives. He believes that the real-time dialectic of resistance and accommodations is what shapes culture. Culture cannot be read retrospectively but has to be studied as an open-ended process of modeling. According to Pickering, all human practice takes the form of modeling—either extending a model or shifting it in cultural space without any universal structures present; this prevents anything substantive from enduring other then temporal patterns.

With this final remark the first point of today's meeting is clarified and temporally settled, to use Pickering's terms, the participants stroll around in the Garden looking at all the non-technological marvels.

PRACTICE

The second topic of today's meeting is practice, and again we will start with Pickering. What Pickering attempts to provide is "a general analysis of scientific practice, which I [Pickering] call the mangle, and some pointers as to how it might be extended toward an understanding of the reciprocal production of science, technology and society (STS)" (Pickering 1995a, 1). This indicates that scientific practice has to be understood as the work of cultural extension where human and non-human agency temporally emerge in practice. [Pickering continues:] "Disciplined human agency and captured material agency are, as I say, constitutively intertwined; they are *interactively stabilized*" (Pickering 1995a, 17). For Pickering, practice is embedded in culture and it is through practice that different elements of culture, including humans, non-humans, concepts, and models evolve together. Ultimately, the only form of practice Pickering acknowledges is practice that is part of the cultural sphere.

Like Pickering, Ihde is interested in scientific practice. In order to understand science in its hermeneutic dimensions, Ihde argues, when we reframe "our understanding of science in terms of interpreting much of its praxis as hermeneutic, we gain certain insights into those operations" (Ihde 1999, 184). The type of hermeneutics Ihde uses and argues for has to be distinguished from classical linguistic hermeneutics; Ihde's hermeneutics are perceptually based and centered on visual trajectories (Ihde 1999, 184). When one engages in an embodied practice through technology, as in the case of human-technology relations, ultimately what one is doing is engaging in an existential relation with the world. It is through action and being in the world that relations to the world are created. [Ihde takes the cue and stands up and clarifies:] "Humans are what they are in terms of the human-world relation, but this relation in existence is actional" (Ihde 1990, 27). Since practice is centered on human bodily action, it requires a hermeneutic phenomenology to understand.

Both our thinkers thus agree that practice is important for understanding human-technology relations from both a material and a social aspect, but the way they go about studying this practice differs. Pickering looks at the real-time dialectics of resistance and accommodation, while Ihde looks for hermeneutic structures centered on the human body. Pickering does not share an interest in the human body and his post-human view is incompatible with a human lifeworld. [Pickering rises again and claims:] "The goals of scientific practice are imaginatively transformed visions of the present. The future states of scientific culture at which practice aims are constructed from existing cultures in a process of modeling (metaphor analogy)" (Pickering 1995a, 19). The process of modeling, which Pickering is fond of and which has to be seen as an open-ended process with no determinate destination, involves a degree of uncertainty. When one constructs a model or engages with a non-human, there are a lot of variants that can occur. Although one might have some expectation of what should happen, one can never fully know in advance if one's plans will be actualized. This notion of modeling resembles Ihde's concept of *multi-stability*. According to Ihde, technologies and non-humans are multi-stable because they follow different trajectories. In other words, there is no determined way to approach a technology, and when a trajectory is chosen, there will still be the possibility for a certain degree of variation. For example, a piece of bamboo can be used as a fishing pole, a punishment-inflicting device, or a house-building tool. Again, I would characterize Ihde's approach as more stable than Pickering's modeling. What they both agree on is that it is through practice that humans and non-humans are shaped and their relations established. It is in practice that models are created and goals revised, leading to stunning inventions or complex theories. Ihde argues that by making a phenomenological analysis of practices, structures will be revealed that can function as guidelines in the use and understanding of technologies. Pickering on the other hand does not believe that such "essences" can become encapsulated in structures. According to Pickering, all there is, onto-logically speaking, is the mangle and the open-ended process of modeling that occurs within it. A concept such as multi-stability would not occur in Picker-ing's writing. For him there is no stability and variants are too weak of an ex-pression. Pickering argues that one should see a given technology as one ele-ment that enters into the process of the mangle alongside the human and the social, with no predictable outcome. The only guidance one will receive is what temporally emerges from the mangle, which can be traced back to Pickering's notion of time and interest in becoming. Ihde instead compares different prac-tices and thereby constructs structures or typologies through a hermeneutic pro-cess, whereas Pickering's interest lies in understanding how these typologies and structures are mangled in practice and not analyzed retrospectively. To sum-marize; Pickering's view on practice involves an indefinite open-endedness in-volving humans, non-humans, the social, and the material, whereas Ihde looks for structures and topologies that can be explained and analyzed through his ex-panded lifeworld analysis.

This ends the second topic of today's meeting. There will now be a little snack break where the participants will eat multi-stable apples in a real-time practice before returning to present their views on human and non-human agency.

HUMAN AND NON-HUMAN AGENCY

[Pickering puts his apple away and starts out:] "One can start from the idea that the world is filled, not in the first instance, with facts and observations, but with agency. The world I want to say, is continually doing things, things that bear upon us not as observation statements upon disembodied intellects but as forces upon material beings" (Pickering 1995a, 6). An example of material agency (non-human agency) can be found in scientific practice; the scientists do some-thing (human agency) to their instruments, then they stand back and wait for the material to act—at this point the actions of the material (material agency) is unknown. The scientists can have an idea about what the material will do, but they will not know before it happens, illustrating the concept of real-time prac-tice. Materials can explode, change color, boil over, or do something else— showing that material force can express unpredictable agency. It is important to mention that materials can have agency but not intentionality, which Pickering reserves for human agency. The scientists form goals and intentions concerning what they are doing; this is something that material agency cannot do.

The mangle is not a one-way process either. By doing "things," materials mangle scientists as much as scientists mangle the materials they encounter. Material agency influences how scientists act because of its unintentional and uncertain agency; this leads the scientists to revise their goals and theories, thereby altering the whole scientific process. In the *dance of agency*, the scientist, his intentions, and the available material are subject. When the scientists reach a temporal end product, they arrive at a state where the material and the social (their goals, intentions, etc.) *interactively stabilize* one another—a stabilization that emerges in a real-time practice. The dance of agency is methodologically applicable outside of science as well. [Pickering, looking quite happy, utters:] "Much of everyday life, I would say, has this character of coping with material agency, agency that comes at us from outside the human realm and that cannot be reduced to anything within that realm" (Pickering 1995a, 6). It is important to note that Pickering does not privilege intentionality and does not accord it a special position in his analysis; rather his theory of the mangle is scale-invariant and thus equally applicable to human intentions and macro-social transformations. Pickering's main interest lies in detailing the assemblages of humans and non-humans engaging with each other in a dance of agency; here the important issue is the temporal emergence and becoming of these post-human assemblages.

[Ihde shakes his head and proclaims:] "As long as I experience at all, I do so in bodily-perceptual ways, and this is the case inside any technologies that I may occupy" (Ihde 1990, 17). Ihde's focus is on how technologies transform the immediately experienced environment; and it is these transformations which he wants to investigate. An example he mentions is wearing a jacket to transform the cold feeling of the wind into a warm feeling. A jacket can be seen as a technology and as a non-human. For Ihde, isolated agency cannot be found in non-humans since humans decide to wear jackets and jackets do their job by keeping us warm. Hence, Ihde does not recognize material agency to be a legitimate way of speaking about non-humans.

Ihde's view on material agency differs from Pickering's in that he does not look at materiality in itself but only in relation to a human lifeworld, a lifeworld that Pickering's analysis is independent of. Ihde claims that the traditional philosophy of science underestimates the importance of instruments and non-humans in science by depicting them in neutral terms. By contrast, Ihde argues that they are non-neutral, and this is a point he makes as early as *Technics and Praxis*, where he claims that by mediating our relations to the world, technologies and non-humans extend and transform human bodily intentionality (Ihde 1979). When technologies extend bodily capacities, the only thing that remains constant in embodiment relations is bodily focus. According to Ihde, technologies need human intentionality to work. [Ihde elaborates:] "For example, the 'behavior' of atoms and their constituents is not directly observable but must be made available through a technologically mediated (instrumental) observation situation. The bubble chamber, accelerators, electron- and computer-enhanced microscopes, all bring into mediated or indirect presence the micro-phenomena which are of interest to the physicist" (Ihde 1990, 23).

In short, as a phenomenologist Ihde denies the existence of a "thing-in-itself." Non-humans are non-neutral and multi-stable, but only insofar as they are constituted in a context, in use. [Ihde in a loud voice states:] "A technological object, whatever else it is, becomes what it 'is' through its uses" (Ihde 1990, 70). In other words, to learn something about a non-human, one cannot simply look at it. One needs to use it in a situation in order to learn about it through a bodily relation.

Our two participants thus share some of the same ideas about what non-human and material agency is. In particular, both agree that there is no radical symmetry between humans and non-humans. [Pickering, addressing Ihde, says:] "As agents, we humans seem to be importantly different from non-human agents like the weather, television sets, or particle accelerators" (Pickering 1995a, 15). At first glance, it seems that Ihde could have made this statement. Yet if we dig a little deeper, we see that a noteworthy difference remains. As previously mentioned, Pickering views his theory as independent of the lifeworld. He believes it is important to apply a post-humanist perspective to all practices, where one tries to see the human and the non-human side simultaneously. By contrast, Ihde's phenomenological/hermeneutic emphasis centers his analysis on relations between humans, technologies, and the world. These are relations where the human side is invariant and the basis of moving out to explore the non-humans. Both agree that there is an intertwining between humans and non-humans, between the material and the social, and both acknowledge that there is an important difference in the human and non-human realm, since there is no counterpart to human intentionality in the material realm. The main difference is that Pickering does not characterize intentionality as a primary factor that needs to be included in every analysis, but as a feature that can be discussed in some instances and abandoned in others. This point leads back to Pickering's claim that his theory is scale-invariant. Ihde on the other hand expands the traditional scope of hermeneutics by including non-humans in his analysis, but he still keeps his perspective anchored in bodily intentionality. Concerning non-humans and agency, they both acknowledge them but deal with them differently. Ihde retains a bodily centered perspective while Pickering highlights assemblages.

Now that it is time to wrap the meeting up, Ihde and Pickering shake hands and start talking about their differences on a less formal level.

LEAVING THE GARDEN

The meeting is coming to an end, a meeting I hope revealed some of the differences and points of agreement between the two participants. I am not going to end this chapter by arguing that Ihde has the better approach or that only Pickering's theory of the mangle is useful. Both of their theories are valuable and useful depending on what you want to examine and analyze. If you want a post-subjective—centered analysis of technology relations then Ihde is the one to read. His work is full of personal experiences and historical examples that explore the social implications of contemporary technology. Pickering's work on the other hand is more interested in becomings and the open-ended process of modeling which constitutes his main notion, the mangle of practice. Pickering's main focus is on how science and the military became a unit, how industrial research got funded during the nineteenth century, and lately with the history of cybernetics (Pickering 1995b).

I believe both thinkers in their own way contribute to a better understanding of humans and non-humans. With these words the meeting is officially over, and we can return to the ordinary world with all its humans, non-humans, and technologies, without which we would no longer feel comfortable or, maybe, be able to survive.

BIBLIOGRAPHY

Ihde, Don. 1979. *Technics and Praxis: A Philosophy of Technology*. Dordrecht: D. Reidel Publishing Co.

———.1990. *Technology and the Lifeworld*. Bloomington and Indianapolis: Indiana University Press.

———. 1991. *Instrumental Realism*. Bloomington and Indianapolis: Indiana University Press

———. 1997. "Why Not Science Critics?" *International Studies in Philosophy* XXIX, no. 1: 45–54.

———. 1999. *Expanding Hermeneutics*. Northwestern University Studies in Phenomenology & Existential Philosophy. Evanston, Ill.: Northwestern University Press.

Kierkegaard, Søren. 1986. *Fear and Trembling*. Translated by Alastair Hannay. New York: Viking Press.

Pickering, Andrew.1995a. *The Mangle of Practice*. Chicago: University of Chicago Press.

———. 1995b. "Cyborg History and the World War II Regime." *Perspectives on Science* 3, no. 1. University of Chicago.

———. 1999. "Japanese Eels to Global Warming: A Posthumanist Perspective on Society and the Environment." Paper presented in the geography department. University of Illinois at Urbana Champaign, colloquium series on "The Environment and Social Change."

———. Forthcoming. "Science as Alchemy." In *Schools of Thought: Twenty-five Years of Interpretive Social Science*, edited by Joan W. Scott and Debra Keates. Princeton, N.J.: Princeton University Press.

———, ed. 1992. *Science as Practice and Culture*. Chicago: University of Chicago Press.

14. Latour and Pickering: Post-human Perspectives on Science, Becoming, and Normativity

Casper Bruun Jensen

I. INTRODUCTION

The following chapter compares and discusses the works of Bruno Latour and Andrew Pickering.[1] Below, I aim not to carry out a classical comparative survey of their works, although I hope to achieve this objective to some extent. The ambition is narrower. I closely analyze specific axes in Latour's and Pickering's frameworks in order to clarify how these scholars, in different ways, profoundly challenge traditional sociological and philosophical analyses of science and move away from social studies of science conceived as social constructivism.

When reading Latour and Pickering, one is transferred into a very different landscape, which could be termed the post-humanist branch of science and technology studies (STS).

There are clear affinities between such approaches and cultural studies of science, in particular the cyborg-feminism of Donna Haraway. But contrary to the often explicit political agendas of these approaches, Latour and Pickering have repeatedly been accused of a normative indecisiveness that is seen as rendering their work problematic or politically naïve. In the following I aim to show how the post-human movement is not so much trying to evade or undermine critical potential as is it trying to become able to re-characterize many technoscientific relationships in ways not based on problematic modernist and humanist assumptions. Below, I carry out a sustained comparative reflection on Latour's Actor-Network Theory (in different guises) and Pickering's mangle of practice and focus in particular on three common but differentiated features, which allow these scholars to take leave of the modern world. First, they demonstrate that humans are not freestanding intentional agents, but rather always are implicated in complex socio-technical assemblages. This realization points to the need for a change in the conceptual tools with which one can approach the study of science and technology in society. I take up this discussion in the following section, which introduces the notion of generalized symmetry and other key concepts. Second, they work to refigure the common-sense understanding of science as a rational endeavor with the purpose of finding the true state of natural (and human) affairs. In the section on epistemology, I analyze their attempts to redefine the scientific activity as a much more entangled activity which cannot be properly characterized by notions of truth and the rational without for that matter working to "undermine" science or take anything away from its practical achievements. This unwillingness to engage with science in a critical mode has led to various criticisms of Latour and Pickering. In the final section, I trace how their post-humanist positions on change in scientific and technological assemblages not so much obviates the need for ethics or normativity as it challenges what could be meant by these terms in a world of continuous becomings.

2. THE NETWORK, THE MANGLE, AND THE QUESTION OF SYMMETRY

The symmetrical approach to the study of science was originally proposed by sociologist of knowledge David Bloor (Bloor 1976; Olesen 1997, 18). He suggested that in studying science, one should use the same set of concepts to make sense of why ideas that we now hold to be true were accepted and why ideas that we now view as false were rejected. He defended this approach because it prevented the adoption of all varieties of Whiggish (presentist) history, in which what is thought to be true is explained by truth, whereas what is thought to be false is explained (away) by beliefs, bias, or bad methods. Michael Callon and Bruno Latour added a new dimension to the notion of symmetry. In the so-called chicken debate with Harry Collins and Steve Yearley, Callon and Latour used the term general symmetry to refer to an analytical leveling of humans and non-humans in analyses of technoscientific practices (deVries 1995, 3–10). The analytical leveling refers to a bracketing of common-sense categorizations of the entities under investigation. Most famously, it implies the suspension of the categories of the "natural" and the "cultural"—since the categorization of an entity as one or the other is viewed as the outcome of a specifically modern way of distributing entities, rather than as a natural and empirically verifiable occurrence.

According to Latour, two ideas have been central to the development of Actor-Network Theory. The first of these is a "semiotics relieved of meaning."

Semiotics is used to bracket the putative essences or substances of entities (such as nature or culture) in order to focus on how they function relative to other actors. However, breaking the limits of semiotics, Latour views this not as a matter of interpretation, but a becoming able to observe the real activities of human and non-human entities as they engage each other. All entities are viewed as active ontological hybrids, working to produce differences by connecting with other actors. Concurrently, the work of the Actor-Network researcher is not to impose on the observed analytical categories (this is nature and this is culture) from the outside, but to trace the developing networks of associations between the multiplicity of involved actors. This explains the motto from *Science in Action:* follow the actors! It also points to how networks can be seen as a "methodological frame for registering heterogeneity."[2]

With this in mind it is possible to see why an actor-network is neither to be understood in an engineering sense, nor as a purely social endeavor. Rather, it should be understood as having a "strong ontological component." "Expressed simply, actor-network is a change of metaphors to describe essences: instead of surfaces you get threads (or rhizomes like in Deleuze)" (Latour 1997a, 47). These take many forms and shapes:

> The attribution of human, inhuman, non-human characteristics, the distribution of capacities between these entities, the relations, that are established between them, the circulation that are entailed by these attributions, the transformation of these attributions, distributions and relations. (Latour 1997a, 53)

A network, then, is not a thing, but it is the registered movement of a thing as it associates with many other elements. It describes not an essence but the result of an ongoing series of negotiations between heterogeneous entities. Consequently, what is interesting to the Actor-Network researcher is never to become able to categorize once and for all an entity as human or non-human, true or false, or natural or cultural. Instead, what matters is to become able to trace the transformations of unstable sets of actors before they are "black-boxed" and naturalized.[3]

While this symmetrical move is the stated aim of the Actor-Network theorists, its practical execution has nevertheless led to problems in developing a descriptive vocabulary for use in practice. Michael Callon has suggested that any language (social, natural, semiotical) can in principle be used for such description, as long as symmetry is strictly adhered to (Callon 1986, 200). But as Latour points out, this has not been without problems:

> However, this solution is somewhat complicated since it can involve all kinds of misunderstandings—and this is exactly what happened with ANT; readers and users said simultaneously that it was a social-constructivist argument, the return of naturalism or a typical French belief in the general extension of texts. (Latour 1997a, 62)

Generalizing and ontologizing the doctrine of symmetry is of consequence for the question of agency. As non-humans and humans are defined by their relations, there are no pure objects or subjects. Instead, the world of ANT is inhabited by quasi-objects, quasi-subjects, and hybrids.[4] Agency, in this view, is a radically historical achievement because it is strengthened, weakened, and transformed as an entity's relations with others evolve, emerge, or disappear. In order to keep in existence an actor must keep relatively aligned with the series of associations that stabilizes it. Sometimes there are happy instances where actors strengthen the agencies of each other immensely, as in the case of Pasteur and the microbes, as Latour explains:

"We see how Pasteur makes his microbes while the microbes make their Pasteur" (Latour 1988). These actors align in such a way that they "point" in the same direction—toward the importance of Pasteur's discovery *and* toward the existence of microbes everywhere.[5] However, in other cases existence may fade. This is what happened to the spontaneously generating organisms of Pasteur's antagonist Pouchet. While these creatures initially flourished in bottles and in scientific articles, they eventually disappeared from these and most other arenas. In Latour's story, the dispute between Pasteur and Pouchet, not a mere battle with words, is a struggle of life and death, of relative existence: the coming into being and fading out of being of entities.

Andrew Pickering replaces the notion of the actor-network with the mangle of practice. The mangle works as a macro-concept for describing how artifacts, natural objects, and humans interact in the ongoing construction of the world. Pickering analyzes these interactions in practice as a "work of cultural extension and transformation in time" (Pickering 1995a, 4). Cultural extension and transformation always takes place in "real time," as opposed to scientists' and philosophers' retrospective accounts based on the end result of the process (Pickering 1995a, 3). Analysis in real time is Pickering's attempt to rebalance STS from the "obsession with knowledge and toward a recognition of science's material powers" and, more generally, from a "representative idiom" to a "performative idiom" (Pickering 1995a, 17). By concerning himself with performativity, Pickering also concerns himself with time. Looking at the real-time work of cultural extension, he finds that science (or any other part of the cultural field) is temporally emergent. From its present state (whatever it is), science moves toward its future states (whatever they will turn out to be) by processes of construction and modeling (Pickering 1995a, 19). Modeling is not determined *a priori* by any of the elements that are part of it; it always works as an open-ended process with a multiplicity of possible outcomes. Hence, no elements can be excluded due to analytical irrelevance prior to the observation of what actually occurs in real-time action.

Broadly, Pickering distinguishes between three kinds of elements that partake in such processes: the conceptual, the social, and the material. He gives priority to none—but suggests that "(scientific) practice is . . . organized around the making (and breaking) of associations or alignments between multiple cultural elements" (Pickering 1995a, 29). As no element is prioritized, symmetry is at play here: human agency does not determine the material world any more than the opposite is the case. Human and non-human, social, material, and conceptual elements are always intertwined in complex ways. What takes place, in science (and other explorative spaces) are processes aiming at interactive stabilizations between heterogeneous cultural elements. This works, in Pickering's phrase, through a dialectics of resistance and accommodation or, differently put, through a dance of agency between diverse elements.

A scientist, for example, has a certain goal to accomplish. She "does something" with her chemicals and apparatuses and then "stands back and waits." She attempts to accommodate these particular elements in the hope of reaching her goal. As a result of this combination the materials react, for instance by exploding. For Pickering this is an instance of material resistance to the scientist's effort, which forces her to try to recombine the elements in a new way. After several turns in this dance of elements, the goal may be reached (although this is not a necessary outcome). Pickering describes such an outcome as the gradual tuning of the participating elements to one another. Through the intervention of the scientist, machinic and material agencies are captured in a specific way (Pickering 1995a, 29). What makes a successful process of tuning possible is not that theory is properly applied to practice. Rather scientists are good at framing material agency and tying heterogeneous elements together in novel ways. But regardless of the intentions and planning capacities of the scientist, unforeseeable events are an inevitable consequence of the way the mangle functions. Pickering claims for this analysis scale-invariance, and views the mangle of practice as a TOE—a theory of everything.

Clearly, this is a symmetrical story, but the level of symmetry is not equivalent to that of Latour. In "On Becoming" Pickering discusses two sorts of becoming termed biological and machinic. Biological becoming is exemplified by weak and strong couplings. A weak coupling might be the evolution of a finch's beak to become better at reaching food. A strong coupling could be the total symbiosis of a bee-orchid environment (Pickering Forthcoming a). While these examples are amenable to processual thinking, the harder case is to think about machinic becoming. Here Pickering parts ways with Latour, since he finds it impossible to keep up the symmetry: ". . . one is inclined to ask oneself questions like: did the inner sporting of inanimate matter lead up to and into the steam engine. . . . The answer to such questions must be: no" (Pickering Forthcoming a). Nonetheless Pickering and Latour are completely in line as regards symmetry insofar as it relates to the "cyborg being and becoming, the intertwined evolution of the human and the nonhuman" (Pickering Forthcoming a).

To Pickering, the world is full of both human and non-human agencies, but they are not of a kind. This is precisely what makes it important to have a notion of material agency as that which "comes at us from outside the human realm and that cannot be reduced to anything within that realm" (Pickering 1995a, 6). Scientists work to capture these material "powers, capacities, and performances" with diverse kinds of machinic agency in the dance of agency. In Pickering, this materialist agential combinatorics replaces what he views as the excessive reliance of Actor-Network theorists on semiotics:

> The actor-network speaks of "delegating" human performances to machines; my suggestion is that the putative symmetry of this operation often breaks down when one tries to imagine delegating machinic functions back to humans. (Pickering 1995a, 15)

Rhetorically, Pickering proposes that we think of ways in which the abilities of a metal-cutter could be delegated back to a human, and answers: "Semiotically, these things can be made equivalent; in practice they are not" (Pickering 1995a, 15). While, in this view, humans and material agencies are intertwined in mutual tuning processes, strict symmetrical claims should be abandoned. Pickering maintains for humans a planning capacity and some intentionality, while highlighting the tremendously varied capacities of diverse material and machinic agents.

Symmetry is often supposed to be disproved by social constructivists and philosophers of science, since it seems obvious that humans are intentional or goal-oriented in ways clearly lacking in non-humans. Pickering adopts this position in his refusal of absolute symmetry. To me, this interpretation seems to depend on a confusion of analytical levels. The ANT notion of generalized symmetry applies to the ontological status of actors; it is not a way of claiming practical equivalence between these. To Latour, no differences (or equivalencies) between actors can be accomplished prior to a successful encounter. Since one is always already immersed in practice, one is never lacking in differences. Only these are no longer clearly distributed between humans and machines but, as we have seen, between hybrid creatures and quasi-objects.

This is also of consequence for a second bone of contention, the status of the social. Pickering is rightly able to claim for himself an analysis of the social, sophisticated in its ability to take into account material agency (Pickering 1995a, 1995b, Forthcoming). But from the perspective of Latour, the notion of the social is one of the very issues at stake in local practices. This position changes the status of the social from a resource into a topic, and renders it unanalyzable as such. While Pickering works with three interrelated spheres of the conceptual, material, and social, Latour would be likely to deny the analytical merit of these broad typological categories. The unwillingness to fully embrace general symmetry makes Pickering inhabit something of an intermediary position between social constructivism and ANT-symmetry that could perhaps be designated partial symmetry.[6]

Another notable difference has to do with Pickering's and Latour's preferred analytical concepts. Pickering has an explicit interest in time and change. As we have seen, change happens through the interactive stabilization of novel combinations of conceptual, material, and social elements. Latour's way of accounting for transformation is by way of the notion of negotiation between actors. Negotiation is dependent on argumentative force, on rhetoric, and even on the coercion of allies.[7] Consequently, an important analytical focus in Latourian networks is on the establishment and securing of meaning. The one who manages to construct a black box and lock off its content is in the best position to control meaning making and naturalize specific interpretations.

Pickering, because of his focus on temporality, worries little about representations, conceptions, and intentions, since they, too, are subject to change in the mangle. They are explicitly of secondary concern: "I do not think that they pose any special problem. I have no detailed examples to discuss, but my suggestion is that they are produced . . . in just the way we have already been discussing" (Pickering 1995a, 99). Intentionality and the capability of making plans are helpful in allowing human agents to systematically connect concepts with empirical observations and to link different strata of elements that are eventually terminated and displayed via machinic agency. But novel displays of material agency get most of the attention in Pickering's story: "Instead of thinking about how representations color our apprehensions of nature, it invites us to think about the machinic termini of our representational chains and how those termini can shift" (Pickering 1995a, 190).

3. EPISTEMOLOGY

What is the status of knowledge in the network or mangle? Neither Latour nor Pickering is much interested in classical epistemology. As post-humanists, both prefer to engage with knowledge at the level of its ontological construction.

According to Latour, truth is not an absolute but a relational achievement. In *Science in Action,* truth is described as the consequence, not the cause, of the argument, since it is constructed by making stable alliances with more and more actors. Later, this argument has been refined, inspired by philosopher of science Isabelle Stengers (Stengers 1997; Latour 1999). Latour still views facts as relative, "circulating entities" which are established through negotiations and trials of strength. He has, however, introduced a criterion of articulation to enable the evaluation of scientific propositions. Constructing articulate propositions is never merely an epistemological matter, but relates to the scientists' ability to enter into ontological configurations with other entities in ways that make it possible for them to disqualify her suggestions. Scientific propositions are articulate when the scientist is able to stage an encounter with his object, which makes it possible for it to act in surprising ways.

In a nice example, Latour presents the case of primatologist and ethnologist Thelma Rowell, who researched sheep behavior with the purpose of trying ". . . to give [her] sheep the opportunity to behave like chimps instead of boring sheep" (Latour 2001, 358). Rowell is actively working to bracket taken-for-granted categories of sheep by reconceptualizing them in the idiom of chimps. As she puts it:

> We were curious to know whether applying our usual expectations of monkeys, and the methods of analysis that go with them, to a "simpler" gregarious social system would reveal primate-like levels of sophistication. Sheep were an appropriate subject, because domestic sheep are popularly taken as the very paradigm of both gregariousness and silliness. (Rowell and Rowell 1993, 214)

New knowledge about sheep, generated through this encounter, is likely to be highly articulate, because it came out of a setting explicitly concerned with the construction of novelty and difference (sheep as chimps) rather than repetition (sheep as sheep). Following Belgian philosopher Vinciane Despret, Latour says, "We are allowed to speak interestingly by what we allow to speak interestingly" (Latour Forthcoming).

Like Latour, Pickering is also uninterested in epistemology per se. He notices the "irremediable historicity" of truth, since knowledge production is situated and dependent on a specific trajectory in time (Pickering 1995a, 33). To Pickering, the atemporal form and content of knowledge is in tension with the actual temporally emergent character of the mangle. He proposes that this tension is the reason why it is rarely possible to apply knowledge directly and unproblematically to new areas of investigation:

> Knowledge does not have the magical quality of "allowing us" to accomplish any particular objective. Where we depart from our base models we are liable to find ourselves left in the lurch by the emergent performances of the material world. (Pickering 2003)

From a performative point of view, however, this is not a cause of worry. Instead of being concerned with representation and correspondence, one focuses on how, in practice, new connections between concepts and the world are made

(Pickering 1995a, 182). In practice, this happens through the dialectics of resistance and accommodation and the gradual interactive stabilization of material, social, and machinic agencies.

No skepticism or anxiety, however, haunts knowledge making in the mangle, since according to the theory one should expect no other foundations for knowledge than just such processes. In the mangle, incommensurabilities therefore reside in the specific machinic captures, which change over time, rather than in abstract theorizing. As new machines simply do not do the same things as old ones, they enable the becoming of different truths.

Knowledge, for Latour, used to be about winning better and stronger allies. To Pickering, it is a matter of managing to stabilize various agencies through tuning processes. A number of critics have pointed at the managerial emphasis of such lines of thought. They have also suggested that the traditional way of conceptualizing science as an agonistic field controlled by the enterprising scientist is, in fact, conservative and politically harmful, if one's aim is to democratize scientific processes (Haraway 1997, 33–35). In what could be viewed as a pre-emptive attempt to forestall such a reading, Latour pointed to the difference between force and potency.

> Conversely, once force is seen to lie in the alliance of weakness, potency vanishes. . . . Whatever displaces the magical impression of potency and escorts it firmly back to the network where it took form I call an "irreduction." (Latour 1988, 213)

As I see it, the commitment to a force in league with weakness has been clarified and enhanced tremendously with the notion of articulation. The degree of articulation indicates how well scientists have been able to give to diverse actors a voice with which to evaluate the adequacy of the propositions scientists have formed about them. I think of articulation as an attempt to enable weaker forces to become expressive about what matters to them, rather than about what matters to the scientist. The notion of articulation also pinpoints an important divergence between post-humanist theories and social constructivism in that it is never interesting simply to describe how social factors influence, contaminate, or problematize the idea of scientific neutrality. Post-humanist STS analyses are about describing the singular ways in which actors are allowed to or prevented from expressing themselves, through their connections with assemblages of heterogeneous others (Strathern 1991). As has Latour, Pickering has moved more and more away from the humanist social constructivist analyses. By looking at hybrid practices as diverse as cybernetics and the Mississippi delta, his concern is now to develop models that can capture and value the heterogeneity and flux of the mangle.[8]

4. NORMATIVITY AND TEMPORALITY

Above, I have discussed the re-definitions employed by Andrew Pickering and Bruno Latour in order to escape epistemology without, for that matter, giving up on knowledge. In this section I want to trace an analogous and related movement by looking more closely at the post-classical ideas of normativity and temporality in the works of Pickering and Latour (Smith and Plotnitsky 1997).

The problem of normativity is thematized a number of times in Latour's writing and intimately interwoven with his general amodern project as set forth in *We Have Never Been Modern*. Philosopher Michel Serres has been a main inspiration in this development. He, as have the "post-modernists," has carried out over the years a "systematic destruction of the metalanguages of essence and existence" (Serres and Latour 1995, 173). However, in strong opposition to post-modern theories, Serres is not arguing for a fragmented philosophy. He uses the metaphor of a vase. As a whole it is very fragile. But shattered into smaller fragments each piece gets stronger and more resistant. Serres claims that the same is the case with post-modern philosophy: "So, the philosophy of fragments is hyperdefensive; it is the results of hypercriticism, of polemics, of battle and hatred. It produces what is most resistant to the strongest aggression" (Serres 1987, 119).[9] Uninterested in polemics, Serres wants to take the risk of constructing on a grand scale, even if this means vulnerability. He calls this endeavor a synthesis of fragility:

> What I seek to form, to compose, to promote—I can't quite find the right word—is a syrrhese, a confluence not a system, a mobile confluence of fluxes. Turbulences, overlapping cyclones and anticyclones, like on the weather map. . . . An assembly of relations. (Serres 1987, 122)

Latour is explicit about the affinity of this line of thought with his own non-critical project, which he also often situates in opposition to "post-moderns." He suggests that everything which the critical humanist "takes to be a justification of more absence, more debunking, more negation, more deconstruction, [network-theory] takes as a proof of presence, deployment, affirmation and construction" (Latour 1997b, 170). ANT is, in fact, often grouped with critical science theorists, but Latour makes it clear that he views the critical stance as reactionary. He claims, for instance, that scientific anarchist Paul Feyerabend has done a disservice to the history and philosophy of science with his "debunking strategy." Debunking is a disservice because it works by creating a dichotomy between science as anarchy and the scientific method. As Latour says, "His is a constant negative argument that the true method is not there, which makes you believe it is important to find the true method" (Latour 1997b, 170).

But, as we saw above, Latour has in fact taken a strong normative stand on the notion of articulation. Paradoxically, however, the normative view he proposes is thoroughly affirmative and non-critical. Scientific work is ethical when it tries to activate and articulate as many actors and make passive as few as possible. In a sense this is a proposal that follows straightforwardly from the premises of ANT. Since no actor is defined *a priori*, everything depends on the constructive work of the actors themselves. This makes it valuable per se to always give the actor for and with whom one engages more possibilities for expressing itself.

As we have seen, Pickering's take on normativity is in some ways different from Latour's. The mangle is characterized by a continual propensity for trans-formation.[10] For Pickering, the processual focus problematizes all notions of normativity since it dissolves the ground from which to criticize. At each in-stance brute chance might interfere and change one's ingrained patterns of thought about what is to be criticized, because "the world makes us in one and the same process as we make the world" (Pickering 1995a, 26).

Pickering views the mangle as inherently anti-disciplinary in its capability to change and displace all boundaries. But he speculates that two complemen-tary types of studies might be identified, their difference depending upon their relation to temporality. One is suggested by the mangle. It is followed through time, displaying the temporally emergent dimensions of science, technology, and society. He sees ANT analyses more like snapshots, synchronic analyses of specific parts of cultural practice. In this proposed minor synthesis the mangle would stand for the temporal study of cultural change whereas cultural studies, as he calls ANT analyses, would trace the "interconnections of heterogeneous cultural elements and strata" not in time but in cultural space (Pickering 1995a, 221). In this suggestion, the mangle and the Actor-Network approach are in fact covering the same cultural territory but are "gestalted" differently; the for-mer with a focus on diachronic, the latter on synchronic aspects of technoscien-tific practice. Pickering eschews taking political stands, proposing that syn-chronic analyses have much better grounds for doing so, as the world stands still in their snapshot perspectives.

Suggestive as a complementary division of labor may sound, I am skeptical about its premises. It seems uncharitable to characterize Latour's analyses as showing a lack of concern in temporal change, when they are interested to the point of obsession in the continual transformations in the relationships between multiple actors. But even if the relevant difference is not between diachronic and synchronic analyses, interesting distinctions can be made. Pickering's notion of temporality is never fully explicated, except for the recurring reference to its transformative capacities. This sounds remarkably close to an adoption of the Kantian conception of time as a synchronic development in a spatial container. In opposition to this view, where time functions as "the motor of the mangle,"

Pickering sometimes presents time as bound up with the becoming of entities (Pickering 2003).

Though unclearly formulated, this second approach, which leaves behind the idea of time as an empirically verifiable sequentiality, seems much closer to Latour, who, following Michel Serres and Gilles Deleuze, thinks of time as folded (Serres 1987; Deleuze 1993). Time folds because actors inhabit many different and interrelated temporalities depending upon the entities they weave together. Latour gives the example of a mousetrap:

> More primitive, more basic than a point in isotopic space, is this subtle weaving together of interactions from many places, times and types of material: the week-old mouse body, the month-old cheese, the age-old trap, the five-year old wood, the night-old action of the exasperated kitchen owner, all of them contributing to this very humble topos-kairos, to an event-producing spot— and it is certainly an event for the mouse who will meet its death, hopefully, tonight. (Latour 1997b)

In the mousetrap, various materials and actions with different temporalities are enfolded, and it is the longevity of the temporalities of these actors which allows stability or patterns to emerge.

5. CONCLUSION

The work of Bruno Latour and Andrew Pickering is sometimes taken for social constructivism, or for a variant of post-modern cultural studies by philosophers and scientists. Social constructivists criticize them for their realist tendencies. And politically engaged students of culture reprimand Latour and Pickering for their lack of critical engagement.

In this paper I have discussed a number of themes with the purpose of clarifying how these symmetrical misunderstandings come about. Latour and Pickering have in common a movement toward a post-human understanding of science and technology. This movement carries with it important redefinitions of several taken-for-granted assumptions about such ideas as nature, culture, truth, rationality, humans, and machines. For these reasons, the critical tools of modernism are also made problematic, and I have discussed the paths Latour and Pickering take to reformulate critical humanist perspectives on science.

I have focused in particular on three aspects. The generalized doctrine of symmetry, formulated by Michel Callon and Bruno Latour, leads us to look for socio-technical assemblages and assume that the distribution of capabilities between entities are at stake in practice, rather than naturally given as human or non-human, cultural or natural. Pickering works with a much more flexible analytical grid than classical social studies of science, but nevertheless typifies three main categories: the social, the conceptual, and the material. For this reason, I termed his position partial symmetry.

Pickering and Latour both focus on the development of knowledge in specific ontological constellations of scientists, materials, and machines. This leads them to suspend interest in epistemology, since their relational approaches stress that knowledge is inseparable from the engagement with concrete entities in real-time action. This is also what makes untenable, from their perspectives, traditional criticism of science as ideology.

In their different formulations, good science is characterized by articulation and becoming. Articulation is the active becoming, through the relationships forged between scientists and other entities, of new modes of existence. I think this last point is crucial: the landscape of post-human STS looks so very different because it takes scientific and other formations seriously—not as bearers of truth or ideologies but as ontological experiments in the invention of novel forms of collectives.

NOTES

1. This chapter was originally written during my 1998–99 visit at the Technoscience Research Seminar at Stony Brook University, directed by Don Ihde. It has since been worked over a number of times, and I would like to thank Don Ihde, Evan M. Selinger, Finn Olesen, and Peter Lauritsen for their comments, which I hope helped to shape up the argument. I am particularly grateful to Andy Pickering who took the time to comment on the paper in several versions.

2. It is important to note that the network is a *methodological* frame; actors do not *fill in* an already constituted network frame, rather they *create* emergent networks through their associations (Latour 1987, 1997a; Callon and Latour 1981).

3. Black-boxing refers to a configuration of actants that is so stable that one can be certain of the output with a given input (Latour 1987). Jeffry Ramsey engages critically with the concept from the point of view of a philosophical interest in epistemology (Ramsey 1992). Kathleen Jordan and Michael Lynch refer to techniques not yet stabilized as black boxes as translucent boxes (Jordan and Lynch 1992). Latour's famous discussion of black-boxing, found in *Science in Action*, is considered to be a "tame version of the argument, tamed for sociologists." He recommends "Irreductions"—the second part of *The Pasteurization of France*—as "much better" (Crawford 1993).

4. In "On Technical Mediation," Latour concludes that artifacts are not mere "things": "They deserve better. They deserve to be housed in our intellectual culture as full-fledged social actors. They mediate our actions? No, they are us" (Latour 1994, 64).

5. This is sometimes referred to as *alignment*.

6. From a Latourian viewpoint, however, such partiality would itself be problematic. See Berg (1988). At the 4S conference in Boston, 2001, anthropologist Stefan Helmreich pointed to the same problem by referring to Andrew Pickering's "humanist post-humanism."

7. The focus on coercion and power as prime sources of network building has been a persistent source of criticism of ANT (Lee and Brown 1994; Elam 1999; Haraway 1997).

8. Andrew Pickering has discussed the politics of becoming in three recent papers (1999; 2000; Forthcoming a). Also see Cussins (1998), Mol (1999), Jensen and Markussen (2001).

9. For a strong reply to this way of characterizing post-modernists and relativists, see Smith (1997).

10. It is, of course, not claimed that everything does change continuously.

BIBLIOGRAPHY

Berg, Marc. 1998. "The Politics of Technology: On Bringing Social Theory into Technological Design." *Science, Technology and Human Values* 23, no. 4: 456–491.

Bloor, David. 1976. *Knowledge and Social Imagery.* Chicago: University of Chicago Press.

Bowker, Geoff, and Bruno Latour. 1987. "A Booming Discipline Short of Discipline: (Social) Studies of Science in France." *Social Studies of Science* 17: 715–748.

Callon, Michael. 1986. "Some Elements of a Sociology of Translation: Domestication of the Scallops and the Fishermen of St. Brieuc Bay." In *Power, Action, and Belief: A New Sociology of Knowledge,* edited by John Law. London: Routledge.

Callon, Michael, and Bruno Latour. 1981. "Unscrewing the Big Leviathan: How Actors Macro-structure Reality and How Sociologists Help Them Do So." In *Advances in Social Theory and Methodology: Toward an Integration of Micro and Macro Sociologies,* edited by Karin Knorr-Cetina and Aron Cicourel. London: Routledge.

Crawford, Hugh T. 1993. "An Interview with Bruno Latour." *Configurations* 1, no. 2: 247–268.

Cussins, Charis. 1998. "Ontological Choreography Agency for Women Patients in an Infertility Clinic." In *Differences in Medicine: Unravelling Practices, Techniques and Bodies,* edited by Marc Berg and Annemarie Mol. Durham, N.C.: Duke University Press.

de Vries, Gerard. 1995. "Should We Send Collins and Latour to Dayton, Ohio?" *EASST Review* 14, no. 4: 3–10.

Deleuze, Gilles. 1993. *The Fold: Leibniz and the Baroque.* London: Athlone Press.

Elam, Mark. 1999. "Living Dangerously with Bruno Latour in a Hybrid World." *Theory, Culture, & Society: Explorations in Critical Social Science* 16, no. 4: 1–24.

Haraway, Donna. 1992. "The Promises of Monsters: A Regenerative Politics of Inappropriate/d Others." In *Cultural Studies,* edited by Lawrence Grossberg et al. New York: Routledge.

———. 1997. *Modest_Witness@Second_Millennium. FemaleMan© _Meets_OncoMouse™.* New York: Routledge.

Helmreich, Stefan. 2001. "Torquing Things Out." Presented at the Annual Meeting for the Social Studies of Science, Cambridge, Massachusetts.

Jensen, Casper Bruun, and Randi Markussen, "Mårup Church and the Politics of Hybridization: On Complexities of Choice." *Social Studies of Science* 31, no. 6 (2001): 795–820.

Jordan, Kathleen, and Michael Lynch. 1992. "The Sociology of a Genetic Engineering

Technique: Ritual and Rationality in the Performance of the 'Plasmid Prep.'" In *The Right Tools for the Job: At Work in Twentieth-Century Life Sciences*, edited by Adele E. Clarke and Joan H. Fujimura. Princeton, N.J.: Princeton University Press.

Latour, Bruno. 1987. *Science in Action: How to Follow Scientists and Engineers through Society*. Cambridge, Mass.: Harvard University Press.

———. 1988. *The Pasteurization of France*. Cambridge, Mass.: Harvard University Press.

———. 1990. "Postmodern? No, Simply Amodern!—Steps towards an Anthropology of Science." *Studies in History and Philosophy of Science* 21: 145–171.

———. 1993. *We Have Never Been Modern*. Cambridge, Mass.: Harvard University Press.

———. 1994. "On Technical Mediation: Philosophy, Sociology, Genealogy." *Common Knowledge* 2, no. 3: 29–64.

———. 1997a. "Om aktør-netværksteori. Nogle få afklaringer og mere end nogle få forviklinger." *Philosophia* 25, nos. 3–4: 47–64.

———. 1997b. "Trains of Thought: Piaget, Formalism and the Fifth Dimension." *Common Knowledge* 3, no. 6: 170–191.

———. 1999. *Pandora's Hope: Essays on the Reality of Science Studies*. Cambridge, Mass.: Harvard University Press.

———. 2000 "A Well-Articulated Primatology: Reflections of a Fellow-Traveller." In *Primate Encounters: Models of Science, Gender and Society*, edited by Shirley Strum and Linda Fedigan. Chicago and London: University of Chicago Press.

———. 2001. "What Rules of Methods for the New Scientific Experiments." Keynote speech, 13th Darmstadt Colloquium.

———. Forthcoming. "Is There Life after Science Studies." In *Theorizing Bodies*, edited by Madeline Akrich and Marc Berg.

Law, John, and John Hassard, eds. 1999. *Actor Network Theory and After*. Oxford: Blackwell.

Lee, Nick, and Steven D. Brown. 1994. "Otherness and the Actor-Network: The Undiscovered Continent." *American Behavioral Scientist* 37, no. 6: 772–790.

Mol, Annemarie. 1999. "Ontological Politics: a Word and Some Questions." In *Actor Network and After*, edited by John Law and John Hassard. Oxford and Keele: Blackwell.

Olesen, Finn. 1997. "Konstruktive studier af videnskab og virkelighed. Fra sociologi til kulturforskning." *Philosophia* 25: 3–47.

Pickering, Andrew. 1995a. *The Mangle of Practice: Time, Agency and Science*. Chicago: University of Chicago Press.

———. 1995b. "Cyborg History and the World War II Regime." *Perspectives on Science* 3: 1–48.

———. 1999. "Japanese Eels to Global Warming: A Posthumanist Perspective on Society and the Environment." Presented at the Colloquium series on "The Environment and Sustainable Development," geography department, University of Illinois at Urbana Champaign.

———. 2000. "In the Thick of Things and the Politics of Becoming." Presented at "Entering the Third Millennium: Philosophy between Its Past and its Future," Bergen, Norway.

———. 2003. "On Becoming: Imagination, Metaphysics, and the Mangle." Chapter 6, this volume.

———. Forthcoming. "The Alchemical Wedding of Science and Industry: Synthetic Dyes and Social Theory."

———, ed. 1992. *Science as Practice and Culture.* Chicago: University of Chicago Press.

Ramsey, Jeffry L. 1992. "On Refusing to Be an Epistemologically Black Box: Instruments in Chemical Kinetics during the 1920s and '30s." *Studies in History and Philosophy of Science* 23, no. 2: 283–304.

Rowell, T. E., and C. A. Rowell. 1993. "The Social Organization of Feral *Ovis aries* Ram Groups in the Pre-Rut Period." *Ethnology* 95: 213–232.

Serres, Michel. 1987. *Statues.* Paris: Francois Bourin.

Serres, Michel, and Bruno Latour. 1995. *Conversations on Science, Culture and Time.* Ann Arbor: University of Michigan Press.

Smith, Barbara H. 1997. *Belief and Resistance: Dynamics of Contemporary Intellectual Controversy.* Cambridge, Mass.: Harvard University Press.

Smith, Barbara H., and Arkady Plotnitsky. 1997. *Mathematics, Science, and Post-Classical Theory.* Durham, N.C.: Duke University Press.

Stengers, Isabelle. 1997. *Power and Invention.* Minneapolis: University of Minnesota Press.

Strathern, Marilyn. 1991. *Partial Connections.* Lanham, Md.: Rowman & Littlefield Publishers.

Traweek, Sharon. 1988. *Beamtimes and Lifetimes: The World of High Energy Physicists.* Cambridge, Mass.: Harvard University Press.

Woolgar, Steve, ed. 1988. *Knowledge and Reflexivity.* London: SAGE.

CONTRIBUTORS

CONTRIBUTORS TO PART ONE

Donna J. Haraway is Professor of the History of Consciousness at the University of California at Santa Cruz. She teaches Science Studies, Feminist Theory, and Women's Studies. Her book *Primate Visions* was paradigmatic for science studies and was followed by *Simians, Cyborgs and Women* and *Modest_Witnes@ Second_Millennium.*

Don Ihde is Distinguished Professor of Philosophy at Stony Brook University. He directs the Technoscience Research Group and is the author of thirteen books, including *Technology and the Lifeworld* and *Instrumental Realism* in this series. His most recent work is *Bodies in Technology.*

Bruno Latour is Professor at the Centre de sociologie de l'innovation at the Ecole des mines in Paris, with appointments at the London School of Economics and the History of Science Department at Harvard University. His work includes *Laboratory Life* with Steven Woolgar, *Science in Action,* and *Pandora's Hope.*

Andrew Pickering is Professor of Sociology at the Unit for Criticism and Interpretive Theory at the University of Illinois at Urbana-Champaign. Coming from a background in both physics and science studies, he authored *Constructing Quarks: A Sociological History of Particle Physics* and *The Mangle of Practice: Time, Agency and Science.*

CONTRIBUTORS TO PART TWO

All the contributors to this project, Part Two, were members of the technoscience research seminar.

Robb Eason is currently a Fellow of the Transatlantic Collegium of Philosophy, a program of Stony Brook University and the Bergischen Universitat of Wuppertal, Germany. His dissertation project is "Contemporary Epistemological Appropriations of Hegel's Philosophy."

Casper Bruun Jensen was a Visiting Fellow at the *technoscience research group* at Stony Brook University. He is currently completing a doctorate in Information and Media Studies at Aarhus University, Denmark. His research concerns controversies surrounding the development and implementation of electronic patient records in Denmark.

Jari Friis Jørgenssen was also a Visiting Fellow at the *technoscience research group* at Stony Brook University. He completed his M.A. from the Institute of Information and Media Studies at Aarhus University on the topic "Cyberculture, Science and AIBO: A Non-modern View on Collectives, Artificial Life and Playful Quasi-Objects."

Evan Selinger is Assistant Professor of Philosophy at the Rochester Institute of Technology. His dissertation, "On Expertise: Descriptive and Normative Problems," was completed while he was working on this technoscience project. He has presented papers in the areas of his interest between phenomenology and science studies at CERN and at the Society for the Social Study of Science in Europe.

Aaron Smith is completing his doctorate at Stony Brook University on Hegel's concept of recognition. He has had a long term-interest in ethics in recent Continental philosophy.

THE INTERVIEWS

The interview with Donna J. Haraway was conducted in Aarhus, Denmark, in conjunction with the conference "Cyborg Identities: The Humanities in Technical Light," October 1999, by Nina Lykke, the editor of *Kvindr, kon & forskning,* and Finn Olesen and Randi Markussen, co-directors of the Media and Information Studies program at Aarhus University.

The interview with Don Ihde was conducted during a session of the *technoscience research seminar*. Questioners included Evan Selinger, Jeremy Hubbell from the Department of History, Srikanth Mallavarapu from the Department of English, and Nikos Plevris, Lecturer from the Technical University in Athens and a Visiting Scholar with the *technoscience research group*. The interview was conducted Spring term, 2001.

The interview with Andrew Pickering was conducted electronically by Casper Bruun Jensen with input from Evan Selinger. It occurred over Spring term, 2001.

The interview with Bruno Latour took place at the international meeting of the Society for the Social Study of Science and the European Society for the Study of Science and Technology in Vienna, Austria, September 2000. Questioners included Don Ihde, Evan Selinger, and Casper Bruun Jensen, as well as Robert Crease, who is Professor of Philosophy at Stony Brook University and the historian of the Brookhaven National Laboratories.

INDEX

CPSIA information can be obtained at www.ICGtesting.com
Printed in the USA
241683LV00002B/20/A